D1189922

CATEGORIES
AND FUNCTORS

This is Volume 39 in
PURE AND APPLIED MATHEMATICS
A Series of Monographs and Textbooks
Editors: PAUL A. SMITH AND SAMUEL EILENBERG
A complete list of titles in this series appears at the end of this volume

CATEGORIES
AND FUNCTORS

Bodo Pareigis

UNIVERSITY OF MUNICH
MUNICH, GERMANY

1970

ACADEMIC PRESS   New York • London

288278

This is the only authorized English translation of *Kategorien und Funktoren - Eine Einführung* (a volume in the series "Mathematische Leitfäden," edited by Professor G. Köthe), originally in German by Verlag B. G. Teubner, Stuttgart. 1969

COPYRIGHT © 1970, BY ACADEMIC PRESS, INC.
ALL RIGHTS RESERVED
NO PART OF THIS BOOK MAY BE REPRODUCED IN ANY FORM,
BY PHOTOSTAT, MICROFILM, RETRIEVAL SYSTEM, OR ANY
OTHER MEANS, WITHOUT WRITTEN PERMISSION FROM
THE PUBLISHERS.

ACADEMIC PRESS, INC.
111 Fifth Avenue, New York, New York 10003

United Kingdom Edition published by
ACADEMIC PRESS, INC. (LONDON) LTD.
Berkeley Square House, London W1X 6BA

LIBRARY OF CONGRESS CATALOG CARD NUMBER: 76-117631

PRINTED IN THE UNITED STATES OF AMERICA

Harriet Irving Library
DEC 7 1970
University of New Brunswick

Contents

1. Preliminary Notions

2. Adjoint Functors and Limits

3. Universal Algebra

4. Abelian Categories

Thinking—is it a social function
or one of the brains?
Stanisław Jerzy Lec

Preface

In their paper on a "General theory of natural equivalences" Eilenberg and MacLane laid the foundation of the theory of categories and functors in 1945. It took about ten years before the time was ripe for a further development of this theory. Early in this century studies of isolated mathematical objects were predominant. During the last decades, however, interest proceeded gradually to the analysis of admissible maps between mathematical objects and to whole classes of objects. This new point of view is appropriately expressed by the theory of categories and functors. Its new language—originally called "general abstract nonsense" even by its initiators—spread into many different branches of mathematics.

The theory of categories and functors abstracts the concepts "object" and "map" from the underlying mathematical fields, for example, from algebra or topology, to investigate which statements can be proved in such an abstract structure. Then these statements will be true in all those mathematical fields which may be expressed by means of this language.

Of course, there are trends today to render the theory of categories and functors independent of other mathematical branches, which will certainly be fascinating if seen for example, in connection with the foundation of mathematics. At the moment, however, the prevailing value of this theory lies in the fact that many different mathematical fields may be interpreted as categories and that the techniques and theorems of this theory may be applied to these fields. It provides the means of comprehension of larger parts of mathematics. It often occurs that certain proofs, for example, in algebra or in topology, use "similar" methods. With this new language it is possible to express these "similarities" in exact terms. Parallel to this fact there is a unification. Thus it will be easier for the mathematician who has command of this language to acquaint himself with the fundamentals of a new mathematical field if the fundamentals are given in a categorical language.

This book is meant to be an introduction to the theory of categories and functors for the mathematician who is not yet familiar with it, as well as for the beginning graduate student who knows some first examples for an application of this theory. For this reason the first chapter has been written in great detail. The most important terms occurring in most mathematical branches in one way or another have been expressed in the language of categories. The reader should consider the examples—most of them from algebra or topology—as applications as well as a possible way to acquaint himself with this particular field.

The second chapter mainly deals with adjoint functors and limits in a way first introduced by Kan.

The third chapter shows how far universal algebra can be represented by categorical means. For this purpose we use the methods of monads (triples) and also of algebraic theories. Here you will find represented one of today's most interesting application of category theory.

The fourth chapter is devoted to abelian categories, a very important generalization of the categories of modules. Here many interesting theorems about modules are proved in this general frame. The embedding theorems at the end of this chapter make it possible to transfer many more results from module categories to arbitrary abelian categories.

The appendix on set theory offers an axiomatic foundation for the set theoretic notions used in the definition of categorical notions. We use the set of axioms of Gödel and Bernays. Furthermore, we give a formulation of the axiom of choice that is particularly suitable for an application to the theory of categories and functors.

I hope that this book will serve well as an introduction and, moreover, enable the reader to proceed to the study of the original literature. He will find some important publications listed at the end of this book, which again include references to the original literature.

Particular thanks are due to my wife Karin. Without her help in preparing the translation I would not have been able to present to English speaking readers the English version of this book.

1

Preliminary Notions

The first sections of this chapter introduce the preliminary notions of category, functor, and natural transformation. The next sections deal mainly with notions that are essential for objects and morphisms in categories. Only the last two sections are concerned with functors and natural transformations in more detail. Here the Yoneda lemma is certainly one of the most important theorems in the theory of categories and functors.

The examples given in Section 1.1 will be partly continued, so that at the end of this chapter—for some categories—all notions introduced will be known in their specific form for particular categories. The verification that the given objects or morphisms in the respective categories have the properties claimed will be left partly to the reader. Many examples, however, will be computed in detail.

1.1 Definition of a Category

In addition to mathematical objects modern mathematics investigates more and more the admissible maps defined between them. One familiar example is given by sets. Besides the sets, which form the mathematical objects in set theory, the set maps are very important. Much information about a set is available if only the maps into this set from all other sets are known. For example, the set containing only one element can be characterized by the fact that, from every other set, there is exactly one map into this set.

Let us first summarize in a definition those properties of mathematical objects and admissible maps which appear in all known applications. As a basis, we take set theory as presented in the Appendix.

Let $\mathscr{C}$ be a class of *objects* $A, B, C,... \in \text{Ob}\,\mathscr{C}$ together with

(1)   A family of mutually disjoint sets $\{\text{Mor}_{\mathscr{C}}(A, B)\}$ for all objects $A, B \in \mathscr{C}$, whose elements $f, g, h,... \in \text{Mor}_{\mathscr{C}}(A, B)$ are called *morphisms* and

(2)   a family of maps

$$\{\mathrm{Mor}_{\mathscr{C}}(A, B) \times \mathrm{Mor}_{\mathscr{C}}(B, C) \ni (f, g) \mapsto gf \in \mathrm{Mor}_{\mathscr{C}}(A, C)\}$$

for all $A, B, C \in \mathrm{Ob}\ \mathscr{C}$, called *compositions*.

$\mathscr{C}$ is called a *category* if $\mathscr{C}$ fulfills the following axioms:

(1)   *Associativity*: For all $A, B, C, D \in \mathrm{Ob}\ \mathscr{C}$ and all $f \in \mathrm{Mor}_{\mathscr{C}}(A, B)$, $g \in \mathrm{Mor}_{\mathscr{C}}(B, C)$, and $h \in \mathrm{Mor}_{\mathscr{C}}(C, D)$ we have

$$h(gf) = (hg)f$$

(2)   *Identity*: For each object $A \in \mathrm{Ob}\ \mathscr{C}$ there is a morphism $1_A \in \mathrm{Mor}_{\mathscr{C}}(A, A)$, called the identity, such that we have

$$f1_A = f \qquad \text{and} \qquad 1_A g = g$$

for all $B, C \in \mathrm{Ob}\ \mathscr{C}$ and all $f \in \mathrm{Mor}_{\mathscr{C}}(A, B)$ and $g \in \mathrm{Mor}_{\mathscr{C}}(C, A)$.

Therefore the class of objects, and the class of morphism sets, as well as the composition of morphisms, always belong to a category $\mathscr{C}$. The compositions have not yet been discussed in our example of sets, whereas the morphisms correspond to the discussed maps. In the case of sets the composition of morphisms corresponds to the juxtaposition of set maps. This juxtaposition is known to be associative. The identity map of a set complies with the axiom of identity. Thus all sets together with the set maps and juxtaposition form a category, which will be denoted by **S**.

Here it becomes clear why one has to consider a class of objects. In fact because of the well-known inconsistencies of classical set theory, the totality of all sets does not itself form a set. One of the known ways out of this difficulty is the introduction of new boundless sets under the name classes. This set theory will be axiomatically treated in the Appendix. A further possibility is to ask axiomatically for the existence of universes where all set theoretic constructions do not exceed a certain cardinal. In some cases this makes possible an elegant formulation of the theorems on categories. It requires, however, a further axiom for set theory. This possibility was essentially used by A. Grothendieck and P. Gabriel. W. Lawvere developed a theory in which categories are axiomatically introduced without using a set theory and from which set theory is derived. Here we shall only use the set theory of Goedel–Bernays (Appendix).

Before examining further examples on categories, we will agree on a sequence of abbreviations. In general, objects will be denoted by capital Latin letters and morphisms by small Latin letters. The fact that A is an object of $\mathscr{C}$ will be expressed by $A \in \mathscr{C}$, and $f \in \mathscr{C}$ means that f is a morphism between two objects in $\mathscr{C}$, that is, there are two uniquely defined objects $A, B \in \mathscr{C}$ such that $f \in \mathrm{Mor}_{\mathscr{C}}(A, B)$. A is called the *domain* of f and B the *range* of f. We also write

$$f : A \to B \quad \text{or} \quad A \xrightarrow{f} B$$

If there is no ambiguity, $\mathrm{Mor}_{\mathscr{C}}(A, B)$ will be abbreviated by $\mathrm{Mor}(A, B)$.

Mor $\mathscr{C}$ denotes the union of the family of morphism sets of a category. Observe that $\mathrm{Mor}_{\mathscr{C}}(A, B)$ may be empty, but that Mor $\mathscr{C}$ contains at least the identities for all objects so that it is empty only for an empty class of objects. Such a category is called an *empty category*. Observe further that for each object $A \in \mathscr{C}$, there is exactly one identity 1_A. If $1_A'$ is another identity for A then we have $1_A' = 1_A' 1_A = 1_A$.

In the following examples only the objects and morphisms of a category will be given. The composition of morphisms will be given only if it is not the juxtaposition of maps. We leave it to the reader to verify the axioms of categories in the following examples.

Examples

1. **S**—*Category of sets:* This is sufficiently described above and in the Appendix.

2. *Category of ordered sets:* An ordered set is a set together with a relation on this set which is reflexive ($a \in A \to a \leqslant a$), transitive ($a \leqslant b$, $b \leqslant c \Rightarrow a \leqslant c$), and antisymmetric ($a \leqslant b$, $b \leqslant a \Rightarrow a = b$). The ordered sets form the objects of this category. A map f between two ordered sets is order preserving if $a \leqslant b$ implies $f(a) \leqslant f(b)$. The order preserving maps form the morphisms of this category.

3. **S***—*Category of pointed sets:* A pointed set is a pair (A, a) where A is a nonempty set and $a \in A$. A pointed map f from (A, a) to (B, b) is a map $f : A \to B$ with $f(a) = b$. The pointed sets form the objects and the pointed maps, the morphisms of this category.

4. **Gr**—*Category of groups:* A group consists of a nonempty set A together with a composition

$$A \times A \ni (a, b) \mapsto ab \in A$$

such that the following axioms hold:

(1) $a(bc) = (ab)c$ for all $a, b, c \in A$
(2)   there is an $e \in A$ with $ea = ae = a$ for all $a \in A$
(3)   for each $a \in A$ there is an $a^{-1} \in A$ with $aa^{-1} = a^{-1}a = e$

A group homomorphism f from a group A into a group B is a map from A into B with $f(aa') = f(a)f(a')$. The groups form the objects and the group homomorphisms, the morphisms of this category.

5. **Ab**—*Category of abelian groups:* A group A is called abelian if $ab = ba$ for all $a, b \in A$. The abelian groups together with the group homomorphisms form the category **Ab**.

6. **Ri**—*Category of unitary, associative rings:* A unitary, associative ring consists of an abelian group A (whose composition is usually written as $(a, b) \mapsto a + b$) together with a further composition

$$A \times A \ni (a, b) \mapsto ab \in A$$

such that the following axioms hold:

(1) $(a + b)c = ac + bc$ for all $a, b, c \in A$
(2) $a(b + c) = ab + ac$ for all $a, b, c \in A$
(3) $(ab)c = a(bc)$ for all $a, b, c \in A$
(4) there is a $1 \in A$ with $1a = a1 = a$ for all $a \in A$

A unitary ring homomorphism f from a unitary, associative ring A into a unitary, associative ring B is a map from A to B with

$$f(a + a') = f(a) + f(a'), \qquad f(aa') = f(a)f(a'), \qquad \text{and} \quad f(1) = 1$$

The unitary, associative rings together with the unitary ring homomorphisms form the category **Ri**.

7. $_R$**Mod**—*Category of unitary R-modules (for a unitary, associative ring R):* A unitary R-(left-)module is an abelian group A [whose composition is usually written as $(a, b) \mapsto a + b$] together with a composition

$$R \times A \ni (r, a) \mapsto ra \in A$$

such that the following axioms hold:

(1) $r(a + a') = ra + ra'$ for all $r \in R, a, a' \in A$
(2) $(r + r')a = ra + r'a$ for all $r, r' \in R, a \in A$
(3) $(rr')a = r(r'a)$ for all $r, r' \in R, a \in A$
(4) $1a = a$ for all $a \in A$

A homomorphism f from a unitary R-module A into a unitary R-module B is a map from A into B with $f(a + a') = f(a) + f(a')$ and $f(ra) = rf(a)$. The unitary R-modules together with the homomorphisms of unitary R-modules form the category $_R$**Mod**. If R is a field, then the R-modules are called vector spaces.

8. **Top**—*Category of topological spaces:* A topological space is a set A together with a subset $\mathcal{O}_A$ of the power set of A such that the following axioms hold:

(1)   if $B_i \in \mathcal{O}_A$ for $i \in I$,   then $\bigcup_{i \in I} B_i \in \mathcal{O}_A$
(2)   if $B_i \in \mathcal{O}_A$ for $i = 1,..., n$,   then $\bigcap_{i=1}^{n} B_i \in \mathcal{O}_A$
(3) $\varnothing \in \mathcal{O}_A$
(4) $A \in \mathcal{O}_A$

The elements of $\mathcal{O}_A$ are called open sets of A. A continuous map f from a topological space A into a topological space B is a map from A into B with $f^{-1}(C) \in \mathcal{O}_A$ for all $C \in \mathcal{O}_B$. The topological spaces together with the continuous maps form the category **Top**.

9. **Htp**—*Category of topological spaces modulo homotopy:* Two continuous maps f and g from a topological space A to a topological space B are called homotopic if there is a continuous map $h : I \times A \to B$ with $h(0, a) = f(a)$ and $h(1, a) = g(a)$ for all $a \in A$, where I is the interval $[0, 1]$ of the real numbers. The open sets $\mathcal{O}_{I \times A}$ of $I \times A$ are arbitrary unions of sets of the form $J \times C$, where $J \subseteq I$ is an open interval and $C \in \mathcal{O}_A$. Homotopy is an equivalence relation for continuous maps. The equivalence classes are called homotopy classes of continuous maps. Juxtaposition of homotopic, continuous maps gives again homotopic, continuous maps. Thus the juxtaposition of maps defines a composition of homotopy classes which is independent of the choice of representatives. The topological spaces together with the homotopy classes of continuous maps and the just discussed composition form the category **Htp**.

10. **Top***—*Category of pointed topological spaces:* A pointed topological space is a pair (A, a) where A is a nonempty topological space and $a \in A$. A pointed continuous map f from (A, a) to (B, b) is a continuous map $f : A \to B$ with $f(a) = b$. The pointed topological spaces together with the pointed continuous maps form the category **Top***.

11. **Htp***—*Category of pointed topological spaces modulo homotopy:* Two pointed continuous maps f and g from a pointed topological space (A, a) into a pointed topological space (B, b) are homotopic if they are homotopic as continuous maps and if $h(r, a) = b$ for all $r \in I$. The pointed topological spaces together with the homotopy classes of pointed continuous maps and the composition of homotopy classes as defined in Example 9 form the category **Htp***.

12.   *Ordered set as a category:* Let A be an ordered set in the sense of Example 2. A defines a category $\mathscr{A}$ with the elements of A as objects. For $a, b \in A = \text{Ob } \mathscr{A}$ we define

$$\text{Mor}_{\mathscr{A}}(a, b) = \begin{cases} \{(a, b)\} & \text{if } a \leqslant b \\ \varnothing & \text{otherwise} \end{cases}$$

The transitivity of the order relation uniquely defines a composition of the morphisms. The reflexivity guarantees the existence of the identity. Since $\text{Mor}_{\mathscr{A}}(a, b)$ has at most one element, the composition is associative.

13.   *Group as a category:* Let A be a group. A defines a category $\mathscr{A}$ with exactly one object B and $\text{Mor}_{\mathscr{A}}(B, B) = A$ such that the composition of the morphisms is the multiplication (composition) of the group.

14.   *Natural numbers as a category:* The natural numbers form an ordered set with the order relation $a \leqslant b$ if and only if $a \mid b$. As in Example 12, the natural numbers form a category.

15.   *Category of correspondences of sets:* A correspondence from a set A to a set B is a subset of $A \times B$. If $f \subseteq A \times B$ and $g \subseteq B \times C$ let

$$gf = \{(a, c) \mid a \in A, \quad c \in C, \quad \text{there is a } b \in B \text{ with } (a, b) \in f \text{ and } (b, c) \in g\}$$

The sets as objects and the correspondences of sets as morphisms form a category.

16.   *Equivalence relation as a category:* Let M be a set and R be an equivalence relation on M. Let the objects be the elements of M. If $(m, m') \in R$, then $\text{Mor}(m, m') = \{(m, m')\}$. If $(m, m') \notin R$, then $\text{Mor}(m, m') = \varnothing$. This defines a category.

   A category $\mathscr{C}$ is called a *discrete category* if $\text{Mor}_{\mathscr{C}}(A, B) = \varnothing$ for any two objects $A \neq B$ in $\mathscr{C}$ and if $\text{Mor}_{\mathscr{C}}(A, A) = \{1_A\}$ for each object A in $\mathscr{C}$. Similarly to Example 12, every class defines a discrete category. Conversely, every discrete category may be interpreted as a class.

   Examples 12, 13, 14, and 16 are categories of a special type, namely those with only a set (instead of a class) of objects. If the objects of a category form a set, then the category is called a *small category* or *diagram scheme*. An explanation for the second name will be given in Section 1.8.

1.2   Functors and Natural Transformations

   We stressed already in Section 1.1 that, together with every kind of mathematical object, the corresponding maps have to be studied as well.

The mathematical objects we defined in Section 1.1 are the categories. The place of the maps will be taken by the functors.

Let $\mathscr{B}$ and $\mathscr{C}$ be categories. Let $\mathscr{F}$ consist of

(1) a map $\mathrm{Ob}\,\mathscr{B} \ni A \mapsto \mathscr{F}(A) \in \mathrm{Ob}\,\mathscr{C}$
(2) a family of maps

$$\{\mathrm{Mor}_{\mathscr{B}}(A, B) \ni f \mapsto F(f) \in \mathrm{Mor}_{\mathscr{C}}(\mathscr{F}(A), \mathscr{F}(B))\}$$

for all $A, B \in \mathrm{Ob}\,\mathscr{B}$

$\mathscr{F}$ is called a *covariant functor* if $\mathscr{F}$ complies with the following axioms:

(1) $\mathscr{F}(1_A) = 1_{\mathscr{F}(A)}$ for all $A \in \mathrm{Ob}\,\mathscr{B}$
(2) $\mathscr{F}(fg) = \mathscr{F}(f)\mathscr{F}(g)$ for all $f \in \mathrm{Mor}_{\mathscr{B}}(B, C)$, $g \in \mathrm{Mor}_{\mathscr{B}}(A, B)$ and for all $A, B, C \in \mathrm{Ob}\,\mathscr{B}$

Let $\mathscr{B}$ and $\mathscr{C}$ be categories. Let $\mathscr{F}$ consist of

(1) a map $\mathrm{Ob}\,\mathscr{B} \ni A \mapsto \mathscr{F}(A) \in \mathrm{Ob}\,\mathscr{C}$
(2) a family of maps

$$\{\mathrm{Mor}_{\mathscr{B}}(A, B) \ni f \mapsto \mathscr{F}(f) \in \mathrm{Mor}_{\mathscr{C}}(\mathscr{F}(B), \mathscr{F}(A))\}$$

for all $A, B \in \mathrm{Ob}\,\mathscr{B}$

$\mathscr{F}$ is called a *contravariant functor* if $\mathscr{F}$ complies with the following axioms:

(1) $\mathscr{F}(1_A) = 1_{\mathscr{F}(A)}$ for all $A \in \mathrm{Ob}\,\mathscr{B}$
(2) $\mathscr{F}(fg) = \mathscr{F}(g)\mathscr{F}(f)$ for all $f \in \mathrm{Mor}_{\mathscr{B}}(B, C)$, $g \in \mathrm{Mor}_{\mathscr{B}}(A, B)$ and for all $A, B, C \in \mathrm{Ob}\,\mathscr{B}$

Since the (co- and contravariant) functors take the place of the maps, we shall often write $\mathscr{F} : \mathscr{B} \to \mathscr{C}$ if $\mathscr{F}$ is a functor from the category $\mathscr{B}$ to the category $\mathscr{C}$. If there is no ambiguity, we shall also write $\mathscr{F}A$ instead of $\mathscr{F}(A)$ and $\mathscr{F}f$ instead of $\mathscr{F}(f)$. A covariant functor will often be called only "functor."

If $\mathscr{B}$, $\mathscr{C}$, and $\mathscr{D}$ are categories and $\mathscr{F} : \mathscr{B} \to \mathscr{C}$ and $\mathscr{G} : \mathscr{C} \to \mathscr{D}$ are functors, then let $\mathscr{G}\mathscr{F} : \mathscr{B} \to \mathscr{D}$ be the functor which results from the composition of the maps defining the functors $\mathscr{F}$ and $\mathscr{G}$. In fact we have

$$\mathscr{G}\mathscr{F}(1_A) = \mathscr{G}(1_{\mathscr{F}(A)}) = 1_{\mathscr{G}\mathscr{F}(A)}$$

and

$$\mathscr{G}\mathscr{F}(fg) = \mathscr{G}(\mathscr{F}(f)\,\mathscr{F}(g)) = \mathscr{G}\mathscr{F}(f)\,\mathscr{G}\mathscr{F}(g)$$

Observe the change in the order of the morphisms if one of the two functors is contravariant. Thus $\mathscr{G}\mathscr{F}$ is covariant if both functors are simultaneously co- or contravariant. If one of the functors is covariant and the other one is contravariant, then $\mathscr{G}\mathscr{F}$ is contravariant.

If $\mathscr{H} : \mathscr{D} \to \mathscr{E}$ is an additional functor, then the composition of functors is associative ($\mathscr{H}(\mathscr{G}\mathscr{F}) = (\mathscr{H}\mathscr{G})\mathscr{F}$) because of the associativity of the composition of maps.

$\mathrm{Id}_{\mathscr{C}} : \mathscr{C} \to \mathscr{C}$ denotes the functor with the identity maps as defining maps. $\mathrm{Id}_{\mathscr{C}}$ is a covariant functor. As above, we have for functors $\mathscr{F}$ and $\mathscr{G}$

$$\mathrm{Id}_{\mathscr{C}}\mathscr{F} = \mathscr{F} \qquad \text{and} \qquad \mathscr{G}\,\mathrm{Id}_{\mathscr{C}} = \mathscr{G}$$

After these considerations one should expect that the categories and functors themselves form a category (of categories). This, however, is not the case in the set theory we use. In fact a category is in general no longer a set but a proper class. Thus, we cannot collect the categories in a new class of objects (see Appendix). In general, the functors, too, are proper classes and cannot be collected in morphism sets. But if we admit only small categories, every category, interpreted as a set of certain sets, is a set, and every functor is a set. Therefore, the category of small categories with functors as morphisms, **Cat**, may be formed.

As an example, we want to mention only a special type of functor. Later on we shall study further examples of functors in more detail. All the categories **S***, **Gr**, **Ab**, **Ri**, $_R$**Mod**, **Top**, and **Top*** have sets with an additional structure as objects. The morphisms are always maps compatible in a special way with the structure of the sets. The composition is always juxtaposition. If one assigns to every object the underlying set and to every morphism the underlying set map, then this defines a covariant functor into **S**, very often called a *forgetful functor*.

Instead of forgetting the structure on the sets completely, one can also forget only part of the structure. For example, the abelian groups are also groups, and the homomorphisms are the same in both cases. The rings are also abelian groups, and the ring homomorphisms are also group homomorphisms. So we get forgetful functors **Ab** $\to$ **Gr** and **Ri** $\to$ **Ab** respectively. Similarly, there are forgetful functors $_R$**Mod** $\to$ **Ab** and **Top*** $\to$ **Top**. If the topological spaces carry an additional structure (e.g., hausdorff, compact, discrete), respective categories are defined thereby. So we get forgetful functors into the category **Top**.

The example **Ab** $\to$ **Gr** and the aforementioned examples have an additional property. An abelian group is a group with a special property. Likewise, a hausdorff topological space is a topological space with a special property. The objects of one category are in each case also objects of the other category. The morphisms of one category are morphisms of the other category. The composition is the same. The identities are preserved by the forgetful functor. A category $\mathscr{A}$ is called a *subcategory* of a category $\mathscr{B}$ if

$$\text{Ob } \mathscr{A} \subseteq \text{Ob } \mathscr{B} \qquad \text{and} \qquad \text{Mor}_{\mathscr{A}}(A, B) \subseteq \text{Mor}_{\mathscr{B}}(A, B)$$

for all $A, B \in \text{Ob } \mathscr{A}$, if the composition of morphisms in $\mathscr{A}$ coincides with the composition of the same morphisms in $\mathscr{B}$, and if the identity of an object in $\mathscr{A}$ is also the identity of the same object viewed as an object in $\mathscr{B}$. Then there is a forgetful functor from $\mathscr{A}$ to $\mathscr{B}$.

We note that **Ri** is not a subcategory of **Ab**. In fact, Ob **Ri** $\subseteq$ Ob **Ab** is not true, although every ring can also be regarded as an abelian group. The corresponding abelian groups of two rings may coincide even if the rings do not coincide. The multiplication may be defined differently.

Let $\mathscr{F} : \mathscr{B} \to \mathscr{C}$ and $\mathscr{G} : \mathscr{B} \to \mathscr{C}$ be two covariant [contravariant] functors. A *natural transformation* $\varphi : \mathscr{F} \to \mathscr{G}$ is a family of morphisms $\{\varphi(A) : \mathscr{F}(A) \to \mathscr{G}(A)\}$ for all $A \in \text{Ob } \mathscr{B}$ such that we have $\varphi(B)\mathscr{F}(f) = \mathscr{G}(f)\varphi(A)$ $[\varphi(A)\mathscr{F}(f) = \mathscr{G}(f)\varphi(B)$, respectively] for all morphisms $f : A \to B$ of $\mathscr{B}$.

In the following there will often be equalities between composed morphisms. The objects which are the domains and the ranges of the separate morphisms will not appear explicitly. Thus, these equations are difficult to comprehend. So we take a detailed representation using arrows, as we already took for single morphisms. This will be called a *diagram*.

In the case of a natural transformation between covariant functors, the defining equation

$$\varphi(B)\,\mathscr{F}(f) = \mathscr{G}(f)\,\varphi(A)$$

may be illustrated by the diagram

$$
\begin{array}{ccc}
\mathscr{F}A & \xrightarrow{\varphi(A)} & \mathscr{G}A \\
{\scriptstyle \mathscr{F}f}\downarrow & & \downarrow{\scriptstyle \mathscr{G}f} \\
\mathscr{F}B & \xrightarrow{\varphi(B)} & \mathscr{G}B
\end{array}
$$

To follow the arrow $\varphi(A)$ from $\mathscr{F}A$ to $\mathscr{G}A$ and then the arrow $\mathscr{G}f$ to $\mathscr{G}B$ substitutes the arrow $\mathscr{G}f\varphi(A)$ from $\mathscr{F}A$ to $\mathscr{G}B$. Correspondingly, $\varphi(B)\mathscr{F}f$ runs through $\mathscr{F}B$. The condition that these two morphisms coincide will be expressed by saying that the diagram is commutative. A diagram with arbitrarily many objects and arrows is called *commutative* if, for any two objects of the diagram, the morphism obtained by following a path between the two objects in the direction of the arrows is independent of the choice of path.

If there is no ambiguity, we shall often write φA instead of $\varphi(A)$. A natural transformation is often called a functorial morphism.

If $\varphi : \mathscr{F} \to \mathscr{G}$ and $\psi : \mathscr{G} \to \mathscr{H}$ are natural transformations, then so is $\psi\varphi$ with $\psi\varphi(A) := \psi(A)\varphi(A)$. We have $(\rho\psi)\varphi = \rho(\psi\varphi)$ because of the associativity of the composition of morphisms. The family $\{1_{\mathscr{F}A} : \mathscr{F}A \to \mathscr{F}A\}$ defines a natural transformation $\mathrm{id}_{\mathscr{F}} : \mathscr{F} \to \mathscr{F}$. For all natural transformations $\varphi : F \to G$ and $\psi : G \to F$, we have

$$\mathrm{id}_{\mathscr{F}}\psi = \psi \qquad \text{and} \qquad \varphi\,\mathrm{id}_{\mathscr{F}} = \varphi$$

Here again it seems as if the functors together with the natural transformations form a category. Here again, set theoretic difficulties arise from the fact that the functors are generally proper classes and cannot be collected in a class of objects. If $\mathscr{A}$ is a small category and $\mathscr{B}$ an arbitrary category, then $\mathscr{A}$ is a set and $\mathscr{B}$ a class. A functor $\mathscr{F} : \mathscr{A} \to \mathscr{B}$, originally defined as a map, is a set by Axiom C4 (Appendix) if it is interpreted as a graph. Similarly, a natural transformation between two functors from $\mathscr{A}$ to $\mathscr{B}$, being a family of morphisms with an index set Ob $\mathscr{A}$, is a set. The natural transformations between two functors from $\mathscr{A}$ to $\mathscr{B}$ are a set, being a subset of the power set of $\bigcup_{A \in \mathscr{A}} \mathrm{Mor}_{\mathscr{B}}(\mathscr{F}A, \mathscr{G}A)$ Therefore, the functors from a small category $\mathscr{A}$ into a category $\mathscr{B}$, together with the natural transformations, form a category $\mathrm{Funct}(\mathscr{A}, \mathscr{B})$, which we call the *functor category*. If the categories $\mathscr{A}$ and $\mathscr{B}$ are not explicitly given, the functor is not considered only as a graph. One also asks that functors between distinct pairs of categories are distinct so that in this general case a functor may well be a proper class, even if the domain of the functor is a small category. If $\mathscr{A}$ is the empty category, then $\mathrm{Funct}(\mathscr{A}, \mathscr{B})$ consists of exactly one functor and exactly one natural transformation, the identity transformation.

An important example of a natural transformation will be presented in the following section.

1.3 Representable Functors

Let $\mathscr{C}$ be a category. Given $A \in \mathscr{C}$ and $f \in \mathrm{Mor}_{\mathscr{C}}(B, C)$, we define a map

$$\mathrm{Mor}_{\mathscr{C}}(A, f) : \mathrm{Mor}_{\mathscr{C}}(A, B) \to \mathrm{Mor}_{\mathscr{C}}(A, C)$$

by $\mathrm{Mor}_{\mathscr{C}}(A, f)(g) := fg$ for all $g \in \mathrm{Mor}_{\mathscr{C}}(A, B)$ and a map

$$\mathrm{Mor}_{\mathscr{C}}(f, A) : \mathrm{Mor}_{\mathscr{C}}(C, A) \to \mathrm{Mor}_{\mathscr{C}}(B, A)$$

by $\mathrm{Mor}_{\mathscr{C}}(f, A)(h) := hf$ for all $h \in \mathrm{Mor}_{\mathscr{C}}(C, A)$.

LEMMA. *Let $\mathscr{C}$ be a category and $A \in \mathscr{C}$. Then $\mathrm{Mor}_\mathscr{C}(A, —) : \mathscr{C} \to \mathbf{S}$
with*

$$\mathrm{Ob}\,\mathscr{C} \ni B \mapsto \mathrm{Mor}_\mathscr{C}(A, B) \in \mathrm{Ob}\,\mathbf{S}$$

$$\mathrm{Mor}_\mathscr{C}(B, C) \ni f \mapsto \mathrm{Mor}_\mathscr{C}(A, f) \in \mathrm{Mor}_\mathbf{S}(\mathrm{Mor}_\mathscr{C}(A, B), \mathrm{Mor}_\mathscr{C}(A, C))$$

is a covariant functor. Furthermore, $\mathrm{Mor}_\mathscr{C}(—, A) : \mathscr{C} \to \mathbf{S}$ with

$$\mathrm{Ob}\,\mathscr{C} \ni B \mapsto \mathrm{Mor}_\mathscr{C}(B, A) \in \mathrm{Ob}\,\mathbf{S}$$

$$\mathrm{Mor}_\mathscr{C}(B, C) \ni f \mapsto \mathrm{Mor}_\mathscr{C}(f, A) \in \mathrm{Mor}_\mathbf{S}(\mathrm{Mor}_\mathscr{C}(C, A), \mathrm{Mor}_\mathscr{C}(B, A))$$

is a contravariant functor.

Proof. We prove only the first assertion. The proof of the second assertion is analogous and may be trivially reduced to the first assertion by later results on the duality of categories.

$\mathrm{Mor}_\mathscr{C}(A, 1_B)(g) = 1_B g = g$ implies $\mathrm{Mor}_\mathscr{C}(A, 1_B) = 1_{\mathrm{Mor}(A,B)}$. Let $f, g \in \mathscr{C}$ be given such that the domain of f is the range of g. Then fg exists. For all morphisms h, we have

$$\mathrm{Mor}_\mathscr{C}(A, fg)(h) = (fg)\,h = f(gh) = \mathrm{Mor}_\mathscr{C}(A, f)\,\mathrm{Mor}_\mathscr{C}(A, g)(h)$$

whenever these expressions are defined.

The functors of this lemma are the most important functors in the theory of categories. So they get a special name: $\mathrm{Mor}_\mathscr{C}(A, –)$ is called covariant and $\mathrm{Mor}_\mathscr{C}(—, A)$ contravariant *representable functor. A is called the *representing object*.

Now we want to give an example of a natural transformation. Let A and B be two sets. The map

$$A \times \mathrm{Mor}_\mathbf{S}(A, B) \ni (a, f) \mapsto f(a) \in B$$

is called the *evaluation map*. For fixed $a \in A$, the evaluation map defines a map from $\mathrm{Mor}(A, B)$ to B, the evaluation of each morphism f at the argument a. Thus we obtain a map $A \to \mathrm{Mor}(\mathrm{Mor}(A, B), B)$, labeled $\varphi(A)$. $\mathrm{Mor}(—, B)$ is a contravariant functor from $\mathbf{S}$ to $\mathbf{S}$. Then $\mathrm{Mor}(\mathrm{Mor}(—, B), B)$, as a composition of two contravariant functors, is a covariant functor from $\mathbf{S}$ to $\mathbf{S}$.

Now we show that φ is a natural transformation from $\mathrm{Id}_\mathbf{S}$ to $\mathrm{Mor}(\mathrm{Mor}(—, B), B)$. Let $g: A \to C$ be an arbitrary map of sets. We have to check the commutativity of the diagram

$$
\begin{array}{ccc}
A & \xrightarrow{\varphi(A)} & \mathrm{Mor}(\mathrm{Mor}(A, B), B) \\
{\scriptstyle g}\downarrow & & \downarrow{\scriptstyle \mathrm{Mor}(\mathrm{Mor}(g,B),B)} \\
C & \xrightarrow{\varphi(C)} & \mathrm{Mor}(\mathrm{Mor}(C, B), B)
\end{array}
$$

For $a \in A$ both $\mathrm{Mor}(\mathrm{Mor}(g, B), B)\varphi(A)(a) = \varphi(A)(a)\,\mathrm{Mor}(g, B)$ and $\varphi(C)\,g(a)$ are maps from $\mathrm{Mor}(C, B)$ into B. Let $f \in \mathrm{Mor}(C, B)$. Then

$$\varphi(A)(a)\,\mathrm{Mor}(g, B)(f) = \varphi(A)(a)(fg) = fg(a) = f(g(a)) = \varphi(C)(g(a))(f)$$

hence, $\varphi(A)(a)\,\mathrm{Mor}(g, B) = \varphi(C)\,g(a)$. So the diagram is commutative.

In linear algebra one finds a corresponding natural transformation from a vector space to its double dual space.

1.4 Duality

We already noticed for contravariant functors that they exchange the composition of morphisms in a peculiar way, or, expressed in the language of diagrams, that the direction of the arrows is reversed after the application of a contravariant functor. This remark will be used for the construction of an important functor.

Let us start with an arbitrary category $\mathscr{C}$. From $\mathscr{C}$ we construct another category $\mathscr{C}^0$ whose class of objects is the class of objects of $\mathscr{C}$ whose morphisms are defined by $\mathrm{Mor}_{\mathscr{C}^0}(A, B) := \mathrm{Mor}_{\mathscr{C}}(B, A)$, and whose compositions are defined by

$$\mathrm{Mor}_{\mathscr{C}^0}(A, B) \times \mathrm{Mor}_{\mathscr{C}^0}(B, C) \ni (f, g) \mapsto fg \in \mathrm{Mor}_{\mathscr{C}^0}(A, C)$$

with fg to be formed in $\mathscr{C}$. It is easy to verify that this composition in $\mathscr{C}^0$ is associative and that the identities of $\mathscr{C}$ are also the identities in $\mathscr{C}^0$. The category $\mathscr{C}^0$ is called the *dual category* of $\mathscr{C}$.

The applications

$$\mathscr{C} \ni A \mapsto A \in \mathscr{C}^0$$

$$\mathrm{Mor}_{\mathscr{C}}(A, B) \ni f \mapsto f \in \mathrm{Mor}_{\mathscr{C}^0}(B, A)$$

and

$$\mathscr{C}^0 \ni A \mapsto A \in \mathscr{C}$$

$$\mathrm{Mor}_{\mathscr{C}^0}(A, B) \ni f \mapsto f \in \mathrm{Mor}_{\mathscr{C}}(B, A)$$

define two contravariant functors, the composition of which is the identity on $\mathscr{C}$ and $\mathscr{C}^0$ respectively. To denote that $A\,[f]$ is considered as an object [a morphism] of $\mathscr{C}^0$ we often write $A^0\,[f^0]$ instead of $A\,[\text{or}\,f]$. By definition, we have for every category $\mathscr{C} = (\mathscr{C}^0)^0$. The functors described here will be labeled by $\mathrm{Op}: \mathscr{C} \to \mathscr{C}^0$ and $\mathrm{Op}: \mathscr{C}^0 \to \mathscr{C}$ respectively. Both functors exchange the direction of the morphisms or, in diagrams, the direction of the arrows and thereby simultaneously the order of the composition, no other composition for categories being defined. In fact we have $f^0 g^0 = (gf)^0$. If we apply this process twice, we get the identity again.

From this point of view, the second part of the lemma in Section 1.3 could be proved in the following way. Instead of examining the maps defined by $\mathrm{Mor}_{\mathscr{C}}(-, A)$: $\mathscr{C} \to \mathbf{S}$, we examine the maps $\mathrm{Mor}_{\mathscr{C}^0}(A, -)$: $\mathscr{C}^0 \to \mathbf{S}$. By the first part of the lemma, these maps form a functor. It is easy to verify that $\mathrm{Mor}_{\mathscr{C}^0}(A, -)\,\mathrm{Op} = \mathrm{Mor}_{\mathscr{C}}(-, A)$ considered as maps from $\mathscr{C}$ to $\mathbf{S}$. Consequently, $\mathrm{Mor}_{\mathscr{C}}(-, A)$ is a contravariant functor. Instead of proving the assertion for $\mathscr{C}$, we proved the "dual assertion" for $\mathscr{C}^0$, the dual assertion being the assertion with the direction of the morphisms reversed. Thus, to each assertion about a category, we get a dual assertion. An assertion is true in a category $\mathscr{C}$ if and only if the dual assertion is true in the category $\mathscr{C}^0$.

We want to describe this so-called duality principle in a more exact way with the set theory presented in the Appendix. Let $\mathfrak{F}(\mathscr{C})$ be a formula with a free class variable $\mathscr{C}$. $\mathfrak{F} = \mathfrak{F}(\mathscr{C})$ is called a theorem on categories if

$$(\wedge \mathscr{C})(\mathscr{C} \text{ is a category} \Rightarrow \mathfrak{F}(\mathscr{C}))$$

is true, that is, if the assertion $\mathfrak{F}(\mathscr{C})$ is true for all categories $\mathscr{C}$. From $\mathfrak{F}$ we derive a new formula $\mathfrak{F}^0 = \mathfrak{F}^0(\mathscr{D})$ with a free class variable $\mathscr{D}$ by

$$\mathfrak{F}^0(\mathscr{D}) = (\vee \mathscr{C})(\mathscr{C} \text{ is a category} \wedge \mathscr{C}^0 = \mathscr{D} \wedge \mathfrak{F}(\mathscr{C}))$$

that is, $\mathfrak{F}^0(\mathscr{D})$ is true for a category $\mathscr{D}$ if and only if $\mathfrak{F}(\mathscr{D}^0)$ is true because $\mathscr{C}^0 = \mathscr{D}$ implies $\mathscr{C} = \mathscr{D}^0$. If $\mathfrak{F}(\mathscr{C})$ is a theorem on categories, we get $\mathfrak{F}^0(\mathscr{C})$ from $\mathfrak{F}(\mathscr{C})$ by reversing the directions of all morphisms appearing in $\mathfrak{F}(\mathscr{C})$. This corresponds exactly to the construction of $\mathfrak{F}(\mathscr{C}^0)$. $\mathfrak{F}^0$ is called the dual formula to $\mathfrak{F}$. Thus we get the following *duality principle*:

Let $\mathfrak{F}$ be a theorem on categories. Then $\mathfrak{F}^0$, the dual formula to $\mathfrak{F}$, is also a theorem on categories, the so-called *dual theorem* to $\mathfrak{F}$.

In fact, if $\mathfrak{F}(\mathscr{C})$ is true for all categories $\mathscr{C}$, then $\mathfrak{F}(\mathscr{C}^0)$ is true for all categories $\mathscr{C}$ and consequently also $\mathfrak{F}^0(\mathscr{C})$.

When we apply this duality principle, we have to bear in mind that we dualize not only the claims of the theorems on categories but also the hypotheses. When we introduce new abbreviating notions, we have to define the corresponding dual notions also.

1.5   Monomorphisms, Epimorphisms, and Isomorphisms

In the theory of categories, one tries to generalize as many notions as possible from special categories, for example the category of sets, to arbitrary categories. An appropriate means of comparison with $\mathbf{S}$ are the morphism sets, or more precisely, the covariant representable functors from an arbitrary category $\mathscr{C}$ into $\mathbf{S}$. So the property $\mathfrak{E}$ could be assigned to an object $A \in \mathscr{C}$ [a morphism $f \in \mathscr{C}$] if A [f] is mapped by each representable functor $\mathrm{Mor}_\mathscr{C}(B, -)$ to a set [a map] in $\mathbf{S}$ with the property $\mathfrak{E}$. In order to recover the original definition in the case $\mathscr{C} = \mathbf{S}$, we have to observe further that the property $\mathfrak{E}$ of a set or map is preserved by $\mathrm{Mor}_\mathbf{S}(B, -)$ and is characterized by this condition.

We find a first application of this principle with the notion of an injective set map. Let $f : C \to D$ be an injective map. Then $\mathrm{Mor}(B, f)$: $\mathrm{Mor}(B, C) \to \mathrm{Mor}(B, D)$ is injective for all $B \in \mathbf{S}$. In fact, $\mathrm{Mor}(B, f)(g) = \mathrm{Mor}(B, f)(h)$ for all $g, h \in \mathrm{Mor}(B, C)$ implies $fg = fh$. So we have $f(g(b)) = f(h(b))$ for all $b \in B$. Since f is injective, $g(b) = h(b)$ for all $b \in B$, that is $g = h$. Consequently, it makes sense to generalize this notion because the converse follows trivially from $B = \{\varnothing\}$.

Let $\mathscr{C}$ be a category and f a morphism in $\mathscr{C}$. f is called a *monomorphism* if the map $\mathrm{Mor}_\mathscr{C}(B, f)$ is injective for all $B \in \mathscr{C}$.

We define the *epimorphism* dual to the notion of the monomorphism. Let $\mathscr{C}$ be a category and f a morphism in $\mathscr{C}$. f is called an epimorphism if the map $\mathrm{Mor}_\mathscr{C}(f, B)$ is injective for all $B \in \mathscr{C}$.

LEMMA 1.
  (a) $f : A \to B$ is a monomorphism in $\mathscr{C}$ if and only if $fg = fh$ implies $g = h$ for all $C \in \mathscr{C}$ and for all $g, h \in \mathrm{Mor}_\mathscr{C}(C, A)$, that is, if f is left cancellable.
  (b) $f : A \to B$ is an epimorphism in $\mathscr{C}$ if and only if $gf = hf$ implies $g = h$ for all $C \in \mathscr{C}$ and for all $g, h \in \mathrm{Mor}_\mathscr{C}(B, C)$, that is, if f is right cancellable.

Proof. (a) and (b) are valid because $\mathrm{Mor}(C, f)(g) = fg$ and $\mathrm{Mor}(f, C)(g) = gf$.

The following two examples show that monomorphisms [epimorphisms] are not always injective [surjective] maps if the morphisms of the category in view can be considered as set maps at all.

Examples

1.   An abelian group G is called divisible if $nG = G$ for each natural number n, that is, if for each $g \in G$ and n there is a $g' \in G$ with $ng' = g$. Let $\mathscr{C}$ be the category of divisible abelian groups and group homomor-

phisms. The residue class homomorphism $\nu : \mathbb{P} \to \mathbb{P}/\mathbb{Z}$ from the rational numbers to the rational numbers modulo the integers is a monomorphism in the category $\mathscr{C}$, for if $f, g: A \to \mathbb{P}$ are two morphisms in $\mathscr{C}$ with $f \neq g$, then there is an $a \in A$ with $f(a) - g(a) = rs^{-1} \neq 0$ and $s \neq \pm 1$. Let $b \in A$ with $rb = a$. Then $r(f(b) - g(b)) = f(a) - g(a) = rs^{-1}$, so $f(b) = g(b) \neq s^{-1}$. Therefore $\nu f(b) \neq \nu g(b)$. Thus, ν is a monomorphism which is not injective as a set map.

2.   In the category **Ri** epimorphisms are not necessarily surjective. The embedding $\lambda : \mathbb{Z} \to \mathbb{P}$, for example, is an epimorphism. Let $g, h : \mathbb{P} \to A$ be given with $g\lambda = h\lambda$. Then $g(n) = h(n)$ for all natural numbers n and $g(1) = h(1) = 1$. Hence $g(n) g(1/n) = 1 = h(n) h(1/n)$. Thus we get $g(1/n) = (g(n))^{-1} = (h(n))^{-1} = h(1/n)$ and more generally $g(p) = h(p)$ for all $p \in \mathbb{P}$, that is, λ is an epimorphism.

3.   We give a third topological example. A topological space A is called hausdorff if for any two distinct points $a, b \in A$ there are two open sets U and V with $a \in U \subseteq A$ and $b \in V \subseteq A$ such that $U \cap V = \varnothing$. The hausdorff topological spaces together with the continuous maps form a subcategory **Hd** of **Top**. A continuous map $f : A \to B$ is called dense if for every open set $U \neq \varnothing$ in B, there is an $a \in A$ with $f(a) \in U$. The embedding $\mathbb{P} \to \mathbb{R}$, for example, is a dense continuous map. We show that each dense continuous map in **Hd** is an epimorphism. Let $f : A \to B$ be such a map. Given $g : B \to C$ and $h : B \to C$ in **Hd** with $g \neq h$ such that $g(b) \neq h(b)$ for some $b \in B$. Then there are open sets U and V with $g(b) \in U \subseteq C$ and $h(b) \in V \subseteq C$ and $U \cap V = \varnothing$. The sets $g^{-1}(U) \subseteq B$ and $h^{-1}(V) \subseteq B$ are open sets with $g^{-1}(U) \cap h^{-1}(V) \ni b$, g and h being continuous. Furthermore, $g^{-1}(U) \cap h^{-1}(V)$ is a nonempty open set so that there is an $a \in A$ with $f(a) \in g^{-1}(U) \cap h^{-1}(V)$. But then $gf(a) \in U$ and $hf(a) \in V$. $U \cap V = \varnothing$ implies $gf(a) \neq hf(a)$, that is, $gf \neq hf$. $\mathbb{P}$ and $\mathbb{R}$ being hausdorff spaces the embedding $\mathbb{P} \to \mathbb{R}$ is an example of an epimorphism which is not surjective as a set map.

COROLLARY (cube lemma).   *Let five of the six sides of the cube*

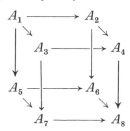

except the top be commutative and let $A_4 \to A_8$ be a monomorphism. Then the top side is also commutative.

Proof. All morphisms in the diagram from A_1 to A_8 are equal, in particular

$$A_1 \to A_3 \to A_4 \to A_8 \quad \text{and} \quad A_1 \to A_2 \to A_4 \to A_8 .$$

Since $A_4 \to A_8$ is a monomorphism, the top side is commutative.

LEMMA 2. *Let f and g be morphisms in a category which may be composed. Then:*

(a) *If fg is a monomorphism, then g is a monomorphism.*
(b) *If f and g are monomorphisms, then fg is a monomorphism.*
(c) *If fg is an epimorphism, then f is an epimorphism.*
(d) *If f and g are epimorphisms, then fg is an epimorphism.*

Proof. The assertions (c) and (d) being dual to the assertions (a) and (b), it is sufficient to prove (a) and (b). Let $gh = gk$, then $fgh = fgk$ and $h = k$. This proves (a). (b) is trivial if we note that monomorphisms are exactly the left-cancellable morphisms.

Example

Now we want to give an example of a category where the epimorphisms are exactly the surjective maps, namely the category of finite groups. The same proof works also for the category **Gr**. First, each surjective map in this category is left cancellable as a set map and consequently as a group homomorphism. So we have to show that each epimorphism $f : G' \to G$ is surjective. We have to show that the subgroup $f(G') = H$ of G coincides with G. Since f can be decomposed into $G' \to H \to G$, the injective map $H \to G$ is an epimorphism [Lemma 2(c)]. We have to show the surjectivity of this map. Let G/H be the set of left residue classes gH with $g \in G$. Furthermore, let $\text{Perm}(G/H \cup \{\infty\})$ be the group of permutations of the union of G/H with a disjoint set of one element. This group is also finite. Let σ be the permutation which exchanges $H \in G/H$ and ∞, and leaves fixed all other elements. Then $\sigma^2 = \text{id}$. Let $t : G \to \text{Perm}(G/H \cup \{\infty\})$ be the map defined by $t(g)(g'H) = gg'H$ and $t(g)(\infty) = \infty$. Then t is a group homomorphism. Let $s : G \to \text{Perm}(G/H \cup \{\infty\})$ be defined by $s(g) = \sigma t(g)\sigma$. Then s is also a group homomorphism. One verifies elementwise that $t(h) = s(h)$ for all $h \in H$. Since $H \to G$ is an epimorphism, we get $t = s$. So for all $g \in G$,

$$gH = t(g)(H) = s(g)(H) = \sigma t(g) \, \sigma(H) = \sigma t(g)(\infty) = \sigma(\infty) = H$$

This proves $H = G$.

Let $\mathscr{C}$ be again an arbitrary category. A morphism $f \in \text{Mor}_{\mathscr{C}}(A, B)$ is called an *isomorphism* if there is a morphism $g \in \text{Mor}_{\mathscr{C}}(B, A)$ such that $fg = 1_B$ and $gf = 1_A$. Two objects $A, B \in \mathscr{C}$ are called *isomorphic* if $\text{Mor}_{\mathscr{C}}(A, B)$ contains an isomorphism. Two morphisms $f : A \to B$ and $g : A' \to B'$ are called *isomorphic* if there are isomorphisms $h : A \to A'$ and $k : B \to B'$ such that the diagram

$$
\begin{array}{ccc}
A & \xrightarrow{\ f\ } & B \\
h \downarrow & & \downarrow k \\
A' & \xrightarrow{\ g\ } & B'
\end{array}
$$

is commutative.

The following assertions are immediately clear. If $f : A \to B$ is an isomorphism with $fg = 1_B$ and $gf = 1_A$, then g is also an isomorphism. We write f^{-1} instead of g because g is uniquely determined by f. The composition of two isomorphisms is again an isomorphism. The identities are isomorphisms. So the relation between objects to be isomorphic is an equivalence relation. Similarly, the relation between morphisms to be isomorphic is an equivalence relation. Isomorphic objects and morphisms are denoted by $A \cong B$ and $f \cong g$ respectively. Now let $\mathscr{F} : \mathscr{C} \to \mathscr{D}$ be a functor and $f \in \mathscr{C}$ an isomorphism with the inverse isomorphism f^{-1}. Then $\mathscr{F}(f)\mathscr{F}(f^{-1}) = \mathscr{F}(ff^{-1}) = \mathscr{F}(1) = 1$ and analogously $\mathscr{F}(f^{-1})\mathscr{F}(f) = 1$. So the fact that f is an isomorphism implies that $\mathscr{F}f$ is also an isomorphism.

A morphism $f \in \text{Mor}_{\mathscr{C}}(A, A)$ whose domain and range is the same object is called an *endomorphism*. Endomorphisms which are also isomorphisms are called *automorphisms*.

LEMMA 3. *If f is an isomorphism, then f is a monomorphism and an epimorphism.*

Proof. Since there is an inverse morphism for f, we get that f is left and right cancellable.

Note that the converse of this lemma is not true. We saw, for example, that $\lambda : \mathbb{Z} \to \mathbb{P}$ in **Ri** is an epimorphism. Since this morphism is injective as a map and since all morphisms in **Ri** are maps, λ is also left cancellable and consequently a monomorphism. λ is obviously not an isomorphism because otherwise λ would have to remain an isomorphism after the application of the forgetful functor into **S**, so λ would have to be bijective. Similarly, $\nu : \mathbb{P} \to \mathbb{P}/\mathbb{Z}$ is a monomorphism and an epimorphism in the category of divisible abelian groups, but not an isomorphism. The same is true in our example of the category of hausdorff topological spaces.

A category $\mathscr{C}$ is called *balanced* if each morphism which is a monomorphism and an epimorphism is an isomorphism. Examples are **S, Gr, Ab,** and $_R$**Mod.**

Let $\varphi : \mathscr{F} \to \mathscr{G}$ be a natural transformation of functors from $\mathscr{C}$ to $\mathscr{D}$. φ is called a *natural isomorphism* if there is a natural transformation $\psi : \mathscr{G} \to \mathscr{F}$ such that $\psi\varphi = \mathrm{id}_\mathscr{F}$ and $\varphi\psi = \mathrm{id}_\mathscr{G}$. Two functors $\mathscr{F}$ and $\mathscr{G}$ are called *isomorphic* if there is a natural transformation between them. Then we write $\mathscr{F} \cong \mathscr{G}$. Two categories are called *isomorphic* if there are functors $\mathscr{F} : \mathscr{C} \to \mathscr{D}$ and $\mathscr{G} : \mathscr{D} \to \mathscr{C}$ such that $\mathscr{G}\mathscr{F} = \mathrm{Id}_\mathscr{C}$ and $\mathscr{F}\mathscr{G} = \mathrm{Id}_\mathscr{D}$. Two categories are called *equivalent* if there are functors $\mathscr{F} : \mathscr{C} \to \mathscr{D}$ and $\mathscr{G} : \mathscr{D} \to \mathscr{C}$ such that $\mathscr{G}\mathscr{F} \cong \mathrm{Id}_\mathscr{C}$ and $\mathscr{F}\mathscr{G} \cong \mathrm{Id}_\mathscr{D}$. The functors $\mathscr{F}$ and $\mathscr{G}$ are called *equivalences* in this case. If $\mathscr{F}$ and $\mathscr{G}$ are contravariant, one often says that $\mathscr{C}$ and $\mathscr{D}$ are *dual* to each other.

If φ is a natural isomorphism with the inverse natural transformation ψ, then ψ is also a natural isomorphism and is uniquely determined by φ. φ is a natural isomorphism if and only if φ is a natural transformation and if $\varphi(A)$ is an isomorphism for all $A \in \mathscr{C}$. In fact the family $\{(\varphi(A))^{-1}\}$ for all $A \in \mathscr{C}$ is again a natural transformation.

We have to distinguish strictly between equivalent and isomorphic categories. If $\mathscr{C}$ and $\mathscr{D}$ are isomorphic, then there is a one-one correspondence between Ob $\mathscr{C}$ and Ob $\mathscr{D}$. If $\mathscr{C}$ and $\mathscr{D}$ are only equivalent, then we have only a one-one correspondence between the isomorphism classes of objects of $\mathscr{C}$ and $\mathscr{D}$ respectively. It may happen that the isomorphism classes of objects in $\mathscr{C}$ are very large, possibly even proper classes, whereas the isomorphism classes of objects in $\mathscr{D}$ consist only of one element each. It is even possible to construct for each category $\mathscr{C}$ an equivalent category $\mathscr{D}$ with this property. In order to do this, we use the axiom of choice in the formulation given in the Appendix. The notion of isomorphism defines an equivalence relation on the class of objects of $\mathscr{C}$. Let Ob $\mathscr{D}$ be a complete set of representatives for this equivalence relation. We complete Ob $\mathscr{D}$ to a category $\mathscr{D}$ by defining $\mathrm{Mor}_\mathscr{D}(A, B) = \mathrm{Mor}_\mathscr{C}(A, B)$ and by using the same composition of morphisms as in $\mathscr{C}$. Obviously $\mathscr{D}$ becomes a category. Let $\mathscr{F} : \mathscr{C} \to \mathscr{D}$ assign to each $A \in \mathscr{C}$ the corresponding representative $\mathscr{F}A$ of the isomorphism class of A. Let $\mathfrak{A}$ be the isomorphism class of A and Φ the class of those isomorphisms which exist between the elements of $\mathfrak{A}$ with range $\mathscr{F}A$. Let two isomorphisms be equivalent if their domain is the same. Then a complete set of representatives defines exactly one isomorphism between each element of $\mathfrak{A}$ and $\mathscr{F}A$. This can be done simultaneously in all isomorphism classes of objects of $\mathscr{C}$. Now let $f : A \to B$ be a morphism in $\mathscr{C}$.

Then we assign to f the morphism $\mathscr{F}f : \mathscr{F}A \to \mathscr{F}B$ defined by

$$\mathscr{F}A \simeq A \xrightarrow{f} B \simeq \mathscr{F}B$$

Because of the commutativity of

$$
\begin{array}{ccccc}
A & \xrightarrow{f} & B & \xrightarrow{g} & C \\
\wr\| & & \wr\| & & \wr\| \\
\mathscr{F}A & \xrightarrow{\mathscr{F}f} & \mathscr{F}B & \xrightarrow{\mathscr{F}g} & \mathscr{F}C
\end{array}
$$

$\mathscr{F}$ is a functor from $\mathscr{C}$ to $\mathscr{D}$. $\mathscr{D}$ being a subcategory of $\mathscr{C}$ we define $\mathscr{G} : \mathscr{D} \to \mathscr{C}$ as the forgetful functor. Trivially $\mathscr{F}\mathscr{G} = \mathrm{Id}_{\mathscr{D}}$. On the other hand, $\mathscr{F}\mathscr{G}A = \mathscr{F}A \simeq A$ for all $A \in \mathscr{C}$. The diagram

$$
\begin{array}{ccc}
\mathscr{F}\mathscr{G}A & \xrightarrow{\mathscr{F}\mathscr{G}f} & \mathscr{F}\mathscr{G}B \\
\wr\| & & \wr\| \\
A & \xrightarrow{f} & B
\end{array}
$$

is commutative for all morphisms $f \in \mathscr{C}$. Thus $\mathscr{C}$ is equivalent to $\mathscr{D}$. We call the category $\mathscr{D}$ a *skeleton* of $\mathscr{C}$.

Observe that by our definition the dual category $\mathscr{C}^0$ of $\mathscr{C}$ is dual to $\mathscr{C}$, but that, conversely, the condition that $\mathscr{D}$ is dual to $\mathscr{C}$ implies only that $\mathscr{D}$ is equivalent to $\mathscr{C}^0$. In this context we also want to mention how contravariant functors may be replaced by covariant functors. Thus it suffices to prove theorems only for covariant functors. As we saw, the isomorphism $\mathrm{Op} : \mathscr{C} \to \mathscr{C}^0$ (because of the contravariance of Op this is also called *antiisomorphism*) has the property $\mathrm{Op}\mathrm{Op} = \mathrm{Id}$. If $\mathscr{F} : \mathscr{C} \to \mathscr{D}$ is a contravariant functor, then $\mathscr{F}\mathrm{Op} : \mathscr{C}^0 \to \mathscr{D}$ and $\mathrm{Op}\mathscr{F} : \mathscr{C} \to \mathscr{D}^0$ are covariant functors, which may again be transformed into $\mathscr{F}$ by an additional composition with Op. If $\mathscr{F}$ and $\mathscr{G}$ are contravariant functors from $\mathscr{C}$ to $\mathscr{D}$ and if $\varphi : \mathscr{F} \to \mathscr{G}$ is a natural transformation, then we get corresponding natural transformations $\varphi\mathrm{Op} : \mathscr{F}\mathrm{Op} \to \mathscr{G}\mathrm{Op}$ and $\mathrm{Op}\varphi : \mathrm{Op}\mathscr{G} \to \mathrm{Op}\mathscr{F}$, as is easily verified. Let $\mathscr{C}$ be a small category, and let us denote the category of contravariant functors from $\mathscr{C}$ to $\mathscr{D}$ by $\mathrm{Funct}^0(\mathscr{C},\mathscr{D})$, then the described applications between co- and contravariant functors define isomorphisms of categories

$$\mathrm{Funct}^0(\mathscr{C}, \mathscr{D}) \simeq \mathrm{Funct}(\mathscr{C}^0, \mathscr{D}) \quad \text{and} \quad \mathrm{Funct}^0(\mathscr{C}, \mathscr{D}) \simeq \mathrm{Funct}(\mathscr{C}, \mathscr{D}^0)^0$$

We leave the verification of the particular properties to the reader. In particular, we get $\mathrm{Funct}(\mathscr{C}, \mathscr{D}) \simeq \mathrm{Funct}(\mathscr{C}^0, \mathscr{D}^0)^0$.

1.6 Subobjects and Quotient Objects

Let $\mathscr{C}$ be a category. Let $\mathfrak{M}$ be the class of monomorphisms of $\mathscr{C}$. We define an equivalence relation on $\mathfrak{M}$ by the following condition. Two monomorphisms $f : A \to B$ and $g : C \to D$ are equivalent if $B = D$ and if there are two morphisms $h : A \to C$ and $k : C \to A$ such that the diagrams

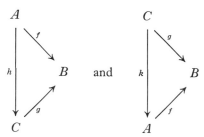

are commutative. Obviously this is an equivalence relation on $\mathfrak{M}$. Let $\mathfrak{U}$ be a complete set of representatives for this equivalence relation. $\mathfrak{U}$ exists by the axiom of choice. Let f and g be equivalent. Then $f = gh$ and $g = fk$, hence $f1_A = f = fkh$ and $g1_C = g = ghk$. Since f and g are left cancellable, we get $1_A = kh$ and $1_C = hk$, thus $A \simeq C$.

Let $B \in \mathscr{C}$. A *subobject* of B is a monomorphism in $\mathfrak{U}$ with range B. A subobject f of B is said to be *smaller* than a subobject g of B if there is a morphism $h \in \mathscr{C}$ such that $f = gh$. By Section 1.5, Lemma 2(a) and since g is cancellable, h is a uniquely determined monomorphism.

LEMMA 1.   *The subobjects of an object $B \in \mathscr{C}$ form an ordered class.*

Proof.   Let $f \leqslant g$ and $g \leqslant h$ be subobjects of B. Then $f = gk$ and $g = hk'$, hence $f = hk'k$, that is, $f \leqslant h$. Furthermore, we get $f \leqslant f$ by $f = f1_A$ if A is the domain of f. Finally, if $f \leqslant g$ and $g \leqslant f$, then f and g are equivalent, so $f = g$.

Instead of the monomorphism which is a subobject we shall often give only its domain and call the domain a subobject. Thus we can again interpret a subobject as an object in $\mathscr{C}$, tacitly assuming that the corresponding monomorphism is known. Observe that a monomorphism is not uniquely determined by the specification of the domain and the range so that an object may be a subobject of another object in different ways. In **S**, for example, there are two different monomorphisms from a one point set into a two point set. If $f \leqslant g$ for subobjects $f : A \to C$ and $g : B \to C$, then we often write $A \subseteq B \subseteq C$.

The ordered class of the subobjects of an object $B \in \mathscr{C}$ is called the *power class* of B. If the power class of each object of a category $\mathscr{C}$ is a set, then $\mathscr{C}$ is called a *locally small category*. Then the power classes are also called *power sets*.

Let $\mathscr{C}$ be a locally small category. Let U be a subset of the power set of the subobjects of $B \in \mathscr{C}$. A subobject $A \in U$ is said to be *minimal* in U if $A' \in U$ and $A' \subseteq A$ always implies $A' = A$. The power set of the subobjects of $B \in \mathscr{C}$ is called *artinian* if, in each nonempty subset of the power set of the subobjects of B, there is a minimal subobject. A subobject $A \in U$ is said to be *maximal* in U if $A' \in U$ and $A \subseteq A'$ always implies $A' = A$. The power set of the subobjects of $B \in \mathscr{C}$ is called *noetherian* if, in each nonempty subset of the power set of the subobjects of B, there is a maximal subobject. If the power set is artinian or noetherian, then we also call B an *artinian* or *noetherian object* respectively. If all objects of $\mathscr{C}$ are artinian or noetherian, then the category $\mathscr{C}$ is said to be *artinian* or *noetherian* respectively. A subset K of the power set of B is called a *chain* if for any two subobjects $A, A' \in K$ we always have $A \subseteq A'$ or $A' \subseteq A$. We say that $B \in \mathscr{C}$ complies with the *minimum condition* [*maximum condition*] *for chains* if each nonempty chain in the power set of B contains a minimal [maximal] element.

LEMMA 2.   *An object $B \in \mathscr{C}$ complies with the minimum condition [maximum condition] for chains if and only if B is artinian [noetherian].*

Proof. If B is artinian, then in particular B complies with the minimum condition for chains. Let B comply with the minimum condition for chains and let U be a subset of the power set of B which does not contain a minimal subobject. Then to each subobject $A_i \in U$ there is a subobject $A_{i+1} \in U$ with $A_{i+1} \subseteq A_i$ and $A_{i+1} \neq A_i$. This will also be written as $A_{i+1} \subset A_i$. So we get a chain K with no minimal element in contradiction to the hypothesis. Thus B is artinian. The equivalence of the maximum condition for chains with the condition that B is noetherian may be shown analogously.

One easily shows that the subobjects in **S**, **Gr**, **Ab**, or **Ri** are the subsets, subgroups, abelian subgroups or subrings with the same unit together with the natural inclusions. In **Top** the subsets of a topological space equipped with a topology in such a way that the inclusion maps are continuous are the subobjects of the topological space. The so-called subspaces of a topological space have additional properties and will be discussed in Section 1.9.

By dualizing we obtain the notion of the *quotient object*, the *copower class* and the *locally cosmall category*. The discussed properties may be dualized similarly.

The property of being a subobject is transitive in **S, Gr, Ab, Ri, Top, S***, and **Top***; that is, if A is a subobject of B and if B is a subobject of C, then A is a subobject of C. This, however, is not the case if one considers quotient objects, for example, in **Ab**, since the quotient object of a quotient object has as elements residue classes of residue classes whereas a quotient object has as elements residue classes (of the original object). So this transitivity cannot be expected in a general form and, in fact, is not implied by our definition of subobjects and quotient objects.

1.7 Zero Objects and Zero Morphisms

An object A in a category $\mathscr{C}$ is called an *initial object* if $\mathrm{Mor}_{\mathscr{C}}(A, B)$ consists of exactly one element for all $B \in \mathscr{C}$. The notion dual to initial object is *final object*. An object is called a *zero object* if it is an initial and a final object.

LEMMA 1.   *All initial objects are isomorphic.*

Proof.   Let A and B be initial objects. Then there is exactly one morphism $f : A \to B$ and exactly one morphism $g : B \to A$. The composition fg [gf] is the unique morphism 1_B [1_A] which exists in $\mathrm{Mor}_{\mathscr{C}}(B, B)$ [$\mathrm{Mor}_{\mathscr{C}}(A, A)$]. Thus f and g are isomorphisms.

LEMMA 2.   *A zero object 0 of a category $\mathscr{C}$ is in a unique way a subobject of each object $B \in \mathscr{C}$ up to isomorphisms of zero objects.*

Proof.   Since $\mathrm{Mor}_{\mathscr{C}}(C, 0)$ consists of exactly one element for all $C \in \mathscr{C}$, the unique morphism $f : 0 \to B$ is a monomorphism for all B, for $\mathrm{Mor}_{\mathscr{C}}(C, f) : \mathrm{Mor}_{\mathscr{C}}(C, 0) \to \mathrm{Mor}_{\mathscr{C}}(C, B)$ is always injective. The subobject of B which represents f must have as domain a zero object isomorphic to 0.

A morphism $f : A \to B$ in C is called a *left zero morphism* if $fg = fh$ for all $g, h \in \mathrm{Mor}_{\mathscr{C}}(C, A)$ and all $C \in \mathscr{C}$. Dually we define a *right zero morphism*. f is called a *zero morphism* if f is a right and left zero morphism.

LEMMA 3.

(a)   *If f is a right zero morphism and g is a left zero morphism and if fg is defined, then fg is a zero morphism.*

(b) *Let A be an initial object. Then $f : A \to B$ is always a right zero morphism.*

(c) *Let 0 be a zero object. Then $f : 0 \to B$ and $g : C \to 0$ and consequently also $fg : C \to B$ are zero morphisms.*

Proof. The assertions are direct consequences of the definitions of the particular notions.

A category $\mathscr{C}$ is called a *category with zero morphisms* if there is a family

$$\{0_{(A,B)} \in \mathrm{Mor}_{\mathscr{C}}(A, B) \qquad \text{for all} \quad A, B \in \mathscr{C}\}$$

with

$$f0_{(A,B)} = 0_{(A,C)} \qquad \text{and} \qquad 0_{(B,C)}g = 0_{(A,B)}$$

for all $A, B, C \in \mathscr{C}$ and all $f \in \mathrm{Mor}_{\mathscr{C}}(B, C)$ and $g \in \mathrm{Mor}_{\mathscr{C}}(A, B)$. The $0_{(A,B)}$ are zero morphisms because $f0_{(A,B)} = 0_{(A,C)} = h0_{(A,B)}$, and correspondingly for the other side. The family $\{0_{(A,B)}\}$ of these zero morphisms is uniquely determined. For if $\{0'_{(A,B)}\}$ is another family of zero morphisms, then

$$0_{(A,B)} = 0_{(A,B)}0'_{(A,A)} = 0'_{(A,B)} \qquad \text{for all} \quad A, B \in \mathscr{C}$$

LEMMA 4.   *A category with a zero object is a category with zero morphisms.*

Proof. The zero morphisms $0_{(A,B)}$ are constructed as in Lemma 3(c). The rest of the assertion is proved by the commutativity of the diagrams

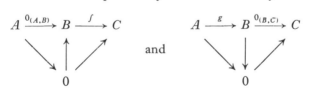

The category $\mathscr{C}$ is a category with zero morphisms if and only if the sets $\mathrm{Mor}_{\mathscr{C}}(A, B)$ are pointed sets and the maps $\mathrm{Mor}_{\mathscr{C}}(f, -)$ and $\mathrm{Mor}_{\mathscr{C}}(-, g)$ are pointed maps (in the sense of Section 1.1, Example 3). Thus $\mathscr{C}$ is said to be a *pointed category*. In $\mathscr{C}$ the distinguished points of $\mathrm{Mor}_{\mathscr{C}}(A, B)$ are uniquely determined by the condition that $\mathrm{Mor}_{\mathscr{C}}(f, -)$ and $\mathrm{Mor}_{\mathscr{C}}(-, g)$ are pointed set maps.

In the category $\mathbf{S}$ an initial object is $\varnothing$ and a final object is $\{\varnothing\}$. Zero objects do not exist. The only zero morphisms have the form $\varnothing \to A$. In the category $\mathbf{S}^*$ each set with one point is a zero object. Thus there are zero morphisms between all objects. Similarly, the set with one point with the corresponding structure is a zero object in the categories **Gr**, **Ab**, and **Top***. In **Top** an initial object is $\varnothing$ and a final object is $\{\varnothing\}$. In **Ri** an initial object is $\mathbb{Z}$, and the set with one point and the trivial ring structure, the so-called zero ring, is a final object. The mono- and epimorphism $\lambda : \mathbb{Z} \to \mathbb{P}$, known from previous examples, is a right zero morphism but not a left zero morphism.

1.8 Diagrams

In this section we want to make precise the notion of a diagram introduced in Section 1.2. Thus a diagram in a category $\mathscr{C}$ will be a functor from a diagram scheme $\mathscr{D}$, that is, from a small category $\mathscr{D}$ (see Section 1.1), into the category $\mathscr{C}$. If the diagram scheme is finite, one says that the diagram is finite, and one illustrates the functor by its image. In this case we write down the objects in the image of the functor $\mathscr{F}$ and the morphisms as arrows between the objects. We omit the identities and often also morphisms which arise from other morphisms by composition. The commutativities which shall hold for all diagrams over the diagram scheme $\mathscr{D}$ are expressed by equality of morphisms in $\mathscr{D}$. Certainly, for certain diagrams additional parts may become commutative because of the particular properties of the objects and morphisms in the image of $\mathscr{F}$.

Observe that the image of a functor, that is, the image of the map of objects and the maps of morphisms, does not form a category in general. In fact it is not necessary that all possible compositions of morphisms in the image are again in the image. For example, let $\mathscr{F} : \mathscr{D} \to \mathscr{C}$ be a functor with $\mathscr{F}A = \mathscr{F}B$ for two different objects $A, B \in \mathscr{D}$. Then two morphisms $f : C \to A$ and $g : B \to D$ cannot be composed in $\mathscr{D}$ but

$$\mathscr{F}C \xrightarrow{\mathscr{F}f} \mathscr{F}A = \mathscr{F}B \xrightarrow{\mathscr{F}g} \mathscr{F}D$$

and thus $\mathscr{F}g\mathscr{F}f$ is not necessarily contained in the image of $\mathscr{F}$. The image of a functor $\mathscr{F}$, however, is a category if $\mathscr{F}$ is an injective map on the class of objects.

As in Section 2.1 we can form the category Funct($\mathscr{D}, \mathscr{C}$). The objects of this category are diagrams. One also calls this category the diagram category. We observe that only the point of view differs from the one in Section 1.2. The category certainly is a functor category. It is interesting to know how the morphisms between two diagrams can be illustrated. Let us clarify this with an example.

Let $\mathscr{D}$ be a category with three objects X, Y, Z and six morphisms 1_X, 1_Y, 1_Z, $x : X \to Y$, $y : Y \to Z$, and $z = yx : X \to Z$. Let $\mathscr{F}$ and $\mathscr{G}$ be two diagrams and let $\varphi : \mathscr{F} \to \mathscr{G}$ be a morphism of diagrams. Then we can present all these data with the diagram

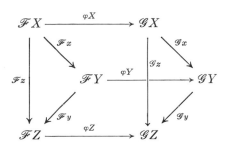

where all four quadrangles are commutative because φ is a natural transformation. The category constructed here is also called the category of commutative triangles in $\mathscr{C}$. The morphisms between diagrams are also families of morphisms, one for each pair of corresponding objects in two diagrams, such that these morphisms commute with the morphisms in the particular diagrams.

Now let us take a fixed diagram in the sense of Section 1.2, which consists of a set of objects and morphisms, and let us ask the question whether this can be considered a diagram in the sense defined above. For that purpose, we form the subcategory $\mathscr{B}$ of $\mathscr{C}$ with the same objects as given in the diagram and with all morphisms of $\mathscr{C}$ between them. $\mathscr{B}$ is a small category. Now let $\{\mathscr{A}_i\}_{i \in I}$ be a family of small subcategories of $\mathscr{B}$, then $\bigcap_{i \in I} \mathscr{A}_i$, defined as the intersection of the corresponding sets of objects together with the intersection of the sets of morphisms, is a small subcategory of $\mathscr{B}$. The composition is the one induced by $\mathscr{B}$. Let us choose for the $\mathscr{A}_i$ only those subcategories that contain all objects and morphisms of the given diagram. Then $\bigcap \mathscr{A}_i$ is the smallest subcategory of $\mathscr{C}$ which contains all objects and all morphisms of the diagram. Thereby the given diagram is completed by additional morphisms which occur as compositions of given morphisms or as identities. The small category we obtained in this way will be considered as the diagram scheme for our diagram.

If the diagram scheme consists of two objects X and Y and of three morphisms 1_X, 1_Y, and $x : X \to Y$, then we call this category $\mathbf{2}$. The diagrams of $\mathrm{Funct}(\mathbf{2}, \mathscr{C})$ are in one-one correspondence to the morphisms of $\mathscr{C}$. Thus one calls $\mathrm{Funct}(\mathbf{2}, \mathscr{C})$ the *morphism category* of $\mathscr{C}$. A morphism in Funct(2, $\mathscr{C}$) between two morphisms $f : A \rightarrow B$ and $g : C \rightarrow D$ is a commutative diagram

$$
\begin{array}{ccc}
A & \longrightarrow & C \\
f\downarrow & & \downarrow g \\
B & \longrightarrow & D
\end{array}
$$

1.9   Difference Kernels and Difference Cokernels

As in Section 1.5, we want to generalize again a notion from **S** to arbitrary categories. For this purpose, let $f : A \rightarrow B$ and $g : A \rightarrow B$ be two set maps in **S**. Then for f and g we can define a set C by

$$
C = \{c \mid c \in A \quad \text{and} \quad f(c) = g(c)\}
$$

For an arbitrary object $D \in \mathbf{S}$ we consider

$$
\text{Mor}(D, C) \xrightarrow{\text{Mor}(D, i)} \text{Mor}(D, A) \underset{\text{Mor}(D,g)}{\overset{\text{Mor}(D,f)}{\rightrightarrows}} \text{Mor}(D, B)
$$

where $i : C \rightarrow A$ is the inclusion. By $fi = gi$, we also have

$$
\text{Mor}(D, f)\,\text{Mor}(D, i) = \text{Mor}(D, g)\,\text{Mor}(D, i).
$$

Conversely, if $h \in \text{Mor}(D, A)$ with $\text{Mor}(D, f)(h) = \text{Mor}(D, g)(h)$, that is, $fh = gh$, then $f(h(d)) = g(h(d))$ for all $d \in D$. Thus all elements of the form $h(d)$ are already in C, that is,

$$
h = (D \xrightarrow{h'} C \xrightarrow{i} A) \qquad \text{or} \qquad h = \text{Mor}(D, i)(h')
$$

Since i is injective and also $\text{Mor}(D, i)$, we can use $\text{Mor}(D, i)$ to identify $\text{Mor}(D, C)$ with the set of morphisms in $\text{Mor}(D, A)$ which are mapped onto the same morphism by $\text{Mor}(D, f)$ and $\text{Mor}(D, g)$. We shall prove in a more general form that this property determines the set C and the injection i uniquely up to an isomorphism, as required for the generalization. We want to reformulate the conditions for the morphism sets. For each pair of morphisms (f, g) from A to B, we constructed a morphism $i : C \rightarrow A$ which satisfies the following condition: If $D \in \mathbf{S}$ and $h \in \text{Mor}(D, A)$ and if $fh = gh$, then there is exactly one morphism $h' \in \text{Mor}(D, C)$ such that $h = ih'$.

Let $\mathscr{C}$ be a category. Let $f : A \rightarrow B$ and $g : A \rightarrow B$ be morphisms in $\mathscr{C}$. A morphism $i : C \rightarrow A$ is called a *difference kernel* of the pair (f, g)

if $fi = gi$ and if to each object $D \in \mathscr{C}$ and to each morphisms $h : D \to A$ with $fh = gh$, there is exactly one morphism $h' : D \to C$ with $h = ih'$. The morphisms considered form the following diagram:

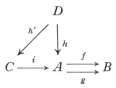

LEMMA 1. *Each difference kernel is a monomorphism.*

Proof. Let i be a difference kernel of (f, g). Let $h, k : D \to C$ be given with $ih = ik$. Then $f(ih) = g(ih)$. Also by definition there is exactly one morphism $h' : D \to C$ with $(ih) = ih'$. But h as well as k comply with this condition. By uniqueness we get $h = k$.

LEMMA 2. *If $i : C \to A$ and $i' : C' \to A$ are difference kernels of the pair (f, g), then there is a uniquely determined isomorphism $k : C \to C'$ such that $i = i'k$.*

Proof. Let us apply the fact that i is a difference kernel to the morphism i'; then we obtain exactly one $k' : C' \to C$ with $i' = ik'$. Correspondingly, one obtains exactly one $k : C \to C'$ with $i = i'k$. Thus the uniqueness of k is already proved. Furthermore, both assertions together imply $i = ik'k$ and $i' = i'kk'$. Since i and i' are monomorphisms by Lemma 1, we get $k'k = 1_C$ and $kk' = 1_{C'}$.

In the special case of **S**, this lemma proves also that if a morphism $i' : C' \to A$ with $fi' = gi'$ complies with the conditions on the diagram of the morphism sets, then i' can be composed with an isomorphism such that the composite is the morphism i. Thus we get from the generalization of the notion given in the beginning only isomorphic sets with uniquely determined isomorphisms. Apart from that, the notion is preserved.

Here we meet for the first time an example of the so-called universal problem. In the class of morphisms h with $fh = gh$ the difference kernel i is universal in the sense that each h of this class may be factored through $i : h = ih'$.

A category $\mathscr{C}$ is said to have difference kernels if there is a difference kernel to each pair of morphisms in $\mathscr{C}$ with common domain and range. We call $\mathscr{C}$ a *category with difference kernels*. Instead of calling the morphism i a difference kernel, we often only call its domain C a difference kernel assuming that the corresponding morphism is known. We acted similarly in the case of subobjects. Since a difference kernel is a monomorphism, there is an equivalent monomorphism which is a subobject. This again is a difference kernel of the same pair of morphisms. Subobjects which are simultaneously a difference kernel of a pair of morphisms are called *difference subobjects*.

Let $\mathscr{C}$ be a category with zero morphisms. Let $f : A \to B$ be a morphism in $\mathscr{C}$. A morphism $g : C \to A$ is called a *kernel* of f if $fg = 0_{(C,B)}$ and if to each morphism $h : D \to A$ with $fh = 0_{(D,B)}$ there is exactly one morphism $k : D \to C$ with $h = gk$.

LEMMA 3. *Let g be a kernel of f. Then g is a difference kernel of $(f, 0_{(A,B)})$.*

Proof. By the properties of the zero morphisms in $\mathscr{C}$, we have that $fh = 0_{(D,B)}$ implies $fh = f0_{(D,A)}$ and conversely. Thus the claim follows directly from the definition.

In particular, kernels are uniquely determined up to an isomorphism, and they form difference subobjects. Since the notions of a kernel and a difference kernel are different notions in general, the kernels which appear as subobjects get the name *normal subobjects*.

Dually to the notions defined in this section we define *difference cokernels, categories with difference cokernels, difference quotient objects, cokernels,* and *normal quotient objects*. For all theorems proved above, there are dual theorems.

The difference kernel of a pair of morphisms (f, g) is denoted by $\mathrm{Ker}(f, g)$ and the difference cokernel by $\mathrm{Cok}(f, g)$. The kernel and cokernel of a morphism f will be denoted by $\mathrm{Ker}(f)$ and $\mathrm{Cok}(f)$ respectively. In all cases, we consider the given notations as objects in the given category and assume that the corresponding morphisms are known.

Categories with difference kernels and difference cokernels are **S**, **S***, **Top, Top***, **Gr, Ab, Ri**, and $_R$**Mod**. We want to give the construction of a difference cokernel in **S**. Let two maps $f, g : A \to B$ be given. Take the smallest equivalence relation on the set B under which $f(a)$ and $g(a)$ are equivalent for all $a \in A$. The equivalence classes of this equivalence relation form a set C, onto which B is mapped in the obvious way. This map is a difference cokernel of (f, g), as may easily be verified. Compare Problem 1.6 for the properties of **Top**. The properties of **Top*** arise analogously from the properties of **S***. In Chapter 3 we shall deal with **S***, **Gr, Ab, Ri**, and $_R$**Mod** in more detail.

1.10   Sections and Retractions

A morphism $f : A \to B$ in a category $\mathscr{C}$ is called a *section* if there is a morphism g in $\mathscr{C}$ such that $gf = 1_A$. f is called a *retraction* if there is a morphism g in $\mathscr{C}$ such that $fg = 1_B$. If f is a section with $gf = 1_A$, then, by definition, g is a retraction and conversely. In general each section determines several retractions, and conversely. The notions section and retraction are dual to each other.

LEMMA 1.   *Each section is a difference kernel.*

Proof.   Let $f : A \to B$ be a section and g be a corresponding retraction. We show that f is a difference kernel of $(fg, 1_B)$. First, $fgf = f = 1_B f$. Let $h : C \to B$ be given with $fgh = 1_B h = h$. Then by $h = f(gh)$ the morphism h may be factored through f. If $h = fh'$, then $gh = gfh' = h'$, that is, the factorization is unique.

LEMMA 2.   *Let $\mathscr{F} : \mathscr{C} \to \mathscr{D}$ be a functor and f be a section in $\mathscr{C}$. Then $\mathscr{F}f$ is a section in $\mathscr{D}$.*

Proof.   Let g be a retraction for f. Then $gf = 1_B$, so $\mathscr{F}g\mathscr{F}f = 1_{\mathscr{F}B}$.

LEMMA 3.   *$f : A \to B$ is a section in the category $\mathscr{C}$ if and only if $\mathrm{Mor}_{\mathscr{C}}(f, C) : \mathrm{Mor}_{\mathscr{C}}(B, C) \to \mathrm{Mor}_{\mathscr{C}}(A, C)$ is surjective for all $C \in \mathscr{C}$.*

Proof.   Let f be a section with a corresponding retraction g, and let $h \in \mathrm{Mor}(A, C)$. Then $h = h(gf) = (hg)f = \mathrm{Mor}(f, C)(hg)$. Conversely, let $\mathrm{Mor}(f, C)$ be surjective for all $C \in \mathscr{C}$. For $C = A$, there is a $g \in \mathrm{Mor}(B, A)$ with $\mathrm{Mor}(f, A)(g) = 1_A$, consequently $fg = 1_A$.

The assertion of this lemma is of special interest in view of the definition of a monomorphism or an epimorphism. When dualizing theorems on categories, be careful not to dualize also the notions used in **S**.

In **S** all injective maps are sections except the map $\varnothing \to A$ with $A \neq \varnothing$. All surjective set maps are retractions. In **Ab** the map $\mathbb{Z} \ni n \mapsto 2n \in \mathbb{Z}$ is a kernel of the residue class homomorphism $\mathbb{Z} \to \mathbb{Z}/2\mathbb{Z}$; however, it is not a section. In fact, if $g : \mathbb{Z} \to \mathbb{Z}$ were a corresponding retraction, then $2g(1) = 1 \in \mathbb{Z}$. But there is no such element $g(1)$ in $\mathbb{Z}$.

1.11   Products and Coproducts

Another important notion in the category of sets is the notion of a product of two sets A and B. The product is the set of pairs

$$A \times B = \{(a, b) \mid a \in A \quad \text{and} \quad b \in B\}$$

Furthermore, there are maps

$$p_A : A \times B \ni (a, b) \mapsto a \in A \qquad \text{and} \qquad p_B : A \times B \ni (a, b) \mapsto b \in B$$

We want to investigate whether this notion can again be generalized in the desired way to morphism sets. First, one obtains for an arbitrary set C

$$\mathrm{Mor_S}(C, A \times B) \cong \mathrm{Mor_S}(C, A) \times \mathrm{Mor_S}(C, B)$$

using the following applications. To $h : C \to A \times B$ one assigns $(p_A h, p_B h) \in \mathrm{Mor}(C, A) \times \mathrm{Mor}(C, B)$, and to a pair $(f, g) \in \mathrm{Mor}(C, A) \times \mathrm{Mor}(C, B)$ one assigns the map $C \ni c \mapsto (f(c), g(c)) \in A \times B$. Furthermore, there are maps $\mathrm{Mor}(C, A \times B) \ni h \mapsto p_A h \in \mathrm{Mor}(C, A)$ and $\mathrm{Mor}(C, A \times B) \ni h \mapsto p_B h \in \mathrm{Mor}(C, B)$, which are transferred by the bijection given above into the maps

$$\mathrm{Mor}(C, A) \times \mathrm{Mor}(C, B) \ni (f, g) \mapsto f \in \mathrm{Mor}(C, A)$$

and

$$\mathrm{Mor}(C, A) \times \mathrm{Mor}(C, B) \ni (f, g) \mapsto g \in \mathrm{Mor}(C, B)$$

In this way the product and the corresponding maps p_A and p_B are transferred to the morphism sets up to isomorphisms. We shall prove in a more general context that this property characterizes products in **S**.

The isomorphism of the morphism sets found above may be also expressed in the following way: To each pair of maps $f : C \to A$ and $g : C \to B$, there is exactly one map $h : C \to A \times B$ such that $f = p_A h$ and $g = g_B h$.

Let $\mathscr{C}$ be a category, and let $A, B \in \mathscr{C}$ be given. A triple $(A \times B, p_A, p_B)$ with $A \times B$ an object in $\mathscr{C}$ and

$$p_A : A \times B \to A \qquad \text{and} \qquad p_B : A \times B \to B$$

morphisms in $\mathscr{C}$ is said to be a *product* of A and B in $\mathscr{C}$ if to each object $C \in \mathscr{C}$ and to each pair (f, g) of morphisms with $f : C \to A$ and $g : C \to B$, there is exactly one morphism $h : C \to A \times B$ such that $f = p_A h$ and $g = p_B h$. Then the morphisms form the following commutative diagram

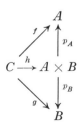

The morphisms p_A and p_B are called *projections*. Often we write (f, g) instead of h. If $C = A \times B$, then $(p_A, p_B) = 1_{A \times B}$ by the uniqueness of (p_A, p_B).

We generalize the notion of a product to an arbitrary family $\{A_i\}_{i \in I}$ of objects in $\mathscr{C}$ where I is a set. An object $\prod_{i \in I} A_i$ together with a family $\{p_i : \prod_{i \in I} A_i \to A_i\}_{i \in I}$ of morphisms is called a *product* of the A_i if to each object $C \in \mathscr{C}$ and to each family $\{f_i : C \to A_i\}_{i \in I}$ of morphisms there is exactly one morphism $h : C \to \prod_{i \in I} A_i$ such that $f_i = p_i h$ for all $i \in I$. The morphisms p_i are called *projections* again, and instead of h, we often write (f_i). As above we have $(p_i) = 1_{\prod A_i}$. If I is a finite set, then we also write $A_1 \times \cdots \times A_n$ instead of $\prod_{i \in I} A_i$ and $(f_1, ..., f_n)$ instead of (f_i). If $I = \varnothing$, then to each object $C \in \mathscr{C}$ there must be exactly one morphism h from C into the empty product E. In this case, the conditions on the morphisms f_i are empty. Thus this requirement says that E is a final object. Conversely each final object is also a product on an empty set of objects.

LEMMA 1. *Let $(A, \{p_i\})$ and $(B, \{q_i\})$ be products of the family $\{A_i\}_{i \in I}$ in $\mathscr{C}$. Then there is a uniquely determined isomorphism $k : A \to B$ such that $p_i = q_i k$.*

Proof. In the commutative diagram (for all $i \in I$)

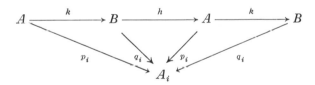

there is a unique k, because $(B, \{q_i\})$ is a product, and a unique h, because $(A, \{p_i\})$ is a product. hk as well as 1_A make both left triangles commutative. $(A, \{p_i\})$ being a product, this morphism must be unique; thus $hk = 1_A$. Correspondingly, one has from both right triangles $kh = 1_B$.

This shows that the product in **S** is already uniquely determined up to an isomorphism by the condition on the morphism sets. Here we have another universal problem. For all families of morphisms into the particular factors with common domain, the product has the property that these families may be factored through the product with a uniquely determined morphism. Often we call product only the corresponding object of a product and assume that the projections are known. If each [finite, nonempty] family of objects in $\mathscr{C}$ has a product, then we call $\mathscr{C}$ a *category, with [finite, nonempty] products*. If $(A, \{p_{i1}\})$ is a product of a family of objects $\{A_i\}_{i\in I}$ in $\mathscr{C}$ and if $h : B \to A$ is an isomorphism, then $(B, \{p_i h\})$ is another product for the A_i.

LEMMA 2. *Assume that in the category $\mathscr{C}$ there is a product for each pair of objects. Then $\mathscr{C}$ is a category with finite, nonempty products.*

Proof. Let $A_1,..., A_n$ be a family of objects in $\mathscr{C}$. We show that $(\cdots (A_1 \times A_2) \times \cdots) \times A_n$ is a product of the A_i. For an induction, it is sufficient to prove that $(A_1 \times \cdots \times A_{n-1}) \times A_n$ is a product of the A_i. Let $p_n : (A_1 \times \cdots \times A_{n-1}) \times A_n \to A_n$ and

$$q : (A_1 \times \cdots \times A_{n-1}) \times A_n \to A_1 \times \cdots \times A_{n-1}$$

be the projections of the outer product and p_i $(i = 1,..., n - 1)$ be the projections of the inner product. Let $\{f_i\}$ be a family of morphisms with common domain B and ranges A_i. Then there is exactly one $h : B \to A_1 \times \cdots \times A_{n-1}$ through which the f_i $(i = 1,..., n - 1)$ may be factored. For h and f_n, there is exactly one $k : B \to (A_1 \times \cdots \times A_{n-1}) \times A_n$ with $qk = h$ and $p_n k = f_n$. Then $p_n k = f_n$ and $p_i qk = f_i$, $i = 1,..., n - 1$. The $p_1 q,..., p_{n-1} q, p_n$ are the projections. k is uniquely determined by the given properties of the factorization.

Similarly to the proof given above, one can also break up infinite products; specifically, one can split off a single factor by

$$\prod_{i\in I} A_i \cong A_j \times \prod_{i\in J} A_i \quad \text{with} \quad J \cup \{j\} = I \quad \text{and} \quad j \notin J$$

Thus, the product is independent of the order of the factors up to an isomorphism and is associative.

LEMMA 3. *Let $\{A_i\}_{i\in I}$ be a family of objects in a category $\mathscr{C}$, and let there be a product $(A, \{p_i\})$ for this family. p_j is a retraction if and only if $\operatorname{Mor}_{\mathscr{C}}(A_j, A_i) \neq \varnothing$ for all $i \in I$ and $i \neq j$.*

Proof. Assume $\operatorname{Mor}_{\mathscr{C}}(A_j, A_i) \neq \varnothing$. Then there is a family of morphisms $f_i : A_j \to A_i$ for all $i \in I$ with $f_j = 1_{A_j}$. The corresponding morphism $f : A_j \to A$ has the property $p_j f = 1_{A_j}$. Conversely, let p_j be a retraction with a section $f : A_j \to A$. Then $p_i f \in \operatorname{Mor}_{\mathscr{C}}(A_j, A_i)$ for all $i \in I$.

The last lemma shows in particular that in a category with zero morphisms the projections of a product are always retractions. In **S** the product of a nonempty set A with $\varnothing$ is the empty set. Thus $p_A : \varnothing \to A$ cannot be a retraction. One easily shows that p_A is not even an epimorphism.

Let $\{A_i\}_{i \in I}$ be a family of objects in a category $\mathscr{C}$ with $A_i = A$ for all $i \in I$. Let B be the product of the A_i with the projections p_i. The identities $1_A : A \to A_i$ induce a morphism $\varDelta : A \to B$ called the *diagonal*. A well-known example for this map is $\mathbb{R} \ni x \mapsto (x, x) \in \mathbb{R} \times \mathbb{R}$ in **S**.

The notions dual to the notions introduced up to now are *coproduct* with the corresponding *injections*, *category with* [*finite, nonempty*] *coproducts*, and *codiagonal*. The coproduct of a family $\{A_i\}_{i \in I}$ will be denoted by $\coprod A_i$. The product has been defined in such a way that

$$\prod \text{Mor}_{\mathscr{C}}(B, A_i) \cong \text{Mor}_{\mathscr{C}}(B, \prod A_i)$$

for all $B \in \mathscr{C}$. Correspondingly, we have for coproducts

$$\prod \text{Mor}_{\mathscr{C}}(A_i, B) \cong \text{Mor}_{\mathscr{C}}(\coprod A_i, B)$$

for all $B \in \mathscr{C}$. In a more general context in Chapter 2, we shall study further properties of products and coproducts.

The categories **S**, **S***, **Top**, **Top***, **Gr**, **Ab**, **Ri**, and $_R$**Mod** are categories with products and coproducts. In all these categories the products coincide with the set-theoretic products with the appropriate structure. The coproduct in **S** and **Top** is the disjoint union, in **S*** and **Top*** it is the union with identification of the distinguished points. In **Ab** and in $_R$**Mod** the finite coproducts coincide with the finite products. (Certainly this is only true for the corresponding objects. The injections are different from the projections, of course.) In **Gr** the coproducts are also called "free products." The coproducts in **Gr** and **Ri** will be discussed in Chapter 3. We give another example from Chapter 3 without going into details about the definition. Let C be a commutative, associative, unitary ring. Let $_C$**Al** be the category of commutative, associative, unitary C algebras. In $_C$**Al** the coproduct is the tensor product of algebras.

1.12 Intersections and Unions

Let B be an object of a category $\mathscr{C}$, and let $f_i : A_i \to B$ be a set of subobjects of B. A subobject $f : A \to B$ which is smaller than the subobjects A_i is called the *intersection* of the A_i if for each $C \in \mathscr{C}$ and each morphism $g : C \to B$ which may be factored through all A_i $(g = f_i h_i)$ there is a morphism $h : C \to A$ with $g = fh$. h is uniquely determined because f is a monomorphism. The intersection of the A_i will be denoted by $\bigcap A_i$. Let $f' : A' \to B$ be a subobject which is larger than the subobjects A_i. Let $C \in \mathscr{C}$, let $g : B \to C$ be a morphism in $\mathscr{C}$, and let $k : C' \to C$ be a subobject such that g restricted to all the A_i may be factored through $k (gf_i = kh_i)$. If these data always imply that the morphism g restricted to A' may be factored through k ($gf' = kh$), then $f' : A' \to B$ is called the *union* of the A_i. Since k is a monomorphism, h is uniquely determined. The union of the A_i will also be denoted by $\bigcup A_i$.

The intersection and the union of the A_i are uniquely determined because the morphisms h in the definition of the intersection and the union are unique. This may be shown similarly to the proof of the uniqueness of the products up to an isomorphism in Section 1.11, Lemma 1. One has to use two subobjects which fulfill the conditions given above, and one has to compare them by the unique factorizations. As subobjects they are not only isomorphic but equal. Since the subobjects form an ordered class, it is easy to show that the intersections as well as the unions are associative, if one observes that the intersection of a subfamily of subobjects is larger than the intersection of the whole family, and that the union of a subfamily is smaller than the union of the whole family. Observe that in the definition all objects of the category $\mathscr{C}$ are admitted as test objects, not only the subobjects of B. It may well be that B does not have sufficiently many subobjects to test whether another subobject is an intersection or union.

If there is an intersection or a union for each [finite, nonempty] family of subobjects of each object, we call the category $\mathscr{C}$ a *category with* [*finite, nonempty*] *intersections* or *unions* respectively. If $\mathscr{C}$ is a locally small category with finite intersections and unions, then the set of subobjects of each object in $\mathscr{C}$ is a lattice. If there are arbitrary intersections and unions in $\mathscr{C}$, then the subobjects of an object form a complete lattice. In Chapter 2 we shall give more criteria for determining whether a category has intersections and unions; thus we do not give any examples here.

Note that the notions intersection and union are not dual to each other. The corresponding dual notions are *cointersection* and *counion*. However, we shall not use these notions.

1.13 Images, Coimages, and Counterimages

Let $f : A \to B$ be a morphism in a category $\mathscr{C}$. The *image* of f is the smallest subobject $g : B' \to B$ of B to which there exists a morphism $h : A \to B'$ with $gh = f$. Since g is a monomorphism, h is uniquely determined. If h is an epimorphism, then h is called the *epimorphic image* of f. The image of f is often denoted by $\mathrm{Im}(f)$, where we assume that the morphism g is known and consider $\mathrm{Im}(f)$ as an object. If there are [epimorphic] images for all morphisms in $\mathscr{C}$, then we call $\mathscr{C}$ a *category with [epimorphic] images*. Dually, we define *[monomorphic] coimages* and denote them by Coim(f). If A' is a subobject of A, then we denote the image of the morphism $A' \to A \to B$ by $f(A')$.

LEMMA 1.   *If $\mathscr{C}$ is a locally small category with intersections, then $\mathscr{C}$ is a category with images.*

Proof.   Form the intersection of all those subobjects of B through which $f : A \to B$ may be factored. This intersection exists and is the smallest subobject with the property that f may be factored through it.

LEMMA 2.   *If $\mathscr{C}$ is a category with images and difference kernels then all images in $\mathscr{C}$ are epimorphic images.*

Proof.   Let $A \xrightarrow{h} \mathrm{Im}(f) \xrightarrow{g} B$ be a factorization of f through its image, and let $k,\ k' : \mathrm{Im}(f) \to C$ be given with $kh = k'h$. Then h may be factored as $A \to \mathrm{Ker}(k, k') \to \mathrm{Im}(f)$. Since $\mathrm{Ker}(k, k') \to \mathrm{Im}(f) \to B$ is a monomorphism and $\mathrm{Im}(f)$ is minimal $\mathrm{Ker}(k, k') = \mathrm{Im}(f)$, thus $k = k'$ and h is an epimorphism.

Let $f : A \to B$ be a morphism in $\mathscr{C}$ and $g : B' \to B$ be a subobject of B. A subobject $A' \to A$ of A is called a *counterimage* of B' under f if there is a morphism $f' : A' \to B'$ such that the diagram

$$
\begin{array}{ccc}
A' & \xrightarrow{\ f'\ } & B' \\
\downarrow & & \downarrow{\scriptstyle g} \\
A & \xrightarrow{\ f\ } & B
\end{array}
$$

is commutative and if for each commutative diagram

$$
\begin{array}{ccc}
C & \longrightarrow & B' \\
\downarrow & & \downarrow{\scriptstyle g} \\
A & \xrightarrow{\ f\ } & B
\end{array}
$$

there is exactly one morphism $h : C \to A'$ such that the diagram

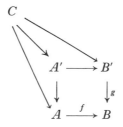

is commutative. This condition asks for more than that A' be only the largest subobject of A which may be transferred by f into B'. But the condition implies this assertion. Thus the counterimage is also uniquely determined. For the counterimage of B' under f, we also write $f^{-1}(B')$, neglecting the monomorphism $f^{-1}(B') \to A$.

Now we want to know which of the relations valid for the notions $f(A)$ and $f^{-1}(A)$ in **S** may be generalized. We collect the most important relations in the following theorem.

THEOREM. *Let* $f : A \to B$ *and* $g : B \to C$ *be morphisms in* $\mathscr{C}$. *Let* $A_1 \subseteq A_2 \subseteq A$ *and* $B_1 \subseteq B_2 \subseteq B$ *and* $C_1 \subseteq C$ *be subobjects of* A, B, *and* C, *respectively. Then we have*

(a) $f(A_1) \subseteq f(A_2)$ *if both sides are defined.*
(b) $f^{-1}(B_1) \subseteq f^{-1}(B_2)$ *if both sides are defined.*
(c) $A_1 \subseteq f^{-1}f(A_1)$ *if the right side is defined.*
(d) $ff^{-1}(B_1) \subseteq B_1$ *if the left side is defined.*
(e) $f^{-1}(B_1) = h(B_1)$ *if f is an isomorphism with the inverse morphism h.*
(f) $f^{-1}(g^{-1}(C_1)) = (gf)^{-1}(C_1)$ *if both sides are defined.*
(g) $g(f(A_1)) = (gf)(A_1)$ *if both sides are defined, if $f(A_1)$ and $g(f(A_1))$ are epimorphic images, and if $\mathscr{C}$ is balanced.*
(h) $f(A_1) = ff^{-1}f(A_1)$ *if $f^{-1}f(A_1)$ is defined.*
(i) $f^{-1}(B_1) = f^{-1}ff^{-1}(B_1)$ *if $ff^{-1}(B_1)$ is defined.*
(j) *For each family of subobjects* $\{A_i\}_{i \in I}$ *of A we have* $\bigcup f(A_i) = f(\bigcup A_i)$ *if $\bigcup A_i$ is defined and $\mathscr{C}$ is a category with images and coimages.*
(k) *For each family of subobjects* $\{B_i\}_{i \in I}$ *of B we have* $\bigcap f^{-1}(B_i) = f^{-1}(\bigcap B_i)$ *if the right side is defined.*

Proof. The assertions (a)–(e) arise directly from the corresponding definitions.

(f)   We start with a commutative diagram

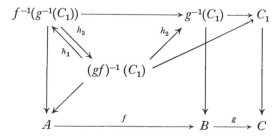

h_1 exists because $(gf)^{-1}(C_1)$ is a counterimage. h_2 exists because $g^{-1}(C_1)$ is a counterimage. Finally, h_3 exists because $f^{-1}(g^{-1}(C_1))$ is a counterimage of $g^{-1}(C_1)$. The monomorphisms from $(gf)^{-1}(C_1)$ and from $f^{-1}(g^{-1}(C_1))$ into A are equivalent, thus the corresponding subobjects are equal.

(g)   We start with the commutative diagram

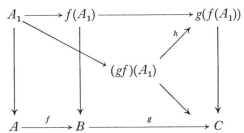

h is a monomorphism because $(gf)(A_1)$ and $g(f(A_1))$ are subobjects of C. h is an epimorphism because $f(A_1)$ and $g(f(A_1))$ are epimorphic images. Thus h is an isomorphism, since $\mathscr{C}$ is balanced.

(h)   We have the commutative diagram

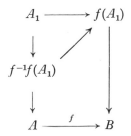

$f(A_1)$ fulfills the property of an image for A_1. Consequently, it fulfills this property also for $f^{-1}(A_1)$.

(i)   is proved similarly to (h).

(j)   We start with the commutative diagram

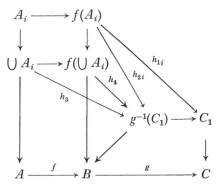

We want to prove that $f(\bigcup A_i)$ is the union of $f(A_i)$. Let there be a morphism h_{1i} for each $i \in I$. Because of the property of a counterimage of $g^{-1}(C_i)$, there is a morphism h_{2i} for all i. Then h_3 exists because $\bigcup A_i$ is a union. h_4 exists because $f(\bigcup A_i)$ is an image. Thus we have a morphism $f(\bigcup A_i) \to C_i$, fulfilling the conditions of a union.

(k)   We start with the commutative diagram

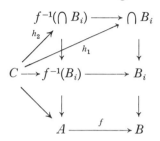

h_1 exists uniquely because $\bigcap$ is an intersection. h_2 exists uniquely such that the diagram becomes commutative, because $f^{-1}(\bigcap B_i)$ is a counterimage. Thus the $f^{-1}(\bigcap B_i)$ is the intersection of the $f^{-1}(B_i)$.

We give some examples of categories satisfying all conditions of this theorem. However, we shall not verify these conditions, since they are implied by later investigations. The categories **S**, **S***, **Gr**, **Ab**, ${}_R$**Mod**, **Top**, **Top***, and **Ri** have epimorphic images, monomorphic coimages, counterimages, intersections, and unions. Except for **Top**, **Top***, and **Ri**, they are all balanced.

LEMMA 3.   *Let $\mathscr{C}$ be a category with epimorphic images. $\mathscr{C}$ is balanced if and only if $\mathscr{C}$ has monomorphic coimages and if these coimages coincide up to an isomorphism with the images of the corresponding morphisms.*

Proof.   Let $\mathscr{C}$ be balanced. Let

$$(A \xrightarrow{f} B) = (A \xrightarrow{g} \mathrm{Im}(f) \xrightarrow{g'} B) = (A \xrightarrow{h} C \xrightarrow{h'} B)$$

with an epimorphism h. We split h' in $(C \xrightarrow{k} \mathrm{Im}(h') \xrightarrow{k'} B)$. Then k' is a monomorphism, through which f may be factored. Thus, there is a morphism $f' : \mathrm{Im}(f) \to \mathrm{Im}(h')$ with $g' = k'f'$. Since $f = g'g = k'f'g = k'kh$, we also have $f'g = kh$, for k' is a monomorphism. Since kh is an epimorphism, f' is an epimorphism. Furthermore, f' is a monomorphism, because g' is a monomorphism. Since $\mathscr{C}$ is balanced, f' is an isomorphism with inverse morphism f^*. Thus, $g = f^*kh$, that is, the quotient object of A, equivalent to $\mathrm{Im}(f)$, is a coimage of f, and the corresponding morphism into B is a monomorphism.

Conversely, let $\mathscr{C}$ be a category with monomorphic coimages which coincide up to an isomorphism with the images, and let $f : A \to B$ be a monomorphism and an epimorphism. Then A is an image of f up to an isomorphism, and B is a coimage of f up to an isomorphism. Thus, f is an isomorphism.

1.14   Multifunctors

After having investigated the essential properties of objects and morphisms, we now have to deal with functors and natural transformations. First, let us take three categories $\mathscr{A}$, $\mathscr{B}$, and $\mathscr{C}$. The product category $\mathscr{A} \times \mathscr{B}$ is defined by $\mathrm{Ob}(\mathscr{A} \times \mathscr{B}) = \mathrm{Ob}(\mathscr{A}) \times \mathrm{Ob}(\mathscr{B})$ and

$$\mathrm{Mor}_{\mathscr{A} \times \mathscr{B}}((A, B), (A', B')) = \mathrm{Mor}_{\mathscr{A}}(A, A') \times \mathrm{Mor}_{\mathscr{B}}(B, B')$$

and the compositions induced by $\mathscr{A}$ and $\mathscr{B}$. Correspondingly, we define the product of n categories. It is easy to verify the axioms for a category. A functor from a product category of two [n] categories into a category $\mathscr{C}$ is called *bifunctor* [*multifunctor*]. Special bifunctors $\mathscr{P}_{\mathscr{A}} : \mathscr{A} \times \mathscr{B} \to \mathscr{A}$ are defined by $\mathscr{P}_{\mathscr{A}}(A, B) = A$ and $\mathscr{P}_{\mathscr{A}}(f, g) = f$, and correspondingly for $\mathscr{P}_{\mathscr{B}}$. They are called projection functors. For n-fold products, they are defined correspondingly.

LEMMA 1.   *Let $\mathscr{F}_B : \mathscr{A} \to \mathscr{C}$ and $\mathscr{G}_A : \mathscr{B} \to \mathscr{C}$ be functors for all $A \in \mathscr{A}$ and $B \in \mathscr{B}$. If we have*

$$\mathscr{F}_B(A) - \mathscr{G}_A(B) \qquad \text{and} \qquad \mathscr{F}_{B'}(f)\,\mathscr{G}_A(g) = \mathscr{G}_{A'}(g)\,\mathscr{F}_B(f)$$

for all A, $A' \in \mathscr{A}$, B, $B' \in \mathscr{B}$ and all morphisms $f : A \to A'$, $g : B \to B'$, then there is exactly one bifunctor $\mathscr{H} : \mathscr{A} \times \mathscr{B} \to \mathscr{C}$ with $\mathscr{H}(A, B) = \mathscr{G}_A(B)$ and $\mathscr{H}(f, g) = \mathscr{F}_{B'}(f)\,\mathscr{G}_A(g)$.

Proof.   We define $\mathscr{H}$ by the conditions for $\mathscr{H}$ given in the lemma. Then one checks at once that $\mathscr{H}(1_A, 1_B) = 1_{\mathscr{H}(A,B)}$ and $\mathscr{H}(f'f, g'g) = \mathscr{H}(f', g')\,\mathscr{H}(f, g)$.

If a bifunctor $\mathscr{H} : \mathscr{A} \times \mathscr{B} \to \mathscr{C}$ is given, then $\mathscr{F}_B(A) = \mathscr{H}(A, B)$ and $\mathscr{F}_B(f) = \mathscr{H}(f, 1_B)$ is a functor from $\mathscr{A}$ into $\mathscr{C}$, and correspondingly, we can define a functor $\mathscr{G}_A$ from $\mathscr{B}$ into $\mathscr{C}$. For these functors, the equations of Lemma 1 are satisfied.

COROLLARY. *Let $\mathscr{H}$ and $\mathscr{H}'$ be bifunctors from $\mathscr{A} \times \mathscr{B}$ into $\mathscr{C}$. A family of morphisms*

$$\varphi(A, B) : \mathscr{H}(A, B) \to \mathscr{H}'(A, B), \qquad A \in \mathscr{A}, \quad B \in \mathscr{B}$$

is a natural tranformation if and only if it is a natural transformation in each variable, that is, if $\varphi(-, B)$ and $\varphi(A, -)$ are natural transformations.

Proof. If we write $\mathscr{H}(f, B)$ instead of $\mathscr{H}(f, 1_B)$, then we get the following commutative diagram

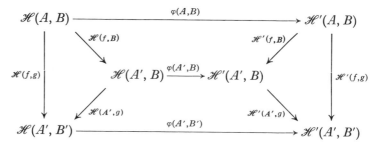

LEMMA 2. *For each category $\mathrm{Mor}_{\mathscr{C}}(-, -) : \mathscr{C}^0 \times \mathscr{C} \to \mathbf{S}$ is a bifunctor.*

Proof. In the lemma of Section 1.3, we proved that $\mathrm{Mor}_{\mathscr{C}}(A, -) : \mathscr{C} \to \mathbf{S}$ and $\mathrm{Mor}_{\mathscr{C}}(-, B) : \mathscr{C}^0 \to \mathbf{S}$ are covariant functors. Furthermore, because of the associativity of the composition of morphisms, we have

$$\mathrm{Mor}_{\mathscr{C}}(f, B') \, \mathrm{Mor}_{\mathscr{C}}(A, g) = \mathrm{Mor}_{\mathscr{C}}(A', g) \, \mathrm{Mor}_{\mathscr{C}}(f, B) = : \mathrm{Mor}_{\mathscr{C}}(f, g)$$

In particular, we have $\mathrm{Mor}_{\mathscr{C}}(f, g)(h) = ghf$, if the right side is defined. Thus by Lemma 1, $\mathrm{Mor}_{\mathscr{C}}(-, -)$ is a bifunctor.

If we do not pass over the dual category $\mathscr{C}^0$ in the first argument of $\mathrm{Mor}_{\mathscr{C}}(-, -)$, then $\mathrm{Mor}_{\mathscr{C}}(-, -)$ is contravariant in the first argument and covariant in the second argument. We denote the representable functor $\mathrm{Mor}_{\mathscr{C}}(A, -)$ by h^A and the representable functor $\mathrm{Mor}_{\mathscr{C}}(-, B)$ by h_B. Because of the commutativity

$$\mathrm{Mor}_{\mathscr{C}}(f, B') \, \mathrm{Mor}_{\mathscr{C}}(A, g) = \mathrm{Mor}_{\mathscr{C}}(A', g) \, \mathrm{Mor}_{\mathscr{C}}(f, B)$$

we have natural transformations

$$\mathrm{Mor}_{\mathscr{C}}(f, -) : \mathrm{Mor}_{\mathscr{C}}(A, -) \to \mathrm{Mor}_{\mathscr{C}}(A', -)$$

and

$$\mathrm{Mor}_{\mathscr{C}}(-, g) : \mathrm{Mor}_{\mathscr{C}}(-, B) \to \mathrm{Mor}_{\mathscr{C}}(-, B')$$

We denote $\text{Mor}_{\mathscr{C}}(f, -)$ by h^f and $\text{Mor}_{\mathscr{C}}(-, g)$ by h_g. These considerations lead to the following lemma.

LEMMA 3. *Let $\mathscr{A}$, $\mathscr{B}$ be small categories and $\mathscr{C}$ be an arbitrary category. Then we have*

$$\text{Funct}(\mathscr{A} \times \mathscr{B}, \mathscr{C}) \simeq \text{Funct}(\mathscr{A}, \text{Funct}(\mathscr{B}, \mathscr{C})) \simeq \text{Funct}(\mathscr{B}, \text{Funct}(\mathscr{A}, \mathscr{C}))$$

Proof. Obviously $\mathscr{A} \times \mathscr{B} \simeq \mathscr{B} \times \mathscr{A}$. Thus it suffices to prove the first isomorphism. If one transfers the considerations on natural transformations made above to the general case of a bifunctor, then the application for the functors is described by Lemma 1. The natural transformations are transferred in accordance with the corollary. For the applications described above, it is easy to verify the properties of a functor and the reversibility.

1.15 The Yoneda Lemma

In this section we want to discuss one of the most important observations on categories. Several times we shall meet set-theoretic difficulties of the kind that one wants to collect proper classes to a set which is not admissible according to the axioms of set theory (see Appendix). Since these classes are not disjoint, we cannot even fall back on a system of representatives. This is true in particular for the natural transformations between two functors $\mathscr{F} : \mathscr{C} \to \mathscr{D}$ and $\mathscr{G} : \mathscr{C} \to \mathscr{D}$. We agree on the following abbreviation: for "$\varphi : \mathscr{F} \to \mathscr{G}$ is a natural transformation" we also write "$\varphi \in \text{Mor}_f(\mathscr{F}, \mathscr{G})$" or "$\text{Mor}_f(\mathscr{F}, \mathscr{G}) \ni \varphi$." Here we do not think of $\text{Mor}_f(\mathscr{F}, \mathscr{G})$ as of a set or class. If $\mathscr{C}$ is a small category, however, then the natural transformations from $\mathscr{F}$ to $\mathscr{G}$ form a set, denoted by $\text{Mor}_f(\mathscr{F}, \mathscr{G})$, by the considerations of Section 1.2. In this case, the abbreviation introduced above has the further meaning "φ is an element of the set $\text{Mor}_f(\mathscr{F}, \mathscr{G})$." The condition that $\mathscr{C}$ is a small category prevents these set theoretic difficulties. Also, for further constructions, we shall generalize the usual notation, and we shall explain in each case the meaning which we attribute to the notation. The notation

$$\text{"}\tau : \text{Mor}_f(\mathscr{F}, \mathscr{G}) \ni \varphi \mapsto x \in X\text{"}$$

shall mean that to each natural transformation from $\mathscr{F}$ into $\mathscr{G}$ there is an element in X, a set or a class, uniquely determined by an instruction explicitly given and denoted by τ. We assign a corresponding meaning to "$\sigma : X \ni x \to \varphi \in \text{Mor}_f(\mathscr{F}, \mathscr{G})$." By "$\text{Mor}_f(\mathscr{F}, \mathscr{G}) \simeq X$" we mean that the application τ is unique and invertible. With these conventions we can carry on the following considerations as if $\mathscr{C}$ were a small category.

THEOREM (Yoneda lemma). *Let $\mathscr{C}$ be a category. Let $\mathscr{F} : \mathscr{C} \to \mathbf{S}$ be a covariant functor, and $A \in C$ be an object. Then the application*

$$\tau : \mathrm{Mor}_f(h^A, \mathscr{F}) \ni \varphi \mapsto \varphi(A)(1_A) \in \mathscr{F}(A)$$

is unique and invertible. The inverse of this application is

$$\tau^{-1} : \mathscr{F}(A) \ni a \mapsto h^a \in \mathrm{Mor}_f(h^A, \mathscr{F})$$

where $h^a(B)(f) = \mathscr{F}(f)(a)$.

Proof. If one notes that $\varphi(A) : h^A(A) = \mathrm{Mor}_{\mathscr{C}}(A, A) \to \mathscr{F}(A)$, then it is clear that τ is uniquely defined. For τ^{-1}, we have to check that h^a is a natural transformation. Later on we shall discuss the connection with the symbol h^f, defined for representable functors

Given $f : B \to C$ in $\mathscr{C}$. Then the diagram

$$
\begin{array}{ccc}
\mathrm{Mor}_{\mathscr{C}}(A, B) & \xrightarrow{\ \mathrm{Mor}(A,f)\ } & \mathrm{Mor}_{\mathscr{C}}(A, C) \\
{\scriptstyle h^a(B)}\downarrow & & \downarrow{\scriptstyle h^a(C)} \\
\mathscr{F}(B) & \xrightarrow{\quad \mathscr{F}(f)\quad } & \mathscr{F}(C)
\end{array}
$$

is commutative, for $h^a(C)\,\mathrm{Mor}(A, f)(g) = h^a(C)(fg) = \mathscr{F}(fg)(a) = \mathscr{F}(f)\mathscr{F}(g)(a) = \mathscr{F}(f)\,h^a(B)(a)$ for all $g \in \mathrm{Mor}_{\mathscr{C}}(A, B)$. Thus τ^{-1} is uniquely defined.

Let $\varphi = h^a$. Then $h^a(A)(1_A) = \mathscr{F}(1_A)(a) = a$. Let $a = \varphi(A)(1_A)$. Then $h^a(B)(f) = \mathscr{F}(f)(a) = \mathscr{F}(f)(\varphi(A)(1_A)) = \varphi(B)\,\mathrm{Mor}(A, f)(1_A) = \varphi(B)(f)$, thus $h^a = \varphi$. This proves the theorem.

Let $\mathscr{F} = h^C$ be a representable functor. Then for $f \in \mathscr{F}(A) = h^C(A) = \mathrm{Mor}(C, A)$ we have the equation

$$h^f(B)(g) = F(g)(f) = fg = \mathrm{Mor}(f, B)(g)$$

that is, the definition for h^f given in the Yoneda lemma coincides in the special case of a representable functor $\mathscr{F}$ with the definition in Section 1.14.

Now we want to investigate what happens with the application τ if we change the functor $\mathscr{F}$ and the representable functor h^A. The commutative diagrams used in the following lemma are to be interpreted in such a way that the given applications coincide.

LEMMA 1. *Let $\mathscr{F}$ and $\mathscr{G}$ be functors from $\mathscr{C}$ into $\mathbf{S}$, and let $\varphi : \mathscr{F} \to \mathscr{G}$ be a natural tranformation. Let $f : A \to B$ be a morphism in $\mathscr{C}$. Then the following diagrams are commutative:*

$$
\begin{array}{ccc}
\mathrm{Mor}_f(h^A, \mathscr{F}) & \xrightarrow{\ \tau\ } & \mathscr{F}(A) \\
{\scriptstyle \mathrm{Mor}_f(h^A, \varphi)}\Big\downarrow & & \Big\downarrow{\scriptstyle \varphi(A)} \\
\mathrm{Mor}_f(h^A, \mathscr{G}) & \xrightarrow{\ \tau\ } & \mathscr{G}(A)
\end{array}
$$

$$
\begin{array}{ccc}
\mathrm{Mor}_f(h^A, \mathscr{F}) & \xrightarrow{\ \tau\ } & \mathscr{F}(A) \\
{\scriptstyle \mathrm{Mor}_f(h^f, \mathscr{F})}\Big\downarrow & & \Big\downarrow{\scriptstyle \mathscr{F}(f)} \\
\mathrm{Mor}_f(h^B, \mathscr{F}) & \xrightarrow{\ \tau\ } & \mathscr{F}(B)
\end{array}
$$

where $\mathrm{Mor}_f(h^A, \varphi)(\psi) = \varphi\psi$ and $\mathrm{Mor}_f(h^f, \mathscr{F})(\psi) = \psi h^f$.

Proof.   Let $\psi : h^A \to \mathscr{F}$ be given. Then

$$\tau\, \mathrm{Mor}_f(h^A, \varphi)(\psi) = \tau(\varphi\psi) = (\varphi\psi)(A)(1_A) = \varphi(A)\,\psi(A)(1_A) = \varphi(A)\,\tau(\psi)$$

Furthermore, we have

$$\tau\, \mathrm{Mor}_f(h^f, \mathscr{F})(\psi) = \tau(\psi h^f) = (\psi h^f)(B)(1_B) = \psi(B)(f)$$
$$= \psi(B)\,\mathrm{Mor}(A, f)(1_A) = \mathscr{F}(f)\,\psi(A)(1_A) = \mathscr{F}(f)\,\tau(\psi)$$

COROLLARY 1.   *Let $\mathscr{C}$ be a small category. Then*

$$\mathrm{Mor}_f(h^-, -) : \mathscr{C} \times \mathrm{Funct}(\mathscr{C}, \mathbf{S}) \to \mathbf{S} \qquad \text{and} \qquad \Phi : \mathscr{C} \times \mathrm{Funct}(\mathscr{C}, \mathbf{S}) \to \mathbf{S}$$

with

$$\mathrm{Mor}_f(h^-, -)(A, \mathscr{F}) = \mathrm{Mor}_f(h^A, \mathscr{F}), \qquad \mathrm{Mor}_f(h^-, -)(f, \varphi) = \mathrm{Mor}_f(h^f, \varphi)$$

and

$$\Phi(A, \mathscr{F}) = \mathscr{F}(A), \qquad \Phi(f, \varphi) = \varphi(B)\,\mathscr{F}(f) = \mathscr{G}(f)\,\varphi(A)$$

are bifunctors. The application τ is a natural isomorphism of these bifunctors.

Proof.   This assertion follows from the preceeding one and from Section 1.14.

The functor in Corollary 1 denoted by Φ will be called the *evaluation functor*. Now we want to apply the new results for representable functors.

COROLLARY 2.   *Let $A, B \in \mathscr{C}$. Then:*

(a) $\operatorname{Mor}_\mathscr{C}(A, B) \ni f \mapsto h^f \in \operatorname{Mor}_f(h^B, h^A)$ *is a bijection.*

(b) *The bijection of* (a) *induces a bijection between the isomorphisms in* $\operatorname{Mor}_\mathscr{C}(A, B)$ *and the natural isomorphisms in* $\operatorname{Mor}_f(h^B, h^A)$.

(c) *For contravariant functors* $\mathscr{F} : \mathscr{C} \to \mathbf{S}$, *we have* $\operatorname{Mor}_f(h_A, \mathscr{F}) \cong \mathscr{F}(A)$.

(d) $\operatorname{Mor}_\mathscr{C}(A, B) \ni f \mapsto h_f \in \operatorname{Mor}_f(h_A, h_B)$ *is a bijection, inducing a bijection between the isomorphisms in* $\operatorname{Mor}_\mathscr{C}(A, B)$ *and the natural isomorphisms in* $\operatorname{Mor}_f(h_A, h_B)$.

Proof.   (a) is the assertion of the Yoneda Lemma for $\mathscr{F} = h^A$. (c) and (d) arise from dualization. (b) By $h^f h^g = h^{gf}$, isomorphisms are carried over the natural isomorphisms. Conversely, let $h^f : h^B \to h^A$ and $h^g : h^A \to h^B$ be inverse natural isomorphisms. Then $h^{gf} = \operatorname{id}_{h^A}$ and $h^{fg} = \operatorname{id}_{h^B}$. We also have $h^{1_A} = \operatorname{id}_{h^A}$ and $h^{1_B} = \operatorname{id}_{h^B}$, thus $gf = 1_A$ and $fg = 1_B$.

The properties of h we used in the preceeding proof show that for a small category $\mathscr{C}$, the application $A \mapsto h^A$, $f \mapsto h^f$ is a contravariant functor $h^- : \mathscr{C} \to \operatorname{Funct}(\mathscr{C}, \mathbf{S})$. We call h^- the *contravariant representation functor*. Correspondingly, $h_- : \mathscr{C} \to \operatorname{Funct}(\mathscr{C}^0, \mathbf{S})$ is the *covariant representation functor*. Both functors have the property that the induced maps on the morphism sets are bijective. A *full functor* is a functor which induces surjective maps on the morphism sets. A *faithful functor* is a functor which induces injective maps on the morphism sets. A faithful functor is sometimes called an embedding. Thus the representation functors are full and faithful.

Already in Section 1.8 we realized that the image of a functor is not necessarily a category. This, however, is the case if the functor $\mathscr{F} : \mathscr{C} \to \mathscr{D}$ is full and faithful. Obviously we only have to check whether for $f : A \to B$ and $g : C \to D$ in $\mathscr{C}$ with $\mathscr{F}B = \mathscr{F}C$ the morphism $\mathscr{F}g\mathscr{F}f$ appears in the image of $\mathscr{F}$. Since $\operatorname{Mor}_\mathscr{D}(\mathscr{F}B, \mathscr{F}C) \cong \operatorname{Mor}_\mathscr{C}(B, C)$ and $\operatorname{Mor}_\mathscr{D}(\mathscr{F}C, \mathscr{F}B) \cong \operatorname{Mor}_\mathscr{C}(C, B)$, there are $h : B \to C$ and $k : C \to B$ with $\mathscr{F}h = 1_{\mathscr{F}B}$ and $\mathscr{F}k = 1_{\mathscr{F}B}$. Since $\mathscr{F}(hk) = 1_{\mathscr{F}B} = \mathscr{F}1_B$ and $\mathscr{F}(kh) = 1_{\mathscr{F}B} = \mathscr{F}1_B$, we get $hk = 1_C$ and $kh = 1_B$. Thus $\mathscr{F}g\mathscr{F}f = \mathscr{F}(g)1_{\mathscr{F}B}\mathscr{F}(f) = \mathscr{F}(g)\mathscr{F}(h)\mathscr{F}(f) = \mathscr{F}(ghf)$.

The full and faithful functors are most important, as we want to show with the following example. Let $\mathscr{F} : \mathscr{C} \to \mathscr{D}$ be full and faithful. Let

$$C_1 \xrightarrow{\ f\ } C_2$$
$$\downarrow{\scriptstyle g}$$
$$C_3$$

be a diagram in $\mathscr{C}$ which is carried over by $\mathscr{F}$ into the diagram

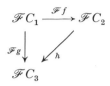

except for the morphism h. Assume that there is a morphism h in $\mathscr{D}$ making the diagram commutative. The question is, if there is also a morphism $h' : C_2 \to C_3$ making the diagram in $\mathscr{C}$ commutative. $\mathscr{F}$ being full and faithful, we may take the counterimage h' of h for this morphism. Thus we decided the question for the existence of morphisms in $\mathscr{C}$ with particular properties in the category $\mathscr{D}$.

LEMMA 2. *Let $\mathscr{F} : \mathscr{C} \to \mathscr{D}$ be a full and faithful functor. Let $\mathscr{A}$ and $\mathscr{B}$ be diagram schemes and $\mathscr{G} : \mathscr{A} \to \mathscr{C}$ and $\mathscr{G}' : \mathscr{B} \to \mathscr{D}$ be diagrams. Let $\mathscr{E} : \mathscr{A} \to \mathscr{B}$ be a functor which is bijective on the objects such that the diagram*

$$\begin{array}{ccc} \mathscr{A} & \xrightarrow{\mathscr{E}} & \mathscr{B} \\ \mathscr{G} \downarrow & & \downarrow \mathscr{G}' \\ \mathscr{C} & \xrightarrow{\mathscr{F}} & \mathscr{D} \end{array}$$

is commutative. Then there is exactly one diagram $\mathscr{H} : \mathscr{B} \to \mathscr{C}$ such that $\mathscr{F}\mathscr{H} = \mathscr{G}'$ and $\mathscr{H}\mathscr{E} = \mathscr{G}$.

Proof. We define $\mathscr{H}$ on the objects of $\mathscr{B}$ by $\mathscr{G}$, since $\mathscr{E}$ is bijective on the objects. For the morphisms of $\mathscr{B}$ we define $\mathscr{H}$ by the maps induced by $\mathscr{G}'$ and $\mathscr{F}^{-1}$. Here we use that $\mathscr{F}$ is full and faithful. With this definition of the map $\mathscr{H}$ one verifies easily that $\mathscr{H}$ is a functor and that $\mathscr{H}$ satisfies the required commutativities.

Let $\mathscr{C}$ be a small category. Let $\mathscr{M}$ be a small full subcategory of $\mathbf{S}$ containing the images of all representable functors from $\mathscr{C}$ to $\mathbf{S}$. In this case we can also talk about the representation functor $h:\mathscr{C}\to\mathrm{Funct}(\mathscr{C},\mathscr{M})$. Correspondingly, we define a representation functor H from $\mathrm{Funct}(\mathscr{C},\mathscr{M})$ which is again a small category, into $\mathrm{Funct}(\mathrm{Funct}(\mathscr{C}, \mathscr{M}), \mathbf{S})$. Both functors are full and faithful. The composition of H and h gives a functor, which is isomorphic to the evaluation functor

$$\Phi : \mathscr{C} \to \mathrm{Funct}(\mathrm{Funct}(\mathscr{C}, \mathscr{M}), \mathbf{S})$$

which is defined according to the evaluation functor

$$\Phi : \mathscr{C} \times \mathrm{Funct}(\mathscr{C}, \mathscr{M}) \to \mathbf{S}$$

This is implied by Corollary 1. Thus the evaluation functor

$$\Phi : \mathscr{C} \to \text{Funct}(\text{Funct}(\mathscr{C}, \mathscr{M}), \mathbf{S})$$

is full and faithful.

Now we want to generalize the assertions of the Yoneda Lemma to functors. We consider functors $\mathscr{F}, \mathscr{G} : \mathscr{C} \to \mathscr{D}$. With $\text{Mor}_{\mathscr{D}}(\mathscr{F}-, -)$ we denote the composed bifunctor from $\mathscr{C} \times \mathscr{D}$ into $\mathbf{S}$ with

$$\text{Mor}_{\mathscr{D}}(\mathscr{F}-, -)(C, D) = \text{Mor}_{\mathscr{D}}(\mathscr{F}C, D)$$

and

$$\text{Mor}_{\mathscr{D}}(\mathscr{F}-, -)(f, g) = \text{Mor}_{\mathscr{D}}(\mathscr{F}f, g)$$

For a natural transformation $\varphi : \mathscr{F} \to \mathscr{G}$, let

$$\text{Mor}_{\mathscr{D}}(\varphi-, -) : \text{Mor}_{\mathscr{D}}(\mathscr{G}-, -) \to \text{Mor}_{\mathscr{D}}(\mathscr{F}-, -)$$

denote the natural transformation which is defined by $\text{Mor}_{\mathscr{D}}(\varphi C, D)(f) = f\varphi(C)$, where $f \in \text{Mor}_{\mathscr{D}}(\mathscr{G}C, D)$. With these notations we obtain the following lemma.

LEMMA 3. *The application*

$$\text{Mor}_f(\mathscr{F}, \mathscr{G}) \ni \varphi \mapsto \text{Mor}_{\mathscr{D}}(\varphi-, -) \in \text{Mor}_f(\text{Mor}_{\mathscr{D}}(\mathscr{G}-, -), \text{Mor}_{\mathscr{D}}(\mathscr{F}-, -))$$

is bijective. It induces a bijection between the natural isomorphisms from $\mathscr{F}$ to $\mathscr{G}$ and the natural isomorphisms from $\text{Mor}_{\mathscr{D}}(\mathscr{G}-, -)$ to $\text{Mor}_{\mathscr{D}}(\mathscr{F}-, -)$.

Proof.   A natural transformation $\psi : \text{Mor}_{\mathscr{D}}(\mathscr{G}-, -) \to \text{Mor}_{\mathscr{D}}(\mathscr{F}-, -)$ is a family of natural transformations $\psi(C) : \text{Mor}_{\mathscr{D}}(\mathscr{G}C, -) \to \text{Mor}_{\mathscr{D}}(\mathscr{F}C, -)$ which is natural in C for all $D \in \mathscr{D}$ (Section 1.14, Corollary). The natural transformations $\psi(C)$ may be represented as $\text{Mor}_{\mathscr{D}}(\varphi C, -)$ with morphisms $\varphi C : \mathscr{F}C \to \mathscr{G}C$ by the Yoneda lemma. Thus it suffices to prove that φC is natural in C, if $\text{Mor}_{\mathscr{D}}(\varphi C, D)$ is natural in C for all $D \in \mathscr{D}$. One direction may be seen if one replaces D by $\mathscr{G}C$ in the diagram

$$
\begin{array}{ccc}
\text{Mor}_{\mathscr{D}}(\mathscr{G}C, D) & \xrightarrow{\text{Mor}(\mathscr{G}f, D)} & \text{Mor}_{\mathscr{D}}(\mathscr{G}C', D) \\
\scriptstyle{\text{Mor}(\varphi C, D)} \downarrow & & \downarrow \scriptstyle{\text{Mor}(\varphi C', D)} \\
\text{Mor}_{D}(\mathscr{F}C, D) & \xrightarrow{\text{Mor}(\mathscr{F}f, D)} & \text{Mor}_{\mathscr{D}}(\mathscr{F}C', D)
\end{array}
$$

and if one computes the image of $1_{\mathscr{G}C}$. The converse is trivial. The assertion on the natural isomorphisms follows from the considerations

in Section 1.5—the isomorphism has to be tested only argumentwise—
and from Corollary 2(b).

We define an equivalence relation on the class of objects in the following way. Two objects are called equivalent if the representable functors,
represented by these objects, are isomorphic. By the Yoneda lemma this
is the same equivalence relation as the one defined by isomorphisms of
objects. Since in categories one considers only the exterior properties of
objects, which are, of course, carried over to isomorphic objects, it makes
sense to generalize the notion of a representable functor. A functor
$\mathscr{F} : \mathscr{C} \to \mathbf{S}$ is called representable, if there is a $C \in \mathscr{C}$ and a natural
isomorphism $\mathscr{F} \cong h^C$. Here the representing object C is only defined up
to an isomorphism. This generalized notion leads to the following
lemma.

LEMMA 4.   *Let $\mathscr{F} : \mathscr{C} \times \mathscr{D} \to \mathbf{S}$ be a bifunctor such that for all $C \in \mathscr{C}$
the functor $\mathscr{F}(C, -) : \mathscr{D} \to \mathbf{S}$ is representable. Then there is a contravariant
functor $\mathscr{G} : \mathscr{C} \to \mathscr{D}$, such that $\mathscr{F} \cong \mathrm{Mor}_{\mathscr{D}}(\mathscr{G}-, -)$.*

Proof.   Let $\mathscr{D}'$ be a skeleton of $\mathscr{D}$. To each $C \in \mathscr{C}$ there exists exactly
one $D \in \mathscr{D}'$ with $\mathscr{F}(C, -) \cong \mathrm{Mor}_{\mathscr{D}}(D, -)$. Let us denote D by $\mathscr{G}(C)$.
The natural isomorphisms $\mathscr{F}(C, -) \cong \mathrm{Mor}_{\mathscr{D}}(D, -)$ are in one-one
correspondence with the elements of a subset $\mathscr{F}'(C, D)$ of $\mathscr{F}(C, D)$ by
the Yoneda lemma. For each $C \in \mathscr{C}$, this subset $\mathscr{F}'(C, D)$ is uniquely
determined. By the axiom of choice, we may assume that to each $C \in \mathscr{C}$
there is exactly one element $c \in \mathscr{F}'(C, D)$. (With the formulation of the
axiom of choice we use, one has to form a disjoint union of the sets
$\mathscr{F}'(C, D)$ with the equivalence relation $c \sim c' \Leftrightarrow \bigvee C$ with $c, c' \in \mathscr{F}'(C, D)$.)
Thus, for each $C \in \mathscr{C}$ there is a natural isomorphism $h^c : \mathrm{Mor}_{\mathscr{D}}(D, -) \to$
$\mathscr{F}(C, -)$. Let $f : C \to C'$ be a morphism in $\mathscr{C}$. Then by the Yoneda lemma
there is exactly one morphism $\mathscr{G}f : \mathscr{G}(C') \to \mathscr{G}(C)$ in $\mathscr{D}$ making the
diagram

$$
\begin{array}{ccc}
\mathrm{Mor}_{\mathscr{D}}(\mathscr{G}(C), -) & \xrightarrow{\ h^c\ } & \mathscr{F}(C, -) \\
{\scriptstyle \mathrm{Mor}_{\mathscr{D}}(\mathscr{G}f, -)} \downarrow & & \downarrow {\scriptstyle \mathscr{F}(f, -)} \\
\mathrm{Mor}_{\mathscr{D}}(\mathscr{G}(C'), -) & \xrightarrow{\ h^{c'}\ } & \mathscr{F}(C', -)
\end{array}
$$

commutative. This uniqueness and the property of a functor of $\mathscr{F}$ imply
that $\mathscr{G}fg = \mathscr{G}g\mathscr{G}f$ and $\mathscr{G}1_C = 1_{\mathscr{G}(C)}$. Thus $\mathscr{G}$ is a contravariant functor
from $\mathscr{C}$ to $\mathscr{D}$ with the required properties.

1.16 Categories as Classes

In Section 1.2 we mentioned that a category may be considered as a special class. Now we want to specify this. First, we deal with the definition of a category that describes only the properties of the morphisms, but does not define the objects. This definition will be slightly narrower than the one given before. First we want to give the definition; then we want to investigate the connection with the definition given in Section 1.1.

A *category* is a class $\mathscr{M}$ together with a subclass $\mathscr{V} \subseteq \mathscr{M} \times \mathscr{M}$ and a map

$$\mathscr{V} \ni (a, b) \mapsto ab \in \mathscr{M}$$

such that

(1)   For all $a, b, c \in \mathscr{M}$ the following are equivalent

    (i) $(a, b), (b, c) \in \mathscr{V}$
    (ii) $(a, b), (ab, c) \in \mathscr{V}$
    (iii) $(a, bc), (b, c) \in \mathscr{V}$
    (iv) $(a, b), (b, c), (a, bc), (ab, c) \in \mathscr{V}$ and $(ab)c = a(bc)$

(2)   For each $a \in \mathscr{M}$ there are $e_l, e_r \in \mathscr{M}$ such that $(e_l, a), (a, e_r) \in \mathscr{V}$ and

$$e_l b = b, \quad b'e_l = b', \quad e_r c = c, \quad c'e_r = c'$$

for all $(e_l, b), (b', e_l), (e_r, c), (c', e_r) \in \mathscr{V}$
Then e_l and e_r are called units.

(3)   Let e, e' be units. Then

$$\{a \mid (e, a), \quad (a, e') \in V\}$$

is a set.

It is easy to verify that the morphisms of a category (in the sense of Section 1.1) satisfy this definition. Conversely, one can get the objects of a category out of the class of morphisms if one assigns to each identity an element, called an object. This, however, does not determine the class of objects uniquely. In this sense the definition given here is narrower. Now we have to prove that each class satisfying the present definition occurs as a class of morphisms in a category (in the old sense).

Let $\mathscr{M}, \mathscr{V}$ satisfy the given definition. We form a category $\mathscr{C}$ (in the old sense) with the units $e \in \mathscr{M}$ as objects. Furthermore, we define

$$\operatorname{Mor}_{\mathscr{C}}(e', e) := \{a \mid (e, a), \quad (a, e') \in \mathscr{V}\}$$

These morphism sets are disjoint. In fact, if

$$a \in \mathrm{Mor}_{\mathscr{C}}(e', e) \cap \mathrm{Mor}_{\mathscr{C}}(e^{**}, e^*)$$

then (e, a), (e^*, a), (e, e^*a), $(e, e^*) \in \mathscr{V}$ thus $e = ee^* = e^*$. Similarly, we get $e' = e^{**}$. For $a \in \mathrm{Mor}_{\mathscr{C}}(e', e)$, $b \in \mathrm{Mor}_{\mathscr{C}}(e^{**}, e^*)$ we have $(a, b) \in \mathscr{V}$ if and only if (ae', e^*b), (a, e'), (e^*, b), $(e', e^*) \in \mathscr{V}$ if and only if $(e', e^*) \in \mathscr{V}$ if and only if $e' = e^*$. In this case we have (e, ab), $(ab, e^{**}) \in \mathscr{V}$, thus $ab \in \mathrm{Mor}_{\mathscr{C}}(e^{**}, e)$. Now it is easy to verify the associativity and the properties of the identities.

To get the connection with set theory as discussed in the appendix, we now define the category as a special class. A class $\mathscr{D}$ is called a category if it satisfies the following axioms:

(a) $\mathscr{D} \subseteq \mathfrak{U} \times \mathfrak{U} \times \mathfrak{U}$
(b) $\mathfrak{D}(\mathscr{D}) \subseteq \mathfrak{W}(\mathscr{D}) \times \mathfrak{W}(\mathscr{D})$
(c) $\mathscr{D}$ is a map
(d)   For $\mathscr{M} = \mathfrak{W}(\mathscr{D})$, $\mathscr{V} = \mathfrak{D}(\mathscr{D})$ and $\mathscr{D} : \mathscr{V} \to \mathscr{M}$ the axioms (1), (2), and (3) given above are satisfied.

Obviously this definition is equivalent to the definition of a category given above.

Problems

1.1.   Covariant representable functors from **S** to **S** preserve surjective maps.

1.2.   Check whether monomorphisms [epimorphisms] in **Ab** and **Top** are injective [surjective] maps.

1.3.   In **Hd** each epimorphisms $f : A \to B$ is a dense map. (Hint: Use as a test object the cofiberproduct of B with itself over A (see Section 2.6).)

1.4.   Show: If $\mathscr{G} : \mathscr{C} \to \mathscr{D}$ is an equivalence of categories and $f \in \mathscr{C}$ is a monomorphism, then $\mathscr{G}f$ is a monomorphism.

1.5.   Let $f : A \to B$ be an epimorphism and a right zero morphism. How many elements are there in $\mathrm{Mor}_{\mathscr{C}}(B, C)$? Compute $\mathrm{Mor}_{\mathbf{Ri}}(\mathbb{P}, \mathbb{P})$.

1.6.   Let A be a subset of a topological space $(B, \mathcal{O}_B)$.

$$\{X \mid X = A \cap Y; \quad Y \in \mathcal{O}_B\}$$

defines a topology on A, the induced topology. $A \subseteq B$, provided with the induced topology, is called a topological subspace of $(B, \mathcal{O}_B)$. The topological subspaces of a topological spaces are (up to equivalence of monomorphisms) exactly the difference subobjects in **Top**. Dualize this assertion. To this end, define for a surjective map $f : B \to C$ a quotient topology on C by

$$\{Z \mid Z \subseteq C; \quad f^{-1}(Z) \in \mathcal{O}_B\}$$

1.7. A subgroup H of a group G is a subset of G which forms a group with the multiplication of G. A subgroup H of G is called a normal subgroup if $gHg^{-1} = H$ for all $g \in G$. Show that the subgroups [normal subgroups] of G are, up to equivalence of monomorphisms, exactly the difference subobjects [normal subobjects] of G in **Gr**.

1.8. If f is an isomorphism, then f is a retraction. The composition of two retractions is a retraction. If fg is a retraction, then f is a retraction.

1.9. If $\mathscr{C}$ is a category with zero morphisms, then the kernel of a monomorphism in $\mathscr{C}$ is a zero morphism.

1.10. Let $\mathscr{C}$ be a category with a zero object 0. Let $A \in \mathscr{C}$, then $(A, 1_A , 0_{(A,0)})$ is a product of A and 0.

1.11. The diagonal is a monomorphism.

1.12. If both sides are defined, then

$$f(A) \subseteq g^{-1}((gf)(A))$$

1.13. Let $\mathscr{P} : \mathbf{S} \to \mathbf{S}$ be defined by

$$\mathscr{P}(A) = \{X \mid X \subseteq A\} \quad \text{and} \quad \mathscr{P}(f)(X) = f^{-1}(X)$$

then $\mathscr{P}$ is a representable, contravariant functor, the *contravariant power set functor*.

1.14. Let $\mathscr{Q} : \mathbf{S} \to \mathbf{S}$ be defined by

$$\mathscr{Q}(A) = \{X \mid X \subseteq A\} \quad \text{and} \quad \mathscr{Q}(f)(X) = f(X)$$

then $\mathscr{Q}$ is a covariant functor, the *covariant power set functor*. Is $\mathscr{Q}$ representable?

1.15. If $\mathscr{F} : \mathbf{S} \to \mathbf{S}$ is a contravariant functor and $f : \mathscr{F}(\{\varnothing\}) \to A$ is an arbitrary map, then there is exactly one natural transformation $\varphi : \mathscr{F} \to \mathrm{Mor}_{\mathbf{S}}(-, A)$ with $\varphi(\{\varnothing\}) = f$. (Observe that $\mathrm{Mor}_{\mathbf{S}}(B, \mathscr{F}(\{\varnothing\})) = (\mathscr{F}(\{\varnothing\}))^B$.)

1.16. Let $\mathscr{F} : \mathbf{S} \to \mathbf{S}$ be a faithful contravariant functor; then there is an element b in $\mathscr{F}(2)$, which is mapped into two different elements of $\mathscr{F}(1)$ by the two maps $\mathscr{F}(2) \to \mathscr{F}(1)$. Here let 1 be a set with one element and 2 be a set with two elements.

1.17. (Pultr) Let $\mathscr{F} : \mathbf{S} \to \mathbf{S}$ be a faithful contravariant functor, then there is a retraction $\rho : \mathscr{F} \to \mathscr{P}$, where $\mathscr{P}$ is the contravariant powerset functor. (By the Yoneda lemma, it is sufficient to prove that there exists a $b \in \mathscr{F}(2)$ for which $\rho(2)(b)$ is the identity on 2. Use problems 13, 15, and 16.)

1.18. In the category of Section 1.1, Example 14, the greatest common divisor of two numbers is the product, and the least common multiple of two numbers is the coproduct.

1.19. Which of the following relations are valid in general, if they are defined?

$$f(\bigcup A_i) \subseteq \bigcup f(A_i)$$
$$f^{-1}(\bigcup A_i) \subseteq \bigcup f^{-1}(A_i)$$
$$f(\bigcap A_i) \supseteq \bigcap f(A_i)$$
$$f^{-1}(\bigcap A_i) \supseteq \bigcap f^{-1}(A_i)$$

2

Adjoint Functors and Limits

One of the most important notions in the entire theory of categories and functors is the notion of the adjoint functor. Therefore, we shall consider it from different points of view: as a universal problem, as a monad, and as a reflexive or coreflexive subcategory. The limits and colimits and many of their properties will be derived from the theorems which we shall prove for adjoint functors. This procedure was introduced by D. N. Kan. The paragraph on monads should be considered preparation for the third chapter. In this field there is still fast development. With the means given here, the interested reader will be able to follow future publications easily.

2.1 Adjoint Functors

In Section 1.15, Lemma 3 we dealt with the question of what the isomorphism $\mathrm{Mor}_{\mathscr{D}}(\mathscr{F}-, -) \cong \mathrm{Mor}_{\mathscr{D}}(\mathscr{G}-, -)$ means for two functors $\mathscr{F}$ and $\mathscr{G}$. Now we want to investigate under which circumstances there is a natural isomorphism $\mathrm{Mor}_{\mathscr{D}}(\mathscr{F}-, -) \cong \mathrm{Mor}_{\mathscr{C}}(-, \mathscr{G}-)$. First, $\mathscr{F} : \mathscr{C} \to \mathscr{D}$ and $\mathscr{G} : \mathscr{D} \to \mathscr{C}$ must be functors. Two such functors are called a *pair of adjoint functors*; $\mathscr{F}$ is called *left adjoint* to $\mathscr{G}$ and $\mathscr{G}$ is called *right adjoint* to $\mathscr{F}$ if there is a natural isomorphism of the bifunctors $\mathrm{Mor}_{\mathscr{D}}(\mathscr{F}-, -) \cong \mathrm{Mor}_{\mathscr{C}}(-, \mathscr{G}-)$ from $\mathscr{C}^0 \times \mathscr{D}$ into **S**.

PROPOSITION 1. *Let the functor $\mathscr{F} : \mathscr{C} \to \mathscr{D}$ be left adjoint to the functor $\mathscr{G} : \mathscr{D} \to \mathscr{C}$. Then $\mathscr{F}$ is determined by $\mathscr{G}$ uniquely up to a natural isomorphism.*

Proof. Let $\mathscr{F}$ and $\mathscr{F}'$ be left adjoint to $\mathscr{G}$, then there is a natural isomorphism $\mathrm{Mor}_{\mathscr{D}}(\mathscr{F}-, -) \cong \mathrm{Mor}_{\mathscr{D}}(\mathscr{F}'-, -)$. Thus, by Section 1.15, Lemma 3 we have $\mathscr{F} \cong \mathscr{F}'$.

If there is a left adjoint functor to $\mathscr{G}$ which is uniquely determined up to an isomorphism, it will also be denoted by $*\mathscr{G}$. If we pass over to the dual categories $\mathscr{C}^0$ and $\mathscr{D}^0$, then we get, from the considerations of Section 1.4, functors $\mathrm{Op}\mathscr{F}\mathrm{Op} = \mathscr{F}^0 : \mathscr{C}^0 \to \mathscr{D}^0$ and $\mathrm{Op}\mathscr{G}\mathrm{Op} = \mathscr{G}^0 : \mathscr{D}^0 \to \mathscr{C}^0$, and we have $\mathrm{Mor}_{\mathscr{C}^0}(\mathscr{G}^0-, -) \cong \mathrm{Mor}_{\mathscr{D}^0}(-, \mathscr{F}^0-)$. Thus $\mathscr{G}^0$ is left adjoint to $\mathscr{F}^0$ and is uniquely determined up to an isomorphism by $\mathscr{F}^0$. Since $\mathscr{G} = \mathscr{G}^{00}$, $\mathscr{G}$ also is uniquely determined by $\mathscr{F}$ up to an isomorphism. Thus the properties of left adjoint functors are transferred to right adjoint functors by dualization. If there is a right adjoint functor to $\mathscr{F}$ which is uniquely determined up to an isomorphism, then it will also be denoted by $\mathscr{F}*$.

COROLLARY 1.   *Let the functors* $\mathscr{F}_i : \mathscr{C} \to \mathscr{D}$ *be left adjoint to the functors* $\mathscr{G}_i : \mathscr{D} \to \mathscr{C}$ *for* $i = 1, 2$. *Let* $\varphi : \mathscr{G}_1 \to \mathscr{G}_2$ *be a natural transformation. Then there is exactly one natural transformation* $*\varphi : \mathscr{F}_2 \to \mathscr{F}_1$, *such that the diagram*

$$\mathrm{Mor}_{\mathscr{C}}(-, \mathscr{G}_1 -) \cong \mathrm{Mor}_{\mathscr{D}}(\mathscr{F}_1 -, -)$$

$$\mathrm{Mor}_{\mathscr{C}}(-, \varphi-) \Big\downarrow \qquad\qquad \Big\downarrow \mathrm{Mor}_{\mathscr{D}}(*\varphi-, -)$$

$$\mathrm{Mor}_{\mathscr{C}}(-, \mathscr{G}_2 -) \cong \mathrm{Mor}_{\mathscr{D}}(\mathscr{F}_2 -, -)$$

is commutative. If $\varphi = \mathrm{id}_{\mathscr{G}_1}$, *then* $*\varphi = \mathrm{id}_{\mathscr{F}_1}$. *For the composition of natural transformations, we have* $*(\varphi\psi) = *\psi*\varphi$.

Proof.   The first assertion is implied by Section 1.15, Lemma 3. The other assertions follow trivially.

COROLLARY 2.   *Let* $\mathscr{C}$ *and* $\mathscr{D}$ *be small categories. The category* $\mathrm{Funct}_R(\mathscr{C},\mathscr{D})$ *of functors from* $\mathscr{C}$ *into* $\mathscr{D}$ *which have right adjoint functors is dual to the category* $\mathrm{Funct}_L(\mathscr{D}, \mathscr{C})$ *of the functors from* $\mathscr{D}$ *into* $\mathscr{C}$, *which have left adjoint functors.*

PROPOSITION 2.   *A functor* $\mathscr{G} : \mathscr{D} \to \mathscr{C}$ *has left adjoint functor if and only if all functors* $\mathrm{Mor}_{\mathscr{C}}(C, \mathscr{G}-)$ *are representable for all* $C \in \mathscr{C}$.

Proof.   This is implied by Section 1.15 Lemma 4.

Now we have to deal in more detail with the natural isomorphisms $\varphi : \mathrm{Mor}_{\mathscr{D}}(\mathscr{F}-, -) \to \mathrm{Mor}_{\mathscr{C}}(-, \mathscr{G}-)$ used in the definition of the adjoint functors. First we assume that φ is an arbitrary natural transformation. Let objects $C \in \mathscr{C}$ and $D \in \mathscr{D}$ be given. Then

$$\varphi(C, D) : \mathrm{Mor}_{\mathscr{D}}(\mathscr{F}C, D) \to \mathrm{Mor}_{\mathscr{C}}(C, \mathscr{G}D).$$

If we choose in particular $D = \mathscr{F}C$, then we get a morphism

$$\varphi(C, \mathscr{F}C)(1_{\mathscr{F}C}) : C \to \mathscr{G}\mathscr{F}C$$

for all $C \in \mathcal{C}$. These morphisms form a natural transformation $\Phi :$ $\mathrm{Id}_{\mathcal{C}} \to \mathcal{GF}$. In fact, if $f : C \to C'$ is a morphism in $\mathcal{C}$, then the diagram

$$\begin{array}{ccccc}
\mathrm{Mor}(\mathcal{F}C, \mathcal{F}C) & \xrightarrow{\mathrm{Mor}(\mathcal{F}C, \mathcal{F}f)} & \mathrm{Mor}(\mathcal{F}C, \mathcal{F}C') & \xleftarrow{\mathrm{Mor}(\mathcal{F}f, \mathcal{F}C')} & \mathrm{Mor}(\mathcal{F}C', \mathcal{F}C') \\
\Big\downarrow{\varphi(C, \mathcal{F}C)} & & \Big\downarrow{\varphi(C, \mathcal{F}C')} & & \Big\downarrow{\varphi(C', \mathcal{F}C')} \\
\mathrm{Mor}(C, \mathcal{GF}C) & \xrightarrow{\mathrm{Mor}(C, \mathcal{GF}f)} & \mathrm{Mor}(C, \mathcal{GF}C') & \xleftarrow{\mathrm{Mor}(f, \mathcal{GF}C')} & \mathrm{Mor}(C', \mathcal{GF}C')
\end{array}$$

is commutative. Thus

$$\begin{aligned}
\Phi(C')f &= \mathrm{Mor}(f, \mathcal{GF}C')\, \varphi(C', \mathcal{F}C')(1_{\mathcal{F}C'}) = \varphi(C, \mathcal{F}C')\, \mathrm{Mor}(\mathcal{F}f, \mathcal{F}C')(1_{\mathcal{F}C'}) \\
&= \varphi(C, \mathcal{F}C')(\mathcal{F}f) = \varphi(C, \mathcal{F}C')\, \mathrm{Mor}(\mathcal{F}C, \mathcal{F}f)(1_{\mathcal{F}C}) \\
&= \mathrm{Mor}(C, \mathcal{GF}f)\, \varphi(C, \mathcal{F}C)(1_{\mathcal{F}C}) = \mathcal{GF}f\Phi(C)
\end{aligned}$$

Conversely, if $\Phi : \mathrm{Id}_{\mathcal{C}} \to \mathcal{GF}$ is a natural transformation, then we define a map

$$\varphi : \mathrm{Mor}_{\mathcal{D}}(\mathcal{F}C, D) \ni f \mapsto \mathcal{G}f\Phi(C) \in \mathrm{Mor}_{\mathcal{C}}(C, \mathcal{G}D)$$

It is natural in C and D because it is a composite of the maps

$$\mathcal{G} : \mathrm{Mor}_{\mathcal{D}}(\mathcal{F}C, D) \to \mathrm{Mor}_{\mathcal{C}}(\mathcal{GF}C, \mathcal{G}D)$$

and

$$\mathrm{Mor}(\Phi C, \mathcal{G}D) : \mathrm{Mor}_{\mathcal{C}}(\mathcal{GF}C, \mathcal{G}D) \to \mathrm{Mor}_{\mathcal{C}}(C, \mathcal{G}D)$$

But both maps are natural in C and D.

LEMMA. *Let* $\mathcal{F} : \mathcal{C} \to \mathcal{D}$ *and* $\mathcal{G} : \mathcal{D} \to \mathcal{C}$ *be functors. The application*

$$\mathrm{Mor}_f(\mathrm{Id}_{\mathcal{C}}, \mathcal{GF}) \ni \Phi \mapsto \mathcal{G}\text{-}\Phi\text{-} \in \mathrm{Mor}_f(\mathrm{Mor}_{\mathcal{D}}(\mathcal{F}-, -), \mathrm{Mor}_{\mathcal{C}}(-, \mathcal{G}-))$$

is bijective. The inverse of this application is

$$\mathrm{Mor}_f(\mathrm{Mor}_{\mathcal{D}}(\mathcal{F}-, -), \mathrm{Mor}_{\mathcal{C}}(-, \mathcal{G}-)) \ni \varphi \mapsto \varphi(-, \mathcal{F}-)(1_{\mathcal{F}-}) \in \mathrm{Mor}_f(\mathrm{Id}_{\mathcal{C}}, \mathcal{GF})$$

Proof. Let Φ be given, then $\mathcal{G}(1_{\mathcal{F}C})\, \Phi(C) = \mathcal{GF}(1_C)\, \Phi(C) = \Phi(C)$. Let φ be given, then

$$\begin{aligned}
\mathcal{G}f(\varphi(C, \mathcal{F}C)(1_{\mathcal{F}C})) &= \mathrm{Mor}_{\mathcal{C}}(C, \mathcal{G}f)\, \varphi(C, \mathcal{F}C)(1_{\mathcal{F}C}) \\
&= \varphi(C, D)\, \mathrm{Mor}_{\mathcal{D}}(\mathcal{F}C, f)(1_{\mathcal{F}C}) = \varphi(C, D)(f)
\end{aligned}$$

Dual to the lemma one proves that

$$\mathrm{Mor}_f(\mathcal{FG}, \mathrm{Id}_{\mathcal{D}}) \cong \mathrm{Mor}_f(\mathrm{Mor}_{\mathcal{C}}(-, \mathcal{G}-), \mathrm{Mor}_{\mathcal{D}}(\mathcal{F}-, -))$$

With the same notations as before, we have the following theorem.

THEOREM 1.   *Let* $\varphi : \mathrm{Mor}_{\mathscr{D}}(\mathscr{F}-, -) \to \mathrm{Mor}_{\mathscr{C}}(-, \mathscr{G}-)$ *and*

$$\psi : \mathrm{Mor}_{\mathscr{C}}(-, \mathscr{G}-) \to \mathrm{Mor}_{\mathscr{D}}(\mathscr{F}-, -)$$

be natural transformations, and let $\Phi : \mathrm{Id}_{\mathscr{C}} \to \mathscr{G}\mathscr{F}$ *and* $\Psi : \mathscr{F}\mathscr{G} \to \mathrm{Id}_{\mathscr{D}}$ *be the natural transformations constructed from* φ *and* ψ*. Then we have* $\varphi\psi = \mathrm{id}_{\mathrm{Mor}(-,\mathscr{G}-)}$ *if and only if*

$$(\mathscr{G} \xrightarrow{\Phi\mathscr{G}} \mathscr{G}\mathscr{F}\mathscr{G} \xrightarrow{\Psi\mathscr{G}} \mathscr{G}) = \mathrm{id}_{\mathscr{G}}$$

Furthermore, we have $\psi\varphi = \mathrm{id}_{\mathrm{Mor}(\mathscr{F}-,-)}$ *if and only if*

$$(\mathscr{F} \xrightarrow{\mathscr{F}\Phi} \mathscr{F}\mathscr{G}\mathscr{F} \xrightarrow{\Psi\mathscr{F}} \mathscr{F}) = \mathrm{id}_{\mathscr{F}}$$

Proof.

$$
\begin{aligned}
\mathscr{G}\Psi(D)\,\Phi\mathscr{G}(D) &= \mathscr{G}\Psi(D)\,\varphi(\mathscr{G}D, \mathscr{F}\mathscr{G}D)(1_{\mathscr{F}\mathscr{G}D}) \\
&= \mathrm{Mor}_{\mathscr{C}}(\mathscr{G}D, \mathscr{G}\Psi(D))\,\varphi(\mathscr{G}D, \mathscr{F}\mathscr{G}D)(1_{\mathscr{F}\mathscr{G}D}) \\
&= \varphi(\mathscr{G}D, D)\,\mathrm{Mor}_{\mathscr{D}}(\mathscr{F}\mathscr{G}D, \Psi(D))(1_{\mathscr{F}\mathscr{G}D}) \\
&= \varphi(\mathscr{G}D, D)(\Psi(D)) \\
&= \varphi(\mathscr{G}D, D)\,\psi(\mathscr{G}D, D)(1_{\mathscr{G}D}) \\
&= \varphi\psi(\mathscr{G}D, D)(1_{\mathscr{G}D})
\end{aligned}
$$

Similarly, one gets

$$
\begin{aligned}
\varphi\psi(C, D)(f) &= \varphi(C, D)\,\psi(C, D)(f) \\
&= \mathscr{G}(\Psi(D)\,\mathscr{F}(f))\,\Phi(C) \\
&= \mathscr{G}\Psi(D)\,\mathscr{G}\mathscr{F}(f)\,\Phi(C) \\
&= \mathscr{G}\Psi(D)\,\Phi\mathscr{G}(D)\,f
\end{aligned}
$$

This proves the assertion.

COROLLARY 3.   *The functor* $\mathscr{F} : \mathscr{C} \to \mathscr{D}$ *if left adjoint to* $\mathscr{G} : \mathscr{D} \to \mathscr{C}$ *if and only if there are natural transformations* $\Phi : \mathrm{Id}_{\mathscr{C}} \to \mathscr{G}\mathscr{F}$ *and* $\Psi : \mathscr{F}\mathscr{G} \to \mathrm{Id}_{\mathscr{D}}$ *with* $(\mathscr{G}\Psi)(\Phi\mathscr{G}) = \mathrm{id}_{\mathscr{G}}$ *and* $(\Psi\mathscr{F})(\mathscr{F}\Phi) = \mathrm{id}_{\mathscr{F}}$.

COROLLARY 4.   *Let* $\mathscr{F}$ *be left adjoint to* $\mathscr{G}$*, then the maps*

$$\mathscr{G} : \mathrm{Mor}_{\mathscr{D}}(\mathscr{F}C, D) \to \mathrm{Mor}_{\mathscr{C}}(\mathscr{G}\mathscr{F}C, \mathscr{G}D)$$

are injective for all $C \in \mathscr{C}$ *and* $D \in \mathscr{D}$*.*

Proof. By the considerations preceeding the lemma, the isomorphism $\mathrm{Mor}_{\mathscr{D}}(\mathscr{F}-, -) \cong \mathrm{Mor}_{\mathscr{C}}(-, \mathscr{G}-)$ is composed of the morphisms

$$\mathscr{G} : \mathrm{Mor}_{\mathscr{D}}(\mathscr{F}-, -) \to \mathrm{Mor}_{\mathscr{C}}(\mathscr{G}\mathscr{F}-, \mathscr{G}-)$$

and

$$\mathrm{Mor}_{\mathscr{C}}(\mathscr{G}\mathscr{F}-, \mathscr{G}-) \to \mathrm{Mor}_{\mathscr{C}}(-, \mathscr{G}-).$$

COROLLARY 5. *Let the categories $\mathscr{C}$ and $\mathscr{D}$ be equivalent by $\mathscr{F} : \mathscr{C} \to \mathscr{D}$ and $\mathscr{G} : \mathscr{D} \to \mathscr{C}$, $\Phi : \mathrm{Id}_{\mathscr{C}} \cong \mathscr{G}\mathscr{F}$ and $\Psi : \mathscr{F}\mathscr{G} \cong \mathrm{Id}_{\mathscr{D}}$, then $\mathscr{F}$ is left adjoint and right adjoint to $\mathscr{G}$.*

Proof. $\Phi\mathscr{G}$ and $\mathscr{G}\Psi$ are isomorphisms. Consequently, $(\mathscr{G}\Psi)(\Phi\mathscr{G})$ and $(\Psi\mathscr{F})(\mathscr{F}\Phi)$ are also isomorphisms. Thus, $\psi\varphi$ and $\varphi\psi$ are isomorphisms and also φ and ψ.

PROPOSITION 3. *A functor $\mathscr{F} : \mathscr{C} \to \mathscr{D}$ is an equivalence if and only if $\mathscr{F}$ is full and faithful and if to each $D \in \mathscr{D}$ there is a $C \in \mathscr{C}$ such that $\mathscr{F}C \cong D$.*

Proof. The conditions are easy to verify if $\mathscr{F}$ is an equivalence. Now let $\mathscr{F}$ be full and faithful and let there be a $C \in \mathscr{C}$ to each $D \in \mathscr{D}$ such that $\mathscr{F}C \cong \mathscr{D}$. We consider the functors $\mathscr{H} : \mathscr{C}' \to \mathscr{C}$ and $\mathscr{G} : \mathscr{D} \to \mathscr{D}'$ which are equivalences between $\mathscr{C}$ and $\mathscr{D}$ and the corresponding skeletons $\mathscr{C}'$ and $\mathscr{D}'$ respectively. Obviously, $\mathscr{F}$ is an equivalence if and only if $\mathscr{G}\mathscr{F}\mathscr{H} : \mathscr{C}' \to \mathscr{D}'$ is an equivalence. $\mathscr{G}\mathscr{F}\mathscr{H}$ is full and faithful and all objects of $\mathscr{D}'$ appear already in the image of $\mathscr{G}\mathscr{F}\mathscr{H}$, since any two isomorphic objects in $\mathscr{D}'$ are already equal. The considerations on the image of a full and faithful functor in Section 1.15 show that different objects of $\mathscr{C}'$ are mapped to different objects by $\mathscr{G}\mathscr{F}\mathscr{H}$. Thus $\mathscr{G}\mathscr{F}\mathscr{H}$ is bijective on the class of objects and on the morphism. Thus the inverse map is a functor and $\mathscr{G}\mathscr{F}\mathscr{H}$ is an isomorphism between $\mathscr{C}'$ and $\mathscr{D}'$.

In Corollary 3 we developed a first criterion for adjoint functors. Before we develop further criteria and investigate in more detail the properties of adjoint functors, we want to give some examples of adjoint functors.

Examples

1. Let $A \in \mathbf{S}$. Forming the product with A defines a functor $A \times - : \mathbf{S} \to \mathbf{S}$. There is a natural isomorphism (natural in $B, C \in \mathbf{S}$)

$$\mathrm{Mor}_{\mathbf{S}}(A \times B, C) \cong \mathrm{Mor}_{\mathbf{S}}(B, \mathrm{Mor}_{\mathbf{S}}(A, C))$$

2. Let **Mo** be the category of monoids, of sets H with a multiplication $H \times H \to H$, such that $(h_1 h_2) h_3 = h_1(h_2 h_3)$ and such that there is a

neutral element $e \in H$ with $eh = h = he$ for all $h \in H$, together with those maps f with $f(h_1 h_2) = f(h_1) f(h_2)$ and $f(e) = e$. Given a monoid H, we define a unitary, associative ring by

$$\mathbb{Z}(H) = \{ f \mid f \in \mathrm{Mor}_S(H, \mathbb{Z}) \quad \text{and} \quad f(h) = 0 \text{ for all but a finite number of } h \in H \}$$

We define $(f + f')(h) = f(h) + f'(h)$. Then $\mathbb{Z}(H)$ becomes an abelian group. The product is defined by $(ff')(h) = \Sigma f(h') f'(h'')$ where the sum is to be taken over those pairs $h', h'' \in H$ with $h'h'' = h$. Since H is a monoid, we get a unitary, associative ring $\mathbb{Z}(H)$. Furthermore, $\mathbb{Z}(-) : \mathbf{Mo} \to \mathbf{Ri}$ is a covariant functor. Now let $R \in \mathbf{Ri}$ and let R' be the monoid defined by the multiplication on R, then also $-' : \mathbf{Ri} \to \mathbf{Mo}$ is a covariant functor. There is a natural isomorphism

$$\mathrm{Mor}_{\mathbf{Ri}}(\mathbb{Z}(-), -) \cong \mathrm{Mor}_{\mathbf{Mo}}(-, -')$$

that is, the functors constructed above are adjoint to each other. This and other functors will be investigated in more detail in Chapter 3.

3.   The following is one of the best known examples which, in fact, led to the development of the theory of adjoint functors. Let R and S be unitary, associative rings. Let A be an R-S-bimodule, that is, and R-left-module and an S-right-module such that $r(as) = (ra)s$ for all $r \in R, s \in S$, and $a \in A$. The set $\mathrm{Mor}_R(A, C)$ with an R-module C is an S-left-module by $(sf)(a) = f(as)$. $\mathrm{Mor}_R(A, -) : {}_R\mathbf{Mod} \to {}_S\mathbf{Mod}$ is even a functor. To this functor there is a left adjoint functor $A \otimes_S - : {}_S\mathbf{Mod} \to {}_R\mathbf{Mod}$ called the tensor product. Thus there is an isomorphism

$$\mathrm{Mor}_R(A \otimes_S B, C) \cong \mathrm{Mor}_S(B, \mathrm{Mor}_R(A, C))$$

which is natural in B and C. Actually this isomorphism is also natural in A.

2.2   Universal Problems

Let us consider again Section 2.1, Example 2. For each monoid H the natural tranformation $\mathrm{Id}_{\mathbf{Mo}} \to (\mathbb{Z}(-))'$ induces a homomorphism of monoids $\rho : H \to (\mathbb{Z}(H))'$ which assigns to each $h \in H$ the map with $f(h') = 1$ for $h = h'$ and $f(h') = 0$ for $h \neq h'$. Let us denote this map by f_h. Now if $g : H \to R$ is a map with $g(h_1 h_2) = g(h_1) g(h_2)$ and $g(e) =$

$1 \in R$, then there is exactly one homomorphism of (unitary) rings $g^* : \mathbb{Z}(H) \to R$ such that the diagram

is commutative. In this diagram we have morphisms of two different categories. In fact, ρ and g are in **Mo** and g^* is in **Ri**. Correspondingly, $\mathbb{Z}(H)$ and R are objects in **Mo** and also objects in **Ri**. Furthermore, we composed a homomorphism of rings g^* with a homomorphism of monoids ρ to a homomorphism of monoids g. We want to give a structure in which these constructions are possible.

Let $\mathscr{C}$ and $\mathscr{D}$ be categories. Let a family of sets

$$\{\mathrm{Mor}_{\mathscr{V}}(A, B) \mid A \in \mathscr{C}, \quad B \in \mathscr{D}\}$$

be given together with two families of maps

$$\mathrm{Mor}_{\mathscr{C}}(A, A') \times \mathrm{Mor}_{\mathscr{V}}(A', B) \to \mathrm{Mor}_{\mathscr{V}}(A, B), \qquad A, A' \in \mathscr{C}, \quad B \in \mathscr{D}$$

$$\mathrm{Mor}_{\mathscr{V}}(A, B') \times \mathrm{Mor}_{\mathscr{D}}(B', B) \to \mathrm{Mor}_{\mathscr{V}}(A, B), \qquad A \in \mathscr{C}, B', \quad B \in \mathscr{D}$$

As usual we write these maps as compositions, that is, if $f \in \mathrm{Mor}_{\mathscr{C}}(A, A')$, $v \in \mathrm{Mor}_{\mathscr{V}}(A', B)$, $v' \in \mathrm{Mor}_{\mathscr{V}}(A, B')$, and $g \in \mathrm{Mor}_{\mathscr{D}}(B', B)$, then we denote the images of (f, v) and (v', g) by vf and gv' respectively.

LEMMA 1. *The disjoint union of the classes of objects of $\mathscr{C}$ and $\mathscr{D}$ together with the family*

$$\{\mathrm{Mor}_{\mathscr{C}}(A, A'), \mathrm{Mor}_{\mathscr{V}}(A, B), \mathrm{Mor}_{\mathscr{D}}(B, B') \mid A, A' \in \mathscr{C}, \quad B, B' \in \mathscr{D}\}$$

of sets, which we consider as disjoint, and together with the compositions of $\mathscr{C}$ and of $\mathscr{D}$ and the above defined compositions form a category $\mathscr{V}(\mathscr{C}, \mathscr{D})$, if the following hold for all $A, A', A'' \in \mathscr{C}$, $B, B', B'' \in \mathscr{D}$ and for all $f \in \mathrm{Mor}_{\mathscr{C}}(A', A)$, $f' \in \mathrm{Mor}_{\mathscr{C}}(A'', A')$, $v \in \mathrm{Mor}_{\mathscr{V}}(A, B)$, $g \in \mathrm{Mor}_{\mathscr{D}}(N, B')$, and $g' \in \mathrm{Mor}_{\mathscr{D}}(B', B'')$

(1) $(vf)f' = v(ff')$
(2) $(g'g)v = v'(gv)$
(3) $(gv)f = g(vf)$
(4) $1_B v = v = v 1_A$

Proof. It is trivial to verify both axioms for categories if we set $\mathrm{Mor}_{\mathscr{V}(\mathscr{C},\mathscr{D})}(B, A) = \varnothing$.

If Lemma 1 holds, then we call the category $\mathscr{V}(\mathscr{C}, \mathscr{D})$ *directly connected category.* The family of sets $\mathrm{Mor}_{\mathscr{V}}(A, B)$ is called a *connection* from $\mathscr{C}$ to $\mathscr{D}$.

If we want to express our example with this structure, then we first have to define a connection from **Mo** to **Ri**. For $H \in$ **Mo** and $R \in$ **Ri**, we define $\mathrm{Mor}_{\mathscr{V}}(H, R) = \mathrm{Mor}_{\mathbf{Mo}}(H, R')$, where R' is the multiplicative monoid of R. By using indices we can make $\mathrm{Mor}_{\mathscr{V}}(H, R)$ disjoint to all morphism sets of **Mo**. The compositions are defined by the composition of the underlying set maps. Thus we get a directly connected category $\mathscr{V}(\mathbf{Mo}, \mathbf{Ri})$. Now to each $H \in$ **Mo** there is a morphism $\rho : H \to \mathbb{Z}(H)$ such that to each morphism $g : H \to R$ for $R \in$ **Ri**, there is exactly one morphism $g^* : \mathbb{Z}(H) \to R$ making the diagram

commutative.

In the general case, a directly connected category gives rise to the following *universal problem.* Let $A \in \mathscr{C}$. Is there an object $U(A) \in \mathscr{D}$ and a morphism $\rho_A : A \to U(A)$, such that to each morphism $g : A \to B$ for $B \in \mathscr{D}$ there is exactly one morphism $g^* : U(A) \to B$ making the diagram

commutative? A pair $(U(A), \rho_A)$ satisfying the above condition is called a *universal solution* of the universal problem.

LEMMA 2. *Let $\mathscr{V}(\mathscr{C}, \mathscr{D})$ be a directly connected category. The universal problem defined by $A \in \mathscr{C}$ has a universal solution if and only if the functor $\mathrm{Mor}_{\mathscr{V}}(A, -) : \mathscr{D} \to \mathbf{S}$ is representable.*

Proof. If $(U(A), \rho_A)$ is a universal solution, then by definition $\mathrm{Mor}(\rho_A, B) : \mathrm{Mor}_{\mathscr{D}}(U(A), B) \cong \mathrm{Mor}_{\mathscr{V}}(A, B)$. Furthermore, by the Yoneda lemma,

$$\mathrm{Mor}(\rho_A, -) : \mathrm{Mor}_{\mathscr{V}(\mathscr{C},\mathscr{D})}(U(A), -) \to \mathrm{Mor}_{\mathscr{V}(\mathscr{C},\mathscr{D})}(A, -)$$

is a natural transformation. Conversely, if

$$\Phi : \mathrm{Mor}_{\mathscr{D}}(U(A), -) \simeq \mathrm{Mor}_{\mathscr{V}}(A, -),$$

then again by the Yoneda lemma $\Phi = \mathrm{Mor}(\Phi(U(A))(1_{U(A)}), -)$ since $U(A) \in \mathscr{D}$. But this means that the natural transformation

$$\mathrm{Mor}_{\mathscr{D}}(U(A), -) \simeq \mathrm{Mor}_{\mathscr{V}}(A, -)$$

maps the morphisms of $\mathrm{Mor}_{\mathscr{D}}(U(A), B)$ into $\mathrm{Mor}_{\mathscr{V}}(A, B)$ by composition with $\Phi(U(A))(1_{U(A)})$. Thus $(U(A), \Phi(U(A))(1_{U(A)}))$ is a universal solution of the problem.

This lemma implies immediately that a universal solution of a universal problem is uniquely determined up to an isomorphism. A directly connected category $\mathscr{V}(\mathscr{C}, \mathscr{D})$ is called *universally directly connected* if the corresponding universal problem has a universal solution for all $A \in \mathscr{C}$.

Often the connection for a directly connected category is given by a functor as

$$\mathrm{Mor}_{\mathscr{V}}(A, B) := \mathrm{Mor}_{\mathscr{C}}(A, \mathscr{G}B)$$

Then we also write $\mathscr{V}_{\mathscr{G}}(\mathscr{C}, \mathscr{D})$. Because of the functor property of $\mathscr{G}$ each covariant functor $\mathscr{G}$ defines a connection. Similarly, each functor $\mathscr{F} : \mathscr{C} \to \mathscr{D}$ defines a connection by

$$\mathrm{Mor}_{\mathscr{V}}(A, B) := \mathrm{Mor}_{\mathscr{D}}(\mathscr{F}A, B)$$

LEMMA 3. *The directly connected category $\mathscr{V}(\mathscr{C}, \mathscr{D})$ is universally directly connected if and only if there is functor $\mathscr{F} : \mathscr{C} \to \mathscr{D}$ such that there exists a natural isomorphism $\mathrm{Mor}_{\mathscr{V}}(-, -) \simeq \mathrm{Mor}_{\mathscr{D}}(\mathscr{F}-, -)$.*

Proof. The lemma follows immediately from Lemma 2 and Section 1.15, Lemma 4.

THEOREM 1. *Let $\mathscr{G} : \mathscr{D} \to \mathscr{C}$ be a covariant functor. The following are equivalent:*

(1) *$\mathscr{G}$ has a left adjoint functor $\mathscr{F} : \mathscr{C} \to \mathscr{D}$.*
(2) *The directly connected category $\mathscr{V}_{\mathscr{G}}(\mathscr{C}, \mathscr{D})$ is universally directly connected.*

In this special case we want to reformulate the universal problem using the definition of the connection. Let $\mathscr{G} : \mathscr{D} \to \mathscr{C}$ be a functor. Let $A \in \mathscr{C}$. We want to find an object $\mathscr{F}A \in \mathscr{D}$ and a morphism $\rho_A : A \to \mathscr{G}\mathscr{F}A$

such that to each morphism $g : A \to \mathscr{G}B$ for each $B \in \mathscr{D}$ there is exactly one morphism $g^* : \mathscr{F}A \to B$ which makes the diagram

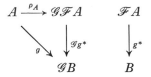

commutative. Here it becomes clear that not g^* is composed with ρ_A but $\mathscr{G}g^*$. The example with which we started at the beginning of this section has exactly this form.

Let two categories $\mathscr{C}$ and $\mathscr{D}$ be given. Let a connection

$$\{\mathrm{Mor}_{\mathscr{V}}(B, A) \mid B \in \mathscr{D}, A \in \mathscr{C}\}$$

be given such that $\mathscr{V}(\mathscr{D}, \mathscr{C})$ is a directly connected category. We also denote this category by $\mathscr{V}'(\mathscr{C}, \mathscr{D})$ and call it *universely connected category*. Observe that now $\mathrm{Mor}_{\mathscr{V}'(\mathscr{C},\mathscr{D})}(B, A)$ is not empty in general, but that $\mathrm{Mor}_{\mathscr{V}'(\mathscr{C},\mathscr{D})}(A, B) = \varnothing$.

Let $\mathscr{V}'(\mathscr{C}, \mathscr{D})$ be an inversely connected category. Here again we define a *universal problem*. Let $A \in \mathscr{C}$. Is there an object $U(A) \in \mathscr{D}$ and a morphism $\rho_A : U(A) \to A$ such that for each morphism $g : B \to A$ for all $B \in \mathscr{D}$ there is exactly one morphism $g^* : B \to U(A)$ making the diagram

commutative? A pair $(U(A), \rho_A)$ satisfying the above condition is called a *universal solution* of the universal problem. If the universal problem in $\mathscr{V}'(\mathscr{C}, \mathscr{D})$ has a universal solution for all $A \in \mathscr{C}$, then $\mathscr{V}'(\mathscr{C}, \mathscr{D})$ is called *universally inversely connected*. Thus we get a new characterization for pairs of adjoint functors $\mathscr{F} : \mathscr{C} \to \mathscr{D}$ and $\mathscr{G} : \mathscr{D} \to \mathscr{C}$.

THEOREM 2. *Let categories $\mathscr{C}$ and $\mathscr{D}$ and a connection be given such that $\mathscr{V}(\mathscr{C}, \mathscr{D})$ is directly connected and $\mathscr{V}'(\mathscr{D}, \mathscr{C})$ is inversely connected with the given connection. Then the following are equivalent:*

(1) *$\mathscr{V}(\mathscr{C}, \mathscr{D})$ is universally directly connected and $\mathscr{V}'(\mathscr{D}, \mathscr{C})$ is universally inversely connected.*

(2) *The morphism sets of the connection are induced by a pair of adjoint functors $\mathscr{F}$ and $\mathscr{G}$ as*

$$\mathrm{Mor}_{\mathscr{A}}(-, -) \cong \mathrm{Mor}_{\mathscr{D}}(\mathscr{F}-, -) \cong \mathrm{Mor}_{\mathscr{C}}(-, \mathscr{G}-)$$

Proof. This assertion is implied by Lemma 3 and the dual of Theorem 1.

2.3 Monads

Let $\mathscr{A}$, $\mathscr{B}$, $\mathscr{C}$, and $\mathscr{D}$ be categories, $\mathscr{F}$, $\mathscr{F}' : \mathscr{A} \to \mathscr{B}$, $\mathscr{G}$, $\mathscr{G}'$, $\mathscr{G}''$: $\mathscr{B} \to \mathscr{C}$, and $\mathscr{H}$, $\mathscr{H}' : \mathscr{C} \to \mathscr{D}$ be functors, and $\varphi : \mathscr{F} \to \mathscr{F}'$, $\psi : \mathscr{G} \to \mathscr{G}'$, $\psi' : \mathscr{G}' \to \mathscr{G}''$, and $\rho : \mathscr{H} \to \mathscr{H}'$ be natural transformations. In Section 2.1 we saw that also $\psi\mathscr{F} : \mathscr{G}\mathscr{F} \to \mathscr{G}'\mathscr{F}$ and $\mathscr{H}\psi : \mathscr{H}\mathscr{G} \to \mathscr{H}\mathscr{G}'$ with $(\psi\mathscr{F})(A) = \psi(\mathscr{F}(A))$ and $(\mathscr{H}\psi)(B) = \mathscr{H}(\psi(B))$ are natural transformations. With this definition one easily verifies the following equations:

$$(\mathscr{H}\mathscr{G})\,\varphi = \mathscr{H}(\mathscr{G}\varphi) \tag{1}$$

$$\rho(\mathscr{G}\mathscr{F}) = (\rho\mathscr{G})\,\mathscr{F} \tag{2}$$

$$(\mathscr{H}\psi)\,\mathscr{F} = \mathscr{H}(\psi\mathscr{F}) \tag{3}$$

$$\mathscr{H}(\psi'\psi)\,\mathscr{F} = (\mathscr{H}\psi'\mathscr{F})(\mathscr{H}\psi\mathscr{F}) \tag{4}$$

$$(\psi\mathscr{F}')(\mathscr{G}\varphi) = (\mathscr{G}'\varphi)(\psi\mathscr{F}) \tag{5}$$

where the last equation follows from the fact that ψ is a natural transformation.

Now let $\mathscr{F} : \mathscr{C} \to \mathscr{D}$ and $\mathscr{G} : \mathscr{D} \to \mathscr{C}$ be a pair of adjoint functors with the natural transformations $\Phi : \mathrm{Id}_{\mathscr{C}} \to \mathscr{G}\mathscr{F}$ and $\Psi : \mathscr{F}\mathscr{G} \to \mathrm{Id}_{\mathscr{D}}$ satisfying the conditions of Section 2.1, Theorem 1. We abbreviate the functor $\mathscr{G}\mathscr{F}$ by $\mathscr{H} = \mathscr{G}\mathscr{F}$. Then we have natural tranformations

$$\epsilon = \Phi : \mathrm{Id}_{\mathscr{C}} \to \mathscr{H} \quad \text{and} \quad \mu = \mathscr{G}\Psi\mathscr{F} : \mathscr{H}\mathscr{H} \to \mathscr{H}$$

With these notations we obtain the following lemma.

LEMMA 1. *The following diagrams are commutative:*

Proof. We use Section 2.1, Theorem 1 and obtain from the definitions

$$\mu(\epsilon\mathscr{H}) = (\mathscr{G}\Psi\mathscr{F})(\Phi\mathscr{G}\mathscr{F}) = ((\mathscr{G}\Psi)\mathscr{F})((\Phi\mathscr{G})\mathscr{F})$$

$$= ((\mathscr{G}\Psi)(\Phi\mathscr{G}))\,\mathscr{F} = \mathrm{id}_{\mathscr{G}}\mathscr{F} = \mathrm{id}_{\mathscr{H}}$$

$$\mu(\mathscr{H}\epsilon) = (\mathscr{G}\Psi\mathscr{F})(\mathscr{G}\mathscr{F}\Phi) = (\mathscr{G}(\Psi\mathscr{F}))(\mathscr{G}(\mathscr{F}\Phi))$$

$$= \mathscr{G}((\Psi\mathscr{F})(\mathscr{F}\Phi)) = \mathscr{G}\,\mathrm{id}_{\mathscr{F}} = \mathrm{id}_{\mathscr{H}}$$

$$\mu(\mu\mathscr{H}) = (\mathscr{G}\Psi\mathscr{F})(\mathscr{G}\psi\mathscr{F}\mathscr{G}\mathscr{F}) = \mathscr{G}(\Psi(\Psi\mathscr{F}\mathscr{G}))\,\mathscr{F} = \mathscr{G}(\Psi(\mathscr{F}\mathscr{G}\Psi))\,\mathscr{F}$$

$$= (\mathscr{G}\Psi\mathscr{F})(\mathscr{G}\mathscr{F}\mathscr{G}\Psi\mathscr{F}) = \mu(\mathscr{H}\mu)$$

A functor $\mathscr{H} : \mathscr{C} \to \mathscr{C}$ whose domain and range categories coincide is called an *endofunctor*. An endofunctor $\mathscr{H}$ together with natural transformations $\epsilon : \mathrm{Id}_{\mathscr{C}} \to \mathscr{H}$ and $\mu : \mathscr{H}\mathscr{H} \to \mathscr{H}$ is called a *monad* if Lemma 1 holds for $(\mathscr{H}, \epsilon, \mu)$. Other terms are triple or dual standard construction. The dual terms are comonad or cotriple or standard construction.

To explain the name, one notes that a monoid is a set H together with two maps $e : \{\varnothing\} \to H$ and $m : H \times H \to H$ such that the diagrams

$$
\begin{array}{ccc}
H & \xrightarrow{\ e \times h\ } & H \times H \\
{\scriptstyle h \times e}\big\downarrow & \searrow^{1_H} & \big\downarrow{\scriptstyle m} \\
H \times H & \xrightarrow{\ m\ } & H
\end{array}
\qquad
\begin{array}{ccc}
H \times H \times H & \xrightarrow{\ m \times h\ } & H \times H \\
{\scriptstyle h \times m}\big\downarrow & & \big\downarrow{\scriptstyle m} \\
H \times H & \xrightarrow{\ m\ } & H
\end{array}
$$

are commutative, where we identified $\{\varnothing\} \times H$ with H. Observe, however, that in the definition of the product we did not use the product of the endofunctors but their composition. The term monad was proposed by S. Eilenberg because of this similarity.

Now we want to deal with the problem of whether all monads are induced by pairs of adjoint functors in the way we proved in Lemma 1. We shall see that this is the case, but that the inducing pairs of adjoint functors are not uniquely determined by the monads. There are, however, two essentially different pairs of adjoint functors satisfying this condition and having certain additional universal properties. These pairs were found by Eilenberg, Moore, and Kleisli. We shall use both constructions with only minimal changes.

THEOREM 1. *Let $(\mathscr{H}, \epsilon, \mu)$ be a monad over the category $\mathscr{C}$. There exist pairs of adjoint functors $\mathscr{S}_{\mathscr{H}} : \mathscr{C} \to \mathscr{C}_{\mathscr{H}}, \mathscr{T}_{\mathscr{H}} : \mathscr{C}_{\mathscr{H}} \to \mathscr{C}$ and $\mathscr{S}^{\mathscr{H}} : \mathscr{C} \to \mathscr{C}^{\mathscr{H}}, \mathscr{T}^{\mathscr{H}} : \mathscr{C}^{\mathscr{H}} \to \mathscr{C}$ inducing the given monad. If $\mathscr{F} : \mathscr{C} \to \mathscr{D}, \mathscr{G} : \mathscr{D} \to \mathscr{C}$*

is another pair of adjoint functors inducing the given monad, then there are uniquely determined functors $\mathscr{K}$ and $\mathscr{L}$ making the diagram

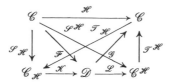

commutative.

Proof. First we give the construction of $\mathscr{S}_{\mathscr{H}}$, $\mathscr{T}_{\mathscr{H}}$, and $\mathscr{C}_{\mathscr{H}}$. The objects of $\mathscr{C}_{\mathscr{H}}$ are the same as the objects of $\mathscr{C}$. Let $A, B \in \mathscr{C}$. The morphisms from A to B in $\mathscr{C}_{\mathscr{H}}$ are the morphisms $f: \mathscr{H}A \to \mathscr{H}B$ for which the diagram

$$
\begin{array}{ccc}
\mathscr{H}\mathscr{H}A & \xrightarrow{\mathscr{H}f} & \mathscr{H}\mathscr{H}B \\
\mu A \downarrow & & \downarrow \mu B \\
\mathscr{H}A & \xrightarrow{f} & \mathscr{H}B
\end{array}
$$

is commutative. By using indices we can determine that the morphism sets in $\mathscr{C}_{\mathscr{H}}$ are disjoint. The compositions are defined as in $\mathscr{C}$. Then $\mathscr{C}_{\mathscr{H}}$ is a category because $\mathscr{H}$ is a functor.

We define the functors $\mathscr{S}_{\mathscr{H}}$ and $\mathscr{T}_{\mathscr{H}}$ by $\mathscr{S}_{\mathscr{H}}A = A$, $\mathscr{S}_{\mathscr{H}}f = \mathscr{H}f$ and $\mathscr{T}_{\mathscr{H}}A = \mathscr{H}A$, $\mathscr{T}_{\mathscr{H}}f = f$. Trivially, $\mathscr{T}_{\mathscr{H}}$ is a functor. The functor properties of $\mathscr{S}_{\mathscr{H}}$ are implied by the fact that μ is a natural transformation. Furthermore, we have $\mathscr{H} = \mathscr{T}_{\mathscr{H}}\mathscr{S}_{\mathscr{H}}$.

To show that $\mathscr{S}_{\mathscr{H}}$ is left adjoint to $\mathscr{T}_{\mathscr{H}}$ we use Section 2.1, Corollary 3. Let $\Phi = \epsilon : \mathrm{Id}_{\mathscr{C}} \to \mathscr{H}$. Define $\Psi : \mathscr{S}_{\mathscr{H}}\mathscr{T}_{\mathscr{H}} \to \mathrm{Id}_{\mathscr{C}_{\mathscr{H}}}$ by $\Psi A = \mu A : \mathscr{H}\mathscr{H}A \to \mathscr{H}A$ considered as a morphism from $\mathscr{H}A$ to A in $\mathscr{C}_{\mathscr{H}}$. ΨA is a morphism in $\mathscr{C}_{\mathscr{H}}$ because of $\mu(\mathscr{H}\mu) = \mu(\mu\mathscr{H})$. Ψ is a natural transformation because of the hypotheses on the morphisms in $\mathscr{C}_{\mathscr{H}}$.

Then we have for objects $A \in \mathscr{C}$ and $A \in \mathscr{C}_{\mathscr{H}}$, respectively,

$$(\Psi\mathscr{S}_{\mathscr{H}})(\mathscr{S}_{\mathscr{H}}\Phi)(A) = (\Psi\mathscr{S}_{\mathscr{H}}(A))(\mathscr{S}_{\mathscr{H}}\Phi(A)) = \mu(A)\,\mathscr{H}\epsilon(A) = 1_{\mathscr{H}A} = 1_{\mathscr{S}_{\mathscr{H}}A}$$

and

$$(\mathscr{T}_{\mathscr{H}}\Psi)(\Phi\mathscr{T}_{\mathscr{H}})(A) = (\mathscr{T}_{\mathscr{H}}\Psi(A))(\Phi\mathscr{T}_{\mathscr{H}}(A)) = \mu(A)\,\epsilon\mathscr{H}(A) = 1_{\mathscr{H}A} = 1_{\mathscr{T}_{\mathscr{H}}A}$$

Since $\mu = \mathscr{T}_{\mathscr{H}}\Psi\mathscr{S}_{\mathscr{H}}$, the monad $(\mathscr{H}, \epsilon, \mu)$ is induced by the pair of adjoint functors $\mathscr{S}_{\mathscr{H}}$ and $\mathscr{T}_{\mathscr{H}}$. $\mathscr{T}_{\mathscr{H}}$ is faithful by Section 2.1, Corollary 4, since all objects of $\mathscr{C}_{\mathscr{H}}$ are in the image of $\mathscr{S}_{\mathscr{H}}$. This also follows directly from the definition.

Now we give $\mathscr{C}^{\mathscr{H}}$, $\mathscr{S}^{\mathscr{H}}$, and $\mathscr{T}^{\mathscr{H}}$. The objects of $\mathscr{C}^{\mathscr{H}}$ are pairs (A, α) where A is an object in $\mathscr{C}$ and $\alpha : \mathscr{H}A \to A$ is a morphism in $\mathscr{C}$ such that the diagrams

$$
\begin{array}{ccc}
A & & \\
\ _{\epsilon A}\searrow\ ^{1_A} & & \\
\mathscr{H}A \xrightarrow{\ \alpha\ } A & &
\end{array}
\qquad
\begin{array}{ccc}
\mathscr{H}\mathscr{H}A & \xrightarrow{\ \mathscr{H}\alpha\ } & \mathscr{H}A \\
\ _{\mu A}\downarrow & & \downarrow^{\alpha} \\
\mathscr{H}A & \xrightarrow{\ \alpha\ } & A
\end{array}
$$

are commutative. The morphisms from (A, α) to (B, β) are morphisms $f : A \to B$ in $\mathscr{C}$ with the diagram

$$
\begin{array}{ccc}
\mathscr{H}A & \xrightarrow{\ \mathscr{H}f\ } & \mathscr{H}B \\
\ _{\alpha}\downarrow & & \downarrow^{\beta} \\
A & \xrightarrow{\ f\ } & B
\end{array}
$$

commutative. The compositions are defined as in $\mathscr{C}$. Then $\mathscr{C}^{\mathscr{H}}$ is a category.

The functors $\mathscr{S}^{\mathscr{H}}$ and $\mathscr{T}^{\mathscr{H}}$ are defined by $\mathscr{S}^{\mathscr{H}}A = (\mathscr{H}A, \mu A)$, $\mathscr{S}^{\mathscr{H}}f = \mathscr{H}f$ and $\mathscr{T}^{\mathscr{H}}(A, \alpha) = A$, $\mathscr{T}^{\mathscr{H}}f = f$. Trivially, $\mathscr{T}^{\mathscr{H}}$ is a functor. $(\mathscr{H}A, \mu A)$ is an object of $\mathscr{C}^{\mathscr{H}}$ because $(\mathscr{H}, \epsilon, \mu)$ is a monad. $\mathscr{H}f$ is a morphism in $\mathscr{C}^{\mathscr{H}}$ because μ is a natural transformation. Furthermore, $\mathscr{H} = \mathscr{T}^{\mathscr{H}}\mathscr{S}^{\mathscr{H}}$.

We use again Section 2.1, Corollary 3 to show that $\mathscr{S}^{\mathscr{H}}$ is left adjoint to $\mathscr{T}^{\mathscr{H}}$. Let $\Phi = \epsilon : \mathrm{Id}_{\mathscr{C}} \to \mathscr{H}$. For each object (A, α) in $\mathscr{C}^{\mathscr{H}}$, we define a morphism $\Psi(A, \alpha) : \mathscr{S}^{\mathscr{H}}\mathscr{T}^{\mathscr{H}}(A, \alpha) \to (A, \alpha)$ by $\alpha : \mathscr{H}A \to A$. $\Psi(A, \alpha)$ is a morphism in $\mathscr{C}^{\mathscr{H}}$ because of the second condition for objects in $\mathscr{C}^{\mathscr{H}}$ and because $\mathscr{S}^{\mathscr{H}}\mathscr{T}^{\mathscr{H}}(A, \alpha) = (\mathscr{H}A, \mu A)$. Ψ is a natural transformation. In fact, we get a commutative diagram

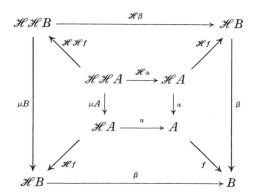

where f is a morphism from (A, α) to (B, β). For objects $A \in \mathscr{C}$ and (A, α) in $\mathscr{C}^{\mathscr{H}}$ we get

$$(\Psi \mathscr{S}^{\mathscr{H}})(\mathscr{S}^{\mathscr{H}} \Phi)(A) = (\Psi \mathscr{S}^{\mathscr{H}}(A))(\mathscr{S}^{\mathscr{H}} \Phi(A)) = \mu(A)\, \mathscr{H} \epsilon(A) = 1_{\mathscr{H}A} = 1_{\mathscr{S} \mathscr{H}_A}$$

and

$$(\mathscr{T}^{\mathscr{H}} \Psi)(\Phi \mathscr{T}^{\mathscr{H}})(A, \alpha) = (\mathscr{T}^{\mathscr{H}} \Psi(A, \alpha))(\Phi \mathscr{T}^{\mathscr{H}}(A, \alpha)) = \alpha \epsilon(A) = 1_A = 1_{\mathscr{T} \mathscr{H}_{(A, \alpha)}}$$

Then we have $\mathscr{T}^{\mathscr{H}} \Psi \mathscr{S}^{\mathscr{H}}(A) = \mathscr{T}^{\mathscr{H}} \Psi(\mathscr{H}A, \mu A) = \mathscr{T}^{\mathscr{H}}(\mu A) = \mu(A)$, thus the monad $(\mathscr{H}, \epsilon, \mu)$ is induced by the pair of adjoint functors $\mathscr{S}^{\mathscr{H}}$ and $\mathscr{T}^{\mathscr{H}}$. By definition $\mathscr{T}^{\mathscr{H}}$ is faithful.

Now let $\mathscr{F} : \mathscr{C} \to \mathscr{D}$ be left adjoint to $\mathscr{G} : \mathscr{D} \to \mathscr{C}$ with the natural transformations $\Phi' : \mathrm{Id}_{\mathscr{C}} \to \mathscr{G} \mathscr{F}$ and $\Psi' : \mathscr{F} \mathscr{G} \to \mathrm{Id}_{\mathscr{D}}$ constructed in Section 2.1, Theorem 1. Let $\mathscr{H} = \mathscr{G} \mathscr{F}$, $\epsilon = \Phi'$, and $\mu = \mathscr{G} \Psi' \mathscr{F}$, that is, let the monad $(\mathscr{H}, \epsilon, \mu)$ be induced by the pair $\mathscr{F}$ and $\mathscr{G}$. We define the functor $\mathscr{K} : \mathscr{C}_{\mathscr{H}} \to \mathscr{D}$ by $\mathscr{K}A = \mathscr{F}A$. Let $f : \mathscr{H}A \to \mathscr{H}B$ be a morphism of objects A and B in $\mathscr{C}_{\mathscr{H}}$. Then we set

$$\mathscr{K}f = (\Psi' \mathscr{F}B)(\mathscr{F}f)(\mathscr{F} \Phi' A).$$

By the definition of f we have $f(\mu B) = (\mu A)(\mathscr{H}f)$. Using the definition of μ, we get $(\mathscr{F}f)(\mathscr{F} \mathscr{G} \Psi' \mathscr{F}A) = (\mathscr{F} \mathscr{G} \Psi' \mathscr{F}B)(\mathscr{F} \mathscr{G} \mathscr{F}f)$, thus $\mathscr{F}f = (\mathscr{F}f)(\mathscr{F} \mathscr{G} \Psi' \mathscr{F}A)(\mathscr{F} \mathscr{G} \mathscr{F} \Phi' A) = (\mathscr{F} \mathscr{G} \Psi' \mathscr{F}B)(\mathscr{F} \mathscr{G} \mathscr{F}f)(\mathscr{F} \mathscr{G} \mathscr{F} \Phi' A) = \mathscr{F} \mathscr{G} \mathscr{K}f$. Since Ψ' is a natural transformation, we get $(\Psi' \mathscr{F}B)(\mathscr{F}f) = (\Psi' \mathscr{F}B)(\mathscr{F} \mathscr{G} \mathscr{K}f) = (\mathscr{K}f)(\Psi' \mathscr{F}A)$. Now let $g : \mathscr{F}B \to \mathscr{F}C$ be another morphism in $\mathscr{C}_{\mathscr{H}}$. Then

$$(\mathscr{K}g)(\mathscr{K}f) = (\mathscr{K}g)(\Psi' \mathscr{F}B)(\mathscr{F}f)(\mathscr{F} \Phi' A) = (\Psi' \mathscr{F}C)(\mathscr{F}g)(\mathscr{F}f)(\mathscr{F} \Phi' A) = \mathscr{K}gf$$

Thus we get that $\mathscr{K}$ is a functor. We have $\mathscr{K} \mathscr{S}_{\mathscr{H}}(A) = \mathscr{F}(A)$ for $A \in \mathscr{C}$ and

$$\mathscr{K} \mathscr{S}_{\mathscr{H}}(f) = \mathscr{K}(\mathscr{H}f) = (\Psi' \mathscr{F}B)(\mathscr{F} \mathscr{G} \mathscr{F}f)(\mathscr{F} \Phi' A)$$
$$= (\Psi' \mathscr{F}B)(\mathscr{F} \Phi' B)(\mathscr{F}f) = \mathscr{F}f$$

for $f \in \mathscr{C}$. Thus we get $\mathscr{K} \mathscr{S}_{\mathscr{H}} = \mathscr{F}$. Furthermore, $\mathscr{G} \mathscr{K}A = \mathscr{G} \mathscr{F}A = \mathscr{H}A = \mathscr{T}_{\mathscr{H}}A$ and

$$\mathscr{G} \mathscr{K}f = (\mathscr{G} \Psi' \mathscr{F}B)(\mathscr{H}f)(\mathscr{H} \Phi' A) = (\mu B)(\mathscr{H}f)(\mathscr{H} \epsilon A)$$
$$= f(\mu A)(\mathscr{H} \epsilon A) = f = \mathscr{T}_{\mathscr{H}}f$$

hence $\mathscr{G} \mathscr{K} = \mathscr{T}_{\mathscr{H}}$.

To prove the uniqueness of $\mathscr{K}$, we assume that there is another functor

$\mathscr{K}' : \mathscr{C}_{\mathscr{H}} \to \mathscr{D}$ which has the same factorization properties. Then $\mathscr{K}'A = \mathscr{F}A = \mathscr{K}A$ because $\mathscr{S}_{\mathscr{H}}$ is the identity on the objects. Let $f : \mathscr{H}A \to \mathscr{H}B$ be a morphism of objects A and B in $\mathscr{C}_{\mathscr{H}}$. Then $\mathscr{G}\mathscr{K}f = \mathscr{T}_{\mathscr{H}}f = \mathscr{G}\mathscr{K}'f$. In particular $\mathscr{F}\mathscr{G}\mathscr{K}f = \mathscr{F}\mathscr{G}\mathscr{K}'f$. Thus we get a commutative diagram

$$\mathscr{F}\mathscr{G}\mathscr{F}A \xrightarrow{\mathscr{F}\mathscr{G}\mathscr{K}f} \mathscr{F}\mathscr{G}\mathscr{F}B$$

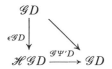

$$\mathscr{F}A \xrightarrow{\quad g \quad} \mathscr{F}B$$

as well for $g = \mathscr{K}f$ as for $g = \mathscr{K}'f$. $\Psi'\mathscr{F}A$ being a retraction we get $\mathscr{K}f = \mathscr{K}'f$ thus $\mathscr{K} = \mathscr{K}'$.

Now we want to construct the functor $\mathscr{L}$. Let $D \in \mathscr{D}$ be given. Then we have a morphism $\mathscr{G}\Psi'D : \mathscr{G}\mathscr{F}\mathscr{G}D \to \mathscr{G}D$. Now $(\mathscr{G}D, \mathscr{G}\Psi'D)$ is an object in $\mathscr{C}^{\mathscr{H}}$ because the diagrams

$$\mathscr{G}D$$
$$\epsilon\mathscr{G}D \downarrow \qquad \searrow$$
$$\mathscr{H}\mathscr{G}D \xrightarrow{\mathscr{G}\Psi'D} \mathscr{G}D$$

and

$$\mathscr{H}\mathscr{H}\mathscr{G}D \xrightarrow{\mathscr{H}\mathscr{G}\Psi'D} \mathscr{H}\mathscr{G}D$$
$$\mu\mathscr{G}D \downarrow \qquad\qquad \downarrow \mathscr{G}\Psi'D$$
$$\mathscr{H}\mathscr{G}D \xrightarrow{\mathscr{G}\Psi'D} \mathscr{G}D$$

are commutative, the first diagram because $\epsilon = \Phi'$, the second diagram because $\mathscr{H} = \mathscr{G}\mathscr{F}$ and $\Psi'(\Psi'\mathscr{F}\mathscr{G}) = \Psi'(\mathscr{F}\mathscr{G}\Psi')$. Thus we define $\mathscr{L}D = (\mathscr{G}D, \mathscr{G}\Psi'D)$. Let $f : D \to D'$ be a morphism in $\mathscr{D}$. Then the diagram

$$\mathscr{G}\mathscr{F}\mathscr{G}D \xrightarrow{\mathscr{G}\mathscr{F}\mathscr{G}f} \mathscr{G}\mathscr{F}\mathscr{G}D'$$
$$\mathscr{G}\Psi'D \downarrow \qquad\qquad \downarrow \mathscr{G}\Psi'D'$$
$$\mathscr{G}D \xrightarrow{\quad \mathscr{G}f \quad} \mathscr{G}D'$$

is commutative. Consequently, $\mathscr{G}f$ is a morphism in $\mathscr{C}^{\mathscr{H}}$. We define $\mathscr{L}f = \mathscr{G}f$. Then $\mathscr{L}$ is a functor and we have $\mathscr{L}\mathscr{F}A = (\mathscr{H}A, \mu A)$ and $\mathscr{L}\mathscr{F}f = \mathscr{H}f$. Furthermore, we have

$$\mathscr{T}^{\mathscr{H}}\mathscr{L}D = \mathscr{T}^{\mathscr{H}}(\mathscr{G}D, \mathscr{G}\Psi'D) \qquad \text{and} \qquad \mathscr{T}^{\mathscr{H}}\mathscr{L}f = \mathscr{G}f$$

Hence, $\mathscr{L}\mathscr{F} = \mathscr{S}^{\mathscr{H}}$ and $\mathscr{T}^{\mathscr{H}}\mathscr{L} = \mathscr{G}$.

We remark that because of

$$\mathscr{K}\Psi A = \mathscr{K}\mu A = (\Psi'\mathscr{F}A)(\mathscr{F}\mathscr{G}\Psi'\mathscr{F}A)(\mathscr{F}\Phi'\mathscr{G}\mathscr{F}A)$$

$$= (\Psi'\mathscr{F}A)(\mathscr{F}(\mathscr{G}\Psi')(\Phi'\mathscr{G})\mathscr{F}A) = \Psi'\mathscr{F}A = \Psi'\mathscr{K}A$$

and

$$\Psi\mathscr{L}D = \Psi(\mathscr{G}D, \mathscr{G}\Psi'D) = \mathscr{G}\Psi'D = \mathscr{L}\Psi'D$$

we have $\mathscr{K}\Psi = \Psi'\mathscr{K}$ and $\Psi\mathscr{L} = \mathscr{L}\Psi'$, where Ψ is the morphism from $\mathscr{S}_{\mathscr{K}}\mathscr{T}_{\mathscr{K}}$ to $\mathrm{Id}_{\mathscr{C}_{\mathscr{K}}}$ and from $\mathscr{S}^{\mathscr{K}}\mathscr{T}^{\mathscr{K}}$ to $\mathrm{Id}_{\mathscr{C}\mathscr{K}}$ respectively.

To prove the uniqueness of $\mathscr{L}$ let $\mathscr{L}' : \mathscr{D} \to \mathscr{C}_{\mathscr{K}}$ be another functor with the required factorization properties. To prove that $\mathscr{L}$ and $\mathscr{L}'$ coincide on the objects, we first show that $\Psi\mathscr{L}' = \mathscr{L}'\Psi'$, which at any rate is true for $\mathscr{L}$. For this reason, we consider the two commutative diagrams

$$
\begin{array}{ccc}
\mathscr{L}'\mathscr{F}\mathscr{G}\mathscr{F}\mathscr{G}D & \xrightarrow{\mathscr{L}'\Psi'\mathscr{F}\mathscr{G}D} & \mathscr{L}'\mathscr{F}\mathscr{G}D \\
{\scriptstyle \mathscr{L}'\mathscr{F}\mathscr{G}\Psi'D} \downarrow & & \downarrow {\scriptstyle \mathscr{L}'\Psi'D} \\
\mathscr{L}'\mathscr{F}\mathscr{G}D & \xrightarrow{\mathscr{L}'\Psi'D} & \mathscr{L}'D
\end{array}
$$

and

$$
\begin{array}{ccc}
\mathscr{S}^{\mathscr{K}}\mathscr{T}^{\mathscr{K}}\mathscr{L}'\mathscr{F}\mathscr{G}D & \xrightarrow{\Psi\mathscr{L}'\mathscr{F}\mathscr{G}D} & \mathscr{L}'\mathscr{F}\mathscr{G}D \\
{\scriptstyle \mathscr{S}^{\mathscr{K}}\mathscr{T}^{\mathscr{K}}\mathscr{L}'\Psi'D} \downarrow & & \downarrow {\scriptstyle \mathscr{L}'\Psi'D} \\
\mathscr{S}^{\mathscr{K}}\mathscr{T}^{\mathscr{K}}\mathscr{L}'D & \xrightarrow{\Psi\mathscr{L}'D} & \mathscr{L}'D
\end{array}
$$

Because of $\mathscr{L}'\mathscr{F}\mathscr{G} = \mathscr{S}^{\mathscr{K}}\mathscr{G} = \mathscr{S}^{\mathscr{K}}\mathscr{S}^{\mathscr{K}}\mathscr{L}'$ the objects and the vertical morphisms in both diagrams are the same. Furthermore,

$$\mathscr{T}^{\mathscr{K}}\Psi\mathscr{S}^{\mathscr{K}} = \mu = \mathscr{G}\Psi'\mathscr{F} = \mathscr{T}^{\mathscr{K}}\mathscr{L}'\Psi'\mathscr{F}$$

Since $\mathscr{T}^{\mathscr{K}}$ is faithful, we also have

$$\Psi\mathscr{L}'\mathscr{F} = \Psi\mathscr{S}^{\mathscr{K}} = \mathscr{L}'\Psi'\mathscr{F} \qquad \text{and} \qquad \Psi\mathscr{L}'\mathscr{F}\mathscr{G}D = \mathscr{L}'\Psi'\mathscr{F}\mathscr{G}D$$

that is, the upper horizontal morphisms in both diagrams coincide too. But since $\mathscr{G}\Psi'D$ is a retraction, and retractions are preserved by functors, we also get $\mathscr{L}'\Psi'D = \Psi\mathscr{L}'D$, hence $\mathscr{L}'\Psi' = \Psi\mathscr{L}'$.

Let $D \in \mathscr{D}$ and $\mathscr{L}'D = (A, \alpha)$. Then $A = \mathscr{T}^{\mathscr{K}}(A, \alpha) = \mathscr{T}^{\mathscr{K}}\mathscr{L}'D = \mathscr{G}D$ and

$$\alpha = \mathscr{T}^{\mathscr{K}}\alpha = \mathscr{T}^{\mathscr{K}}\Psi(A, \alpha) = \mathscr{T}^{\mathscr{K}}\Psi\mathscr{L}'D = \mathscr{T}^{\mathscr{K}}\mathscr{L}'\Psi'D = \mathscr{G}\Psi'D$$

hence $\mathscr{L}'D = \mathscr{L}D$. Now let $f : D \to D'$ in $\mathscr{D}$ be given, then $\mathscr{T}^{\mathscr{H}}\mathscr{L}f = \mathscr{G}f = \mathscr{T}^{\mathscr{H}}\mathscr{L}'f$. Since $\mathscr{T}^{\mathscr{H}}$ is faithful, we get $\mathscr{L}f = \mathscr{L}'f$; thus, $\mathscr{L} = \mathscr{L}'$. This proves the theorem.

The objects of the category $\mathscr{C}^{\mathscr{H}}$ are called $\mathscr{H}$ *algebras* and the objects of the form $\mathscr{S}^{\mathscr{H}}(A)$ are called *free $\mathscr{H}$ algebras*.

COROLLARY.   *In the diagram of Theorem 1 the functors* $\mathscr{T}_{\mathscr{H}}$, $\mathscr{T}^{\mathscr{H}}$, *and* $\mathscr{K}$ *are faithful. If one of the functors* $\mathscr{H}$, $\mathscr{S}_{\mathscr{H}}$, $\mathscr{S}^{\mathscr{H}}$, *or* $\mathscr{F}$ *is faithful, then all these functors are faithful.*

Proof.   The constructions of the proof of Theorem 1 imply that $\mathscr{T}_{\mathscr{H}}$ and $\mathscr{T}^{\mathscr{H}}$ are faithful. Because $\mathscr{T}_{\mathscr{H}} = \mathscr{G}\mathscr{K}$, $\mathscr{K}$ is also faithful. If $\mathscr{H}$ is faithful, then $\mathscr{F}$ is faithful, because $\mathscr{H} = \mathscr{G}\mathscr{F}$. Now assume that $\mathscr{F}$ is faithful, then by Section 2.1, Corollary 4 the functor $\mathscr{H} = \mathscr{G}\mathscr{F}$ is faithful. Replacing $\mathscr{F}$ by the functors $\mathscr{S}_{\mathscr{H}}$ and $\mathscr{S}^{\mathscr{H}}$ respectively, in both conclusions completes the proof.

LEMMA 2.   *Let* $(\mathscr{H}, \epsilon, \mu)$ *be a monad over the category* $\mathscr{C}$, *and let* (A, α) *be an $\mathscr{H}$ algebra. Then there is a free $\mathscr{H}$ algebra* (B, β) *and a retraction* $f : B \to A$ *in* $\mathscr{C}$, *which is a morphism of $\mathscr{H}$ algebras.*

Proof.   By

$\alpha : \mathscr{H}A \to A$ is a retraction. Furthermore, $\mu : \mathscr{H}\mathscr{H}A \to \mathscr{H}A$ is a free $\mathscr{H}$ algebra. By

$$
\begin{array}{ccc}
\mathscr{H}\mathscr{H}A & \xrightarrow{\;\mathscr{H}\alpha\;} & \mathscr{H}A \\
{\scriptstyle\mu A}\downarrow & & \downarrow{\scriptstyle\alpha} \\
\mathscr{H}A & \xrightarrow{\;\;\alpha\;\;} & A
\end{array}
$$

α is a morphism of $\mathscr{H}$ algebras.

It is especially interesting to know under which circumstances the functor $\mathscr{L} : \mathscr{D} \to \mathscr{C}^{\mathscr{H}}$ constructed in Theorem 1 is an isomorphism of categories. In this case one can consider $\mathscr{D}$ as the category of $\mathscr{H}$ algebras. A functor $\mathscr{G} : \mathscr{D} \to \mathscr{C}$ will be called *monadic* if $\mathscr{G}$ has a left adjoint functor $\mathscr{F}$ such that the functor $\mathscr{L} : \mathscr{D} \to \mathscr{C}^{\mathscr{H}}$ defined by the monad $\mathscr{G}\mathscr{F} = \mathscr{H}$ is an isomorphism of categories.

Before we start to investigate this question in more detail, we need some further notions. First we want to make an assertion on the way functors behave relative to diagrams. Let $\mathscr{G} : \mathscr{D} \to \mathscr{C}$ be a covariant functor. Let $\mathfrak{E}$ be a categorical property of diagrams (e.g., $f : A \to B$ is a monomorphism, D is a commutative diagram, $B \to D$ is a product of the diagram D). Assume that with each diagram D in $\mathscr{C}$ with property $\mathfrak{E}$, the diagram $\mathscr{G}(D)$ in $\mathscr{D}$ also has property $\mathfrak{E}$. In this case one says that $\mathscr{G}$ *preserves* property $\mathfrak{E}$. Assume that each diagram D in $\mathscr{C}$ for which the diagram $\mathscr{G}(D)$ in $\mathscr{D}$ has property $\mathfrak{E}$ has itself property $\mathfrak{E}$, then we say that $\mathscr{G}$ *reflects* property $\mathfrak{E}$. Let D be a diagram in $\mathscr{C}$ with property $\mathfrak{E}$ and with the additional property that there is an extension D'' in $\mathscr{D}$ of the diagram $\mathscr{G}(D)$ with the property $\mathfrak{E}*$. If under these conditions, there is exactly one diagram extension D' of D in $\mathscr{C}$, with $\mathscr{G}(D') = D''$, and if this extension has property $\mathfrak{E}*$, then we say that $\mathscr{G}$ *creates* the property $\mathfrak{E}*$.

A simple example for the last definition is the assertion that the functor $\mathscr{G}$ *creates isomorphisms*. This assertion means that to each object $C \in \mathscr{C}$ and to each isomorphism $f'' : \mathscr{G}(C) \to C''$ in $\mathscr{D}$ there is exactly one morphism $f' : C \to C'$ in $\mathscr{C}$ with $\mathscr{G}(f') = f''$ and $\mathscr{G}(C') = C''$, and that then this morphism f' is even an isomorphism. The property $\mathfrak{E}$ says only that the diagram D is a diagram with one single object and one morphism. The property $\mathfrak{E}*$ says that the only morphism of the diagram with two objects, which is not the identity, is an isomorphism. The functor $\mathfrak{E}$ of Section 2.4, Theorem 2 is an example of a functor which creates isomorphisms. In this simple case one even omits the specification of property $\mathfrak{E}$.

A pair of morphisms $f_0, f_1 : A \to B$ is called *contractible* if there is a morphism $g : B \to A$ such that $f_0 g = 1_B$ and $f_1 g f_0 = f_1 g f_1$.

Let $h : B \to C$ be a difference cokernel of a contractible pair $f_0, f_1 : A \to B$, then there is exactly one morphism $k : C \to B$ with $hk = 1_C$ and $kh = f_1 g$. For $f_1 g : B \to B$ we have $(f_1 g) f_0 = (f_1 g) f_1$. Since h is a difference cokernel of (f_0, f_1), there is exactly one $k : C \to B$ with $kh = f_1 g$. Furthermore, we have $hkh = hf_1 g = hf_0 g = h1_B = 1_C h$, and thus $hk = 1_C$ because h is an epimorphism.

Conversely, let $f_0, f_1 : A \to B$ be a contractible pair with the morphism $g : B \to A$. If $h : B \to C$ and $k : C \to B$ are morphisms with $hf_0 = hf_1$, $hk = 1_C$, and $kh = f_1 g$, then h is a difference cokernel of (f_0, f_1). In fact, if $x : B \to U$ is a morphism with $xf_0 = xf_1$, then $x = xf_0 g = xf_1 g = xkh$. If $x = yh$, then $xk = y$. Thus, a difference cokernel of a contractible pair is a commutative diagram

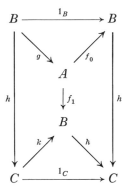

This implies the following lemma.

LEMMA 3. *Each functor preserves difference cokernels of contractible pairs.*

Recalling the definition of an $\mathscr{H}$ algebra for a monad $(\mathscr{H}, \epsilon, \mu)$, we see immediately that (A, α) is an $\mathscr{H}$ algebra if and only if the diagram

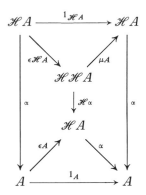

is commutative, that is, if α is a difference cokernel of the contractible pair $(\mu A, \mathscr{H}\alpha)$.

Let $\mathscr{G} : \mathscr{D} \to \mathscr{C}$ be a functor. A pair of morphism $f_0, f_1 : A \to B$ in $\mathscr{D}$ is said to be $\mathscr{G}$-*contractible* if $(\mathscr{G}f_0, \mathscr{G}f_1)$ is contractible in $\mathscr{C}$. $\mathscr{G}$ *creates difference cokernels of* $\mathscr{G}$-*contractible pairs* if to each $\mathscr{G}$-contractible pair $f_0, f_1 : A \to B$ in $\mathscr{D}$ for which $(\mathscr{G}f_0, \mathscr{G}f_1)$ has a difference cokernel $h' : \mathscr{G}B \to C'$ in $\mathscr{C}$, there is exactly one morphism $h : B \to C$ in $\mathscr{D}$ with $\mathscr{G}h = h'$, and if this morphism h is a difference cokernel of (f_0, f_1).

LEMMA 4. *Let* $\mathscr{G} : \mathscr{D} \to \mathscr{C}$ *be a monadic functor. Then* $\mathscr{G}$ *creates difference cokernels of* $\mathscr{G}$-*contractible pairs.*

Proof. For a monad $(\mathscr{H}, \epsilon, \mu)$ we can assume $\mathscr{D} = \mathscr{C}^{\mathscr{H}}$ and $\mathscr{G} = \mathscr{T}^{\mathscr{H}}$. Let $f_0, f_1 : (A, \alpha) \to (B, \beta)$ be a $\mathscr{T}^{\mathscr{H}}$-contractible pair, and let $g : B \to A$ be the corresponding morphism. Assume that there is a difference cokernel $h : B \to C$ of $f_0, f_1 : A \to B$ ($f_i = \mathscr{T}^{\mathscr{H}} f_i$). Then also $\mathscr{H} h$ is a difference cokernel of $(\mathscr{H} f_0, \mathscr{H} f_1)$. Thus, we get a commutative diagram

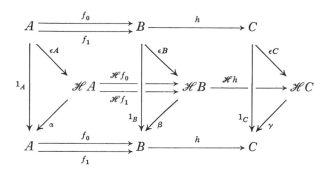

where $\gamma : \mathscr{H} C \to C$ is determined by the factorization property of the difference cokernel. Thus the first condition for an $\mathscr{H}$ algebra holds for (C, γ).

Since $\mu : \mathscr{H} \mathscr{H} \to \mathscr{H}$ is a natural transformation, $\mu C : \mathscr{H} \mathscr{H} C \to \mathscr{H} C$ is uniquely determined by $\mu A : \mathscr{H} \mathscr{H} A \to \mathscr{H} A$ and $\mu B : \mathscr{H} \mathscr{H} B \to \mathscr{H} B$ as a morphism between the difference cokernels. The commutative diagrams

$$
\begin{array}{ccc}
\mathscr{H} \mathscr{H} A & \xrightarrow{\mathscr{H} \alpha} & \mathscr{H} A \\
{\scriptstyle \mu A} \downarrow & & \downarrow {\scriptstyle \sim} \\
\mathscr{H} A & \xrightarrow{\alpha} & A
\end{array}
$$

and

$$
\begin{array}{ccc}
\mathscr{H} \mathscr{H} B & \xrightarrow{\mathscr{H} \beta} & \mathscr{H} B \\
{\scriptstyle \mu B} \downarrow & & \downarrow {\scriptstyle \beta} \\
\mathscr{H} B & \xrightarrow{\beta} & B
\end{array}
$$

induce a commutative diagram

$$
\begin{array}{ccc}
\mathscr{H} \mathscr{H} C & \xrightarrow{\mathscr{H} \gamma} & \mathscr{H} C \\
{\scriptstyle \mu C} \downarrow & & \downarrow {\scriptstyle \gamma} \\
\mathscr{H} C & \xrightarrow{\gamma} & C
\end{array}
$$

using f_0, f_1 together with the usual conclusions for difference cokernels. Thus (C, γ) is an $\mathscr{H}$ algebra.

Since $\mathscr{T}^{\mathscr{H}}$ is faithful, the morphism h in $\mathscr{C}^{\mathscr{H}}$ is uniquely determined by the morphism h in $\mathscr{C}$. Furthermore, h is a morphism of $\mathscr{H}$ algebras with $hf_0 = hf_1$. Now let $k : (B, \beta) \to (D, \delta)$ be another morphism of $\mathscr{H}$ algebras with $kf_0 = kf_1$; then there exists exactly one morphism $x : C \to D$ in $\mathscr{C}$ with $k = xh$. Thus $\mathscr{H}k = \mathscr{H}x\mathscr{H}h$. But since $\mathscr{H}h$ is a difference cokernel of $\mathscr{H}f_0$ and $\mathscr{H}f_1$, we get again, with the usual conclusions for difference cokernels, that $\delta\mathscr{H}x = x\gamma$. Thus, x is a morphism of $\mathscr{H}$ algebras. This proves that $h : (B, \beta) \to (C, \gamma)$ is a difference cokernel in $\mathscr{C}^{\mathscr{H}}$.

THEOREM 2 (Beck). *A functor $\mathscr{G} : \mathscr{D} \to \mathscr{C}$ is monadic if and only if $\mathscr{G}$ has a left adjoint functor $\mathscr{F}$, and if $\mathscr{G}$ creates difference cokernels of $\mathscr{G}$-contractible pairs.*

Proof. Because of Lemma 4, it is sufficient to prove that a functor $\mathscr{G}$, which has a left adjoint functor $\mathscr{F}$, and which creates difference cokernels of $\mathscr{G}$-contractible pairs, is monadic. Here it suffices to construct an inverse functor for the functor $\mathscr{L}$ of Theorem 1. Let (A, α) be an $\mathscr{H}$ algebra with $\mathscr{H} = \mathscr{G}\mathscr{F}$. Then $\mu A, \mathscr{H}\alpha : \mathscr{H}\mathscr{H}A \to \mathscr{H}A$ is a contractible pair with the difference cokernel $\alpha : \mathscr{H}A \to A$. Since $\mathscr{G}(\Psi'\mathscr{F}A) = \mu A$ and $\mathscr{G}(\mathscr{F}\alpha) = \mathscr{H}\alpha$, the pair $\Psi'\mathscr{F}A, \mathscr{F}\alpha : \mathscr{F}\mathscr{H}A \to \mathscr{F}A$ is a $\mathscr{G}$-contractable pair which has a difference cokernel in $\mathscr{C}$. The hypothesis implies that there is exactly one difference cokernel $a : \mathscr{F}A \to C$ in $\mathscr{D}$ with $\mathscr{G}a = \alpha$ and $\mathscr{G}C = A$. We define $\mathscr{L}'(A, \alpha) = C$.

If $f : (A, \alpha) \to (B, \beta)$ is a morphism of $\mathscr{H}$ algebras, and if $\mathscr{L}'(B, \beta) = D$ and $b : \mathscr{F}B \to D$ is the difference cokernel of $(\Psi'\mathscr{F}B, \mathscr{F}\beta)$, then the commutative diagram

$$
\begin{array}{ccccc}
\mathscr{F}\mathscr{G}\mathscr{F}A & \underset{\mathscr{F}\alpha}{\overset{\Psi'\mathscr{F}A}{\rightrightarrows}} & \mathscr{F}A & \overset{a}{\longrightarrow} & C \\
{\scriptstyle\mathscr{F}\mathscr{G}\mathscr{F}f}\downarrow & & \downarrow{\scriptstyle\mathscr{F}f} & & \downarrow{\scriptstyle g} \\
\mathscr{F}\mathscr{G}\mathscr{F}B & \underset{\mathscr{F}\beta}{\overset{\Psi'\mathscr{F}B}{\rightrightarrows}} & \mathscr{F}B & \overset{b}{\longrightarrow} & D
\end{array}
$$

implies the existence and the uniqueness of the morphism g with $\mathscr{G}(g) = f$. Let $\mathscr{L}'(f) = g$. Since g is defined as a morphism between difference cokernels, $\mathscr{L}'$ is a functor.

Now we verify that $\mathscr{L}\mathscr{L}' = \mathrm{Id}_{\mathscr{C}^{\mathscr{H}}}$ and $\mathscr{L}'\mathscr{L} = \mathrm{Id}_{\mathscr{D}}$. We have $\mathscr{L}\mathscr{L}'(A, \alpha) = (\mathscr{G}C, \mathscr{G}\Psi'C) = (A, \mathscr{G}\Psi'C)$. Since Ψ' is a natural transformation, the diagram

$$\mathscr{H}\mathscr{H}A \xrightarrow{\;\mathscr{H}\alpha\;} \mathscr{H}A$$

with the vertical maps $\mathscr{G}\Psi'\mathscr{F}A$ and $\mathscr{G}\Psi'C$, and bottom map $\mathscr{H}A \xrightarrow{\;\alpha\;} A$

with $\alpha = \mathscr{G}a$ and $A = \mathscr{G}C$ is commutative. $\mathscr{G}\Psi'\mathscr{F}A = \mu A$ and $(\mathscr{G}\Psi'C)\,(\mathscr{H}\alpha) = \alpha(\mu A) = \alpha(\mathscr{H}\alpha)$ and the fact that $\mathscr{H}\alpha$ is an epimorphism as a difference cokernel imply $\alpha = \mathscr{G}\Psi'C$. Furthermore, we have $\mathscr{L}\mathscr{L}'(f) = \mathscr{L}(g) = \mathscr{G}(g) = f$, where g is chosen as above. Then $\mathscr{L}'\mathscr{L}(C) = \mathscr{L}'(\mathscr{G}C, \mathscr{G}\Psi'C)$. Since $\mathscr{G}\Psi'C$ is a difference cokernel of the contractible pair

$$\mathscr{G}\Psi'\mathscr{F}\mathscr{G}C, \mathscr{G}\mathscr{F}\mathscr{G}\Psi'C : \mathscr{G}\mathscr{F}\mathscr{H}\mathscr{G}C \to \mathscr{G}\mathscr{F}\mathscr{G}C$$

(the corresponding morphism is $\Phi'\mathscr{H}\mathscr{G}C$), the morphism $\Psi'C : \mathscr{F}\mathscr{G}C \to C$ is a difference cokernel of $(\Psi'\mathscr{F}\mathscr{G}C, \mathscr{F}\mathscr{G}\Psi'C)$ because of the hypothesis on $\mathscr{G}$. Thus, $\mathscr{L}'\mathscr{L}C = C$. Furthermore, $\mathscr{L}'\mathscr{L}f = \mathscr{L}'\mathscr{G}f$. Since the diagram

$$\mathscr{F}\mathscr{G}C \xrightarrow{\;\Psi'C\;} C$$

with vertical maps $\mathscr{F}\mathscr{G}f$ and f, and bottom map $\mathscr{F}\mathscr{G}D \xrightarrow{\;\Psi'D\;} D$

is commutative, and since f is a morphism between difference cokernels, we have $\mathscr{L}'\mathscr{G}f = f$.

LEMMA 5.   *Let $\mathscr{G} : \mathscr{D} \to \mathscr{C}$ be a functor which creates difference cokernels of $\mathscr{G}$-contractible pairs. Then $\mathscr{G}$ creates isomorphisms.*

Proof.   Let $g : C \to D$ be an isomorphism in $\mathscr{C}$ and let $C = \mathscr{G}A$ with $A \in \mathscr{D}$. Then $1_A, 1_A : A \to A$ is a $\mathscr{G}$-contractible pair with the difference cokernel $g : C \to D$ in $\mathscr{C}$. Thus there is exactly one $f : A \to B$ with $\mathscr{G}f = g$. Furthermore, f is a difference cokernel of $1_A, 1_A : A \to A$. But also $1_A : A \to A$ is a difference cokernel of this pair, consequently f is an isomorphism in $\mathscr{D}$.

2.4   Reflexive Subcategories

Let $\mathscr{D}$ be a category and $\mathscr{C}$ a subcategory of $\mathscr{D}$. Let $\mathscr{E} : \mathscr{C} \to \mathscr{D}$ be the embedding defined by the subcategory. $\mathscr{C}$ is called a *reflexive subcategory*, if there is a left adjoint functor $\mathscr{R} : \mathscr{D} \to \mathscr{C}$ to $\mathscr{E}$. The functor $\mathscr{R}$

is called the *reflector* and the object $\mathscr{R}D \in \mathscr{C}$, assigned to an object $D \in \mathscr{D}$, is called the *reflection* of D.

Since $\mathscr{C}$ is a subcategory of $\mathscr{D}$, the universal problem corresponding to a reflexive subcategory is easily represented. Let $C \in \mathscr{C}$ and $D \in \mathscr{D}$. There exists a morphism $f : D \to \mathscr{R}D$ in $\mathscr{D}$ induced by the natural transformation $\mathrm{Id}_{\mathscr{D}} \to \mathscr{E}\mathscr{R}$. If $g : D \to C$ is another morphism in $\mathscr{D}$, then there exists exactly one morphism h in the subcategory $\mathscr{C}$ which makes the diagram

$$D \xrightarrow{\ f\ } \mathscr{R}D$$
$$\searrow{}_{g} \qquad \downarrow{}^{h}$$
$$C$$

commutative.

Dual to the notions defined above, a subcategory $\mathscr{E} : \mathscr{C} \to \mathscr{D}$ is called a *coreflexive subcategory*, if $\mathscr{E}$ has a right adjoint functor $\mathscr{R} : \mathscr{D} \to \mathscr{C}$. Correspondingly, $\mathscr{R}$ is called the *coreflector* and $\mathscr{R}D$ the *coreflection* of the object $D \in \mathscr{D}$.

We give some examples for which the reader who is familiar with the corresponding fields will easily verify that they define reflexive or coreflexive subcategories. Some of the examples will be dealt with in more detail in later sections. Reflexive subcategories include (1) the full subcategory of the topological T_i-spaces ($i = 0, 1, 2, 3$) in **Top**, (2) the full subcategory of the regular spaces in **Top**, (3) the full subcategory of the totally disconnected spaces in **Top**, (4) the full subcategory of the compact hausdorff spaces in the full subcategory of the normal hausdorff spaces of **Top**, (5) the full subcategory of the torsion free groups in **Ab**, (6) **Ab** in **Gr**, and (7) the full subcategory of the commutative, associative, unitary rings in **Ri**. The full subcategory of the torsion groups in **Ab** gives an example of a coreflexive subcategory. Other examples for coreflexive subcategories are the full subcategory of locally connected spaces in **Top**, and the full subcategory of locally arcwise connected spaces in **Top**.

LEMMA. *Let $\mathscr{C}$ be a full, reflexive subcategory of the category $\mathscr{D}$ with reflector $\mathscr{R}$. Then the restriction of $\mathscr{R}$ to the subcategory $\mathscr{C}$ is isomorphic to* $\mathrm{Id}_{\mathscr{C}}$.

Proof. Since $\mathscr{C}$ is a full subcategory, we get for each $C \in \mathscr{C}$ that the morphism $1_C : C \to C$ is a universal solution for the universal problem defined by $\mathscr{E} : \mathscr{C} \to \mathscr{D}$. By the uniqueness of the universal solution $\mathscr{R}C \cong C$ is natural in C for all $C \in \mathscr{C}$.

In the case of a reflexive subcategory we have a simple presentation of the universal problem defined by the adjoint functors; thus it is interesting to know when a pair of adjoint functors induces a reflexive subcategory. The following theorem gives a sufficient condition.

THEOREM 1.   *Let the functor $\mathscr{F} : \mathscr{C} \to \mathscr{D}$ be left adjoint to the functor $\mathscr{G} : \mathscr{D} \to \mathscr{C}$ and let $\mathscr{G}$ be injective on the objects. Then $\mathscr{G}(\mathscr{D})$ is a reflexive subcategory of $\mathscr{C}$ with reflector $\mathscr{G}\mathscr{F}$.*

Proof.   The image of $\mathscr{G}$ is a subcategory of $\mathscr{C}$ be a remark at the beginning of Section 1.8. We define factorizations of the functors by the following commutative diagram of categories:

where $\mathscr{C}' = \mathscr{G}(\mathscr{D})$. By Section 2.1, Corollary 4 we have that

$$\mathscr{G} : \mathrm{Mor}_{\mathscr{D}}(\mathscr{F}-, -) \to \mathrm{Mor}_{\mathscr{C}}(\mathscr{G}\mathscr{F}-, \mathscr{G}-)$$

is injective. Thus, $\mathscr{G}' : \mathrm{Mor}_{\mathscr{D}}(\mathscr{F}-, -) \to \mathrm{Mor}_{\mathscr{C}'}(\mathscr{G}'\mathscr{F}-, \mathscr{G}'-)$ is a natural isomorphism by the definition of $\mathscr{C}'$. We get

$$\mathrm{Mor}_{\mathscr{C}'}(\mathscr{G}'\mathscr{F}-, \mathscr{G}'-) \simeq \mathrm{Mor}_{\mathscr{D}}(\mathscr{F}-, -) \simeq \mathrm{Mor}_{\mathscr{C}}(-, \mathscr{G}-) \simeq \mathrm{Mor}_{\mathscr{C}}(-, \mathscr{E}\mathscr{G}'-)$$

Since each object in $\mathscr{C}'$ may uniquely be represented as $\mathscr{G}'D$, and since $\mathscr{G}'$ is full, we get $\mathrm{Mor}_{\mathscr{C}'}(\mathscr{F}'-, -) \simeq \mathrm{Mor}_{\mathscr{C}}(-, \mathscr{E}-)$. $\mathscr{F}'$ and $\mathscr{G}\mathscr{F}$ coincide up to the embedding of $\mathscr{C}'$ into $\mathscr{C}$.

PROPOSITION.   *Let $\mathscr{C}'$ be a reflexive subcategory of $\mathscr{C}$ with reflector $\mathscr{R}$. For all $A \in \mathscr{C}'$ the morphism $f : A \to \mathscr{R}A$ defined by the corresponding universal problem is a section in $\mathscr{C}$.*

Proof.   Let $\mathscr{E} : \mathscr{C}' \to \mathscr{C}$ be the embedding. By Section 2.1, Theorem 1 we have $(\mathscr{E} \xrightarrow{\Phi\mathscr{E}} \mathscr{E}\mathscr{R}\mathscr{E} \xrightarrow{\mathscr{E}\Psi} \mathscr{E}) = \mathrm{id}_{\mathscr{E}}$, thus $(A \xrightarrow{f} \mathscr{R}A \xrightarrow{\mathscr{E}\Psi A} A) = 1_A$ for all $A \in C'$. Observe that f is a morphism in C, whereas $\mathscr{E}\Psi A$ is even in $\mathscr{C}'$.

THEOREM 2.   *Let $\mathscr{E} : \mathscr{C} \to \mathscr{D}$ be a full, reflexive subcategory. If for each $C \in \mathscr{C}$ also each $D \in \mathscr{D}$ with $C \simeq D$ in $\mathscr{D}$ is an object in $\mathscr{C}$, then $\mathscr{E}$ is a monadic functor.*

Proof. Let $\mathscr{H} = \mathscr{E}\mathscr{R}$ and $\mathscr{R}$ be the reflector to $\mathscr{E}$, then $\epsilon(D) : D \to \mathscr{E}\mathscr{R}D$ is the universal solution of the universal problem defined by $\mathscr{E}$. Let $\delta : \mathscr{H}D \to D$ be a $\mathscr{D}$ morphism, such that

is commutative. Then $\epsilon(D) \, \delta\epsilon(D) = \epsilon(D)$. Since $\mathscr{E}$ is full, we get $\epsilon(D)\delta = \mathscr{E}(f)$ with $f : \mathscr{R}D \to \mathscr{R}D$. By the universal property of $\epsilon(D)$ and the commutativity of

$$D \xrightarrow{\ \epsilon(D)\ } \mathscr{E}\mathscr{R}D$$

$$\epsilon(D) \searrow \qquad \downarrow \mathscr{E}(f)$$

$$\mathscr{E}\mathscr{R}D$$

we get $f = 1_{\mathscr{R}D}$, thus $\epsilon(D)\delta = 1_{\mathscr{H}D}$. This proves that $\epsilon(D) \to \mathscr{H}D$ is an isomorphism and $D \in \mathscr{C}$. Furthermore, because $(\Psi\mathscr{R}D)(\mathscr{R}\epsilon(D)) = 1_{\mathscr{R}D} = (\mathscr{R}\delta)(\mathscr{R}\epsilon(D))$, we also have $\Psi\mathscr{R}D = \mathscr{R}\delta$, thus $\mu(D) = \mathscr{H}\delta$. This implies that

$$\mathscr{H}\mathscr{H}D \xrightarrow{\ \mathscr{H}\delta\ } \mathscr{H}D$$

$$\mu(D) \downarrow \qquad\qquad \downarrow \delta$$

$$\mathscr{H}D \xrightarrow{\ \delta\ } D$$

is commutative, and (D, δ) is an $\mathscr{H}$ algebra.

If $D \in \mathscr{C}$, then there exists exactly one $\delta : \mathscr{H}D \to D$ with $\delta\epsilon(D) = 1_D$, because $\epsilon(D)$ is a universal solution.

Let $f : D \to D'$ be a morphism and $D, D' \in \mathscr{C}$. Let (D, δ) and (D', δ') be the corresponding $\mathscr{H}$-algebras. Then

$$
\begin{array}{ccccc}
D & \xrightarrow{\ \epsilon(D)\ } & \mathscr{H}D & \xrightarrow{\ \delta\ } & D \\
\downarrow{\scriptstyle f} & & \downarrow{\scriptstyle \mathscr{H}f} & & \downarrow{\scriptstyle f} \\
D' & \xrightarrow{\ \epsilon(D')\ } & \mathscr{H}D' & \xrightarrow{\ \delta'\ } & D'
\end{array}
$$

is commutative, thus f is a morphism of $\mathscr{H}$-algebras. Hence $\mathscr{L} : \mathscr{C} \to \mathscr{D}^{\mathscr{H}}$ is an isomorphism of categories.

2.5 Limits and Colimits

Let $\mathscr{A}$ be a diagram scheme, $\mathscr{C}$ a category and $\mathrm{Funct}(\mathscr{A}, \mathscr{C})$ be the diagram category introduced in Section 1.8. We define a functor $\mathscr{K} : \mathscr{C} \to \mathrm{Funct}(\mathscr{A}, \mathscr{C})$ by $\mathscr{K}(C)(A) = C$, $\mathscr{K}(C)(f) = 1_C$ and $\mathscr{K}(g)(A) = g$ for all $C \in \mathscr{C}$, $A \in \mathscr{A}$, $f \in \mathscr{A}$, and $g \in \mathscr{C}$, and we call $\mathscr{K}$ the *constant functor*. In the inversely connected category $\mathscr{V}_{\mathscr{K}}(\mathrm{Funct}(\mathscr{A}, \mathscr{C}), \mathscr{C})$, with the connection $\mathrm{Mor}_{\mathscr{V}}(C, \mathscr{F}) = \mathrm{Mor}_f(\mathscr{K}C, \mathscr{F})$, the functor $\mathscr{K}$ defines a universal problem for each diagram $\mathscr{F} \in \mathrm{Funct}(\mathscr{A}, \mathscr{C})$. We want to find an object $U(\mathscr{F})$ in $\mathscr{C}$ and a morphism $\rho_{\mathscr{F}} : U(\mathscr{F}) \to \mathscr{F}$, such that to each morphism $\varphi : C \to \mathscr{F}$ there is exactly one morphism $\varphi^* : C \to U(\mathscr{F})$ with $\rho_{\mathscr{F}}\varphi^* = \varphi$.

If $\mathscr{A}$ is the empty category, then $\mathrm{Funct}(\mathscr{A}, \mathscr{C})$ consists of one object and one morphism. $\mathscr{K}$ maps all objects of $\mathscr{C}$ to the object of $\mathrm{Funct}(\mathscr{A}, \mathscr{C})$ and all morphisms to the morphism of $\mathrm{Funct}(\mathscr{A}, \mathscr{C})$. Since $\mathrm{Mor}_f(\mathscr{K}C, \mathscr{F})$ has one element, the object $U(\mathscr{F})$ must satisfy the condition that from each object $C \in \mathscr{C}$ there is exactly one morphism into $U(\mathscr{F})$. Thus, $U(\mathscr{F})$ is a final object.

We formulate the universal problem more explicitly. First, a morphism $\varphi \in \mathrm{Mor}_{\mathscr{V}}(C, \mathscr{F}) = \mathrm{Mor}_f(\mathscr{K}C, \mathscr{F})$ is a family of morphisms $\varphi(A) : C \to \mathscr{F}A$, such that for each morphism $f : A \to A'$ in $\mathscr{A}$ the diagram

$$
\begin{array}{ccc}
C & \xrightarrow{\varphi(A)} & \mathscr{F}A \\
& \searrow{\scriptstyle \varphi(A')} & \downarrow{\scriptstyle \mathscr{F}f} \\
& & \mathscr{F}A'
\end{array}
$$

is commutative. In particular $\rho_{\mathscr{F}}$ is such a family of morphisms $\rho_{\mathscr{F}}(A) : U(\mathscr{F}) \to \mathscr{F}A$, to make the corresponding diagrams commutative. This family of morphisms has to have the property that to each family $\varphi \in \mathrm{Mor}_f(\mathscr{K}C, \mathscr{F})$ there is exactly one morphism $\varphi^* : C \to U(\mathscr{F})$ such that the diagram

$$
\begin{array}{ccc}
& C & \\
{\scriptstyle \varphi^*}\downarrow & & \searrow{\scriptstyle \varphi(A)} \\
U(\mathscr{F}) & \xrightarrow[\rho_{\mathscr{F}}(A)]{} & \mathscr{F}A
\end{array}
$$

is commutative for all $A \in \mathscr{A}$.

If there is a universal solution for the universal problem defined by $\mathscr{F}$, then this universal solution is called the *limit* of the diagram $\mathscr{F}$ and is denoted by $\varprojlim \mathscr{F}$. The morphisms $\rho_{\mathscr{F}}(A) : \varprojlim \mathscr{F} \to \mathscr{F}A$ are called *projections* and are denoted by $p_A = \rho_{\mathscr{F}}(A)$. If the diagram $\mathscr{F}$ is given as a set of objects C_i and of morphisms in $\mathscr{C}$, then we often write $\varprojlim C_i$ instead of $\varprojlim \mathscr{F}$.

Since the notions introduced here are very important, we also define the dual notion explicitly. The constant functor $\mathscr{K}$ defines a directly connected category $\mathscr{V}_{\mathscr{K}}(\mathrm{Funct}(\mathscr{A}, \mathscr{C}), \mathscr{C})$ with the connection

$$\mathrm{Mor}_{\mathscr{V}}(\mathscr{F}, C) = \mathrm{Mor}_f(\mathscr{F}, \mathscr{K}C).$$

The universal problem which belongs to a diagram $\mathscr{F}$ may be explicitly expressed in the following way. Each morphism $\varphi \in \mathrm{Mor}_{\mathscr{V}}(\mathscr{F}, C) = \mathrm{Mor}_f(\mathscr{F}, \mathscr{K}C)$ is a family of morphisms $\varphi(A) : \mathscr{F}A \to C$, such that to each morphism $f : A \to A'$ in $\mathscr{A}$ the diagram

$$
\begin{array}{ccc}
\mathscr{F}A & \xrightarrow{\varphi(A)} & C \\
{\scriptstyle \mathscr{F}f}\downarrow & \nearrow{\scriptstyle \varphi(A')} & \\
\mathscr{F}A' & &
\end{array}
$$

is commutative. Then in particular $\rho_{\mathscr{F}}$ is such a family of morphisms $\rho_{\mathscr{F}}(A) : \mathscr{F}A \to U(\mathscr{F})$, which makes the corresponding diagrams commutative. We require that this family of morphisms has the property that to each $\varphi \in \mathrm{Mor}_f(\mathscr{F}, \mathscr{K}C)$ there is exactly one morphism $\varphi^* : U(\mathscr{F}) \to C$ such that for all $A \in \mathscr{A}$ the diagram

$$
\begin{array}{ccc}
\mathscr{F}A & \xrightarrow{\rho_{\mathscr{F}}(A)} & U(\mathscr{F}) \\
& \searrow{\scriptstyle \varphi(A)} & \downarrow{\scriptstyle \varphi^*} \\
& & C
\end{array}
$$

is commutative.

If there is a universal solution for the universal problem defined by $\mathscr{F}$, then this solution is called the *colimit* of the diagram $\mathscr{F}$ and is denoted by $\varinjlim \mathscr{F}$. The morphisms $\rho_{\mathscr{F}}(A) : \mathscr{F}A \to \varinjlim \mathscr{F}$ are called *injections*. If the diagram $\mathscr{F}$ is given as a set of objects C_i and a set of morphisms in $\mathscr{C}$, then we often write $\varinjlim C_i$ instead of $\varinjlim \mathscr{F}$.

If there is a limit [colimit] for each $\mathscr{F} \in \mathrm{Funct}(\mathscr{A}, \mathscr{C})$, then $\mathscr{C}$ is called a *category with $\mathscr{A}$-limits [$\mathscr{A}$-colimits]*. If there are limits [colimits] in $\mathscr{C}$ for all diagrams $\mathscr{F}$ over all diagram schemes $\mathscr{A}$, then $\mathscr{C}$ is called *complete* [*cocomplete*]. Correspondingly, we define a *finitely complete* [respectively, *cocomplete*] category, if there are limits [colimits] in $\mathscr{C}$ for all diagrams over finite diagram schemes $\mathscr{A}$.

LEMMA 1. *Let $\mathscr{F} : \mathscr{A} \to \mathscr{C}$ be a diagram. If the limit or colimit exists, then it, respectively, is uniquely determined up to an isomorphism.*

Proof. Limits and colimits are unique up to an isomorphism because they are a universal solution.

LEMMA 2. *A category $\mathscr{C}$ is a category with $\mathscr{A}$-limits [$\mathscr{A}$-colimits] if and only if the constant functor $\mathscr{K} : \mathscr{C} \to \mathrm{Funct}(\mathscr{A}, \mathscr{C})$ has a right adjoint [left adjoint] functor.*

Proof. Since the limits are universal solutions, the lemma is implied by Section 2.2, Theorem 1.

The explicit formulation of the universal problem defining a limit allows us also to define a limit for functors $\mathscr{F} : \mathscr{B} \to \mathscr{C}$ with an arbitrary category $\mathscr{B}$. But limits of these large diagrams will not always exist, even if $\mathscr{C}$ is complete. Compare the examples at the end of this section.

Now we want to collect all diagrams over a category $\mathscr{C}$ (not only those with a fixed diagram scheme) to a category. We have two interesting possibilities for this. The category to be constructed will be called the *large diagram category*, and we denote it by $\mathfrak{Dg}(\mathscr{C})$. The objects of $\mathfrak{Dg}(\mathscr{C})$ are pairs $(\mathscr{A}, \mathscr{F})$, where $\mathscr{A}$ is a diagram scheme and $\mathscr{F} : \mathscr{A} \to \mathscr{C}$ is a diagram. The morphisms between two objects $(\mathscr{A}, \mathscr{F})$ and $(\mathscr{A}', \mathscr{F}')$ are pairs $(\mathscr{G}, \varphi)$, where $\mathscr{G} : \mathscr{A} \to \mathscr{A}'$ is a functor and $\varphi : \mathscr{F} \to \mathscr{F}'\mathscr{G}$ is a natural transformation. Now, if morphisms $(\mathscr{G}, \varphi) : (\mathscr{A}, \mathscr{F}) \to (\mathscr{A}', \mathscr{F}')$ and $(\mathscr{G}', \varphi') : (\mathscr{A}', \mathscr{F}') \to (\mathscr{A}'', \mathscr{F}'')$ are given, then let the composition of these two morphisms be $(\mathscr{G}'\mathscr{G}, (\varphi'\mathscr{G})\varphi)$. With this definition, $\mathfrak{Dg}(\mathscr{C})$ forms a category.

We also construct another large diagram category $\mathfrak{Dg}'(\mathscr{C})$ with the same objects as in $\mathfrak{Dg}(\mathscr{C})$, in which, however, a morphism from $(\mathscr{A}, \mathscr{F})$ to $(\mathscr{A}', \mathscr{F}')$ is a pair $(\mathscr{G}, \varphi)$ with a functor $\mathscr{G} : \mathscr{A} \to \mathscr{A}'$ and a natural transformation $\varphi : \mathscr{F}'\mathscr{G} \to \mathscr{F}$. The composition in $\mathfrak{Dg}'(\mathscr{C})$ is

$$(\mathscr{G}', \varphi')(\mathscr{G}, \varphi) = (\mathscr{G}'\mathscr{G}, \varphi(\varphi'\mathscr{G})).$$

For each diagram scheme $\mathscr{A}$, the category $\mathrm{Funct}(\mathscr{A}, \mathscr{C})$ is a subcategory of $\mathfrak{Dg}(\mathscr{C})$ with the application $\mathscr{F} \mapsto (\mathscr{A}, \mathscr{F})$ and $\varphi \mapsto (\mathrm{Id}_{\mathscr{A}}, \varphi)$. Similarly, $\mathrm{Funct}(\mathscr{A}, \mathscr{C})^0$ is a subcategory of $\mathfrak{Dg}'(\mathscr{C})$. Both subcategories are not full because there may be other endofunctors of $\mathscr{A}$ than $\mathrm{Id}_{\mathscr{A}}$.

Let $\mathcal{O}$ be a discrete category with only one object. The composition of the constant functor $\mathscr{K} : \mathscr{C} \to \mathrm{Funct}(\mathcal{O}, \mathscr{C})$ with the embedding $\mathrm{Funct}(\mathcal{O}, \mathscr{C}) \to \mathfrak{Dg}(\mathscr{C})$ will also be called the *constant functor* and will be denoted by $\mathfrak{K} : \mathscr{C} \to \mathfrak{Dg}(\mathscr{C})$. Similarly, we get a constant functor $\mathfrak{K} : \mathscr{C}^0 \to \mathfrak{Dg}'(\mathscr{C})$.

PROPOSITION 1.   *The category $\mathscr{C}$ is cocomplete if and only if the constant functor $\Re : \mathscr{C} \to \mathfrak{Dg}(\mathscr{C})$ has a left adjoint functor.*

Proof.   Let us denote $\mathrm{Mor}_{\mathfrak{Dg}(\mathscr{C})}((\mathscr{A}, \mathscr{F}), \Re C)$ by $\mathrm{Mor}((\mathscr{A}, \mathscr{F}), \Re C)$. $\Re$ has a left adjoint functor if and only if $\mathrm{Mor}((\mathscr{A}, \mathscr{F}), \Re-)$ is representable for all $(\mathscr{A}, \mathscr{F})$ (Section 1.15, Lemma 4). Let $(\mathscr{G}, \varphi) \in \mathrm{Mor}((\mathscr{A}, \mathscr{F}), \Re C)$, then $\mathscr{G} : \mathscr{A} \to \mathcal{O}$ is uniquely determined, and we have a natural transformation $\varphi : \mathscr{F} \to \mathscr{K}_{\mathscr{A}} C$, where $\mathscr{K}_{\mathscr{A}} : \mathscr{C} \to \mathrm{Funct}(\mathscr{A}, \mathscr{C})$ is the constant functor. The functor corresponding to $\Re C$ composed with $\mathscr{G}$ assigns to each object in $\mathscr{A}$ the object $C \in \mathscr{C}$ and to each morphism in $\mathscr{A}$ the morphism $1_C \in \mathscr{C}$. Thus $\mathrm{Mor}((\mathscr{A}, \mathscr{F}), \Re C) \cong \mathrm{Mor}_f(\mathscr{F}, \mathscr{K}_{\mathscr{A}} C)$. It is easy to verify that this isomorphism is natural in C; $\mathrm{Mor}((\mathscr{A}, \mathscr{F}), \Re-) \cong \mathrm{Mor}_f(\mathscr{F}, \mathscr{K}_{\mathscr{A}}-)$. The functor $\mathrm{Mor}_f(\mathscr{F}, \mathscr{K}_{\mathscr{A}}-)$ is representable for all $(\mathscr{A}, \mathscr{F})$ if and only if $\mathscr{C}$ is cocomplete (Lemma 2).

PROPOSITION 2.   *The category $\mathscr{C}$ is complete if and only if the constant functor $\Re : \mathscr{C}^0 \to \mathfrak{Dg}'(\mathscr{C})$ has a left adjoint functor.*

Proof.   This proposition is implied by Proposition 1 if one replaces $\mathscr{C}$ by $\mathscr{C}^0$. In fact, $\mathfrak{Dg}(\mathscr{C}^0) \cong \mathfrak{Dg}'(\mathscr{C})$.

In particular, the following notations make sense. Let $\mathscr{F} : \mathscr{A} \to \mathscr{C}$ and $\mathscr{G} : \mathscr{A} \to \mathscr{C}$ be functors, and let $\varphi : \mathscr{F} \to \mathscr{G}$ be a natural transformation. Then let $\varinjlim \varphi = \varinjlim(\mathrm{Id}_{\mathscr{A}}, \varphi)$ and $\varprojlim \varphi = \varprojlim(\mathrm{Id}_{\mathscr{A}}, \varphi)$, where $\varinjlim$ and $\varprojlim$ denote the left adjoint functor for $\Re$ with values in $\mathscr{C}$ of Proposition 1 and Proposition 2 respectively (also in the case of Proposition 2). We write also

$$\varinjlim \varphi : \varinjlim \mathscr{F} \to \varinjlim \mathscr{G} \qquad \text{and} \qquad \varprojlim \varphi : \varprojlim \mathscr{F} \to \varprojlim \mathscr{G}$$

Let $\mathscr{F} : \mathscr{A} \to \mathscr{C}$, $\mathscr{G} : \mathscr{B} \to \mathscr{C}$, and $\mathscr{H} : \mathscr{A} \to \mathscr{B}$ be functors, such that the diagram

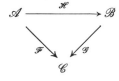

is commutative. We assume that here both $\mathscr{A}$ and $\mathscr{B}$ are small categories. Then we define $\varinjlim \mathscr{H} : \varinjlim \mathscr{F} \to \varinjlim \mathscr{G}$ and $\varprojlim \mathscr{H} : \varprojlim \mathscr{F} \to \varprojlim \mathscr{G}$ by $\varinjlim \mathscr{H} = \varinjlim(\mathscr{H}, \mathrm{id}_{\mathscr{F}})$ and $\varprojlim \mathscr{H} = \varprojlim(\mathscr{H}, \mathrm{id}_{\mathscr{F}})$ respectively.

Now we want to investigate when a small category $\mathscr{A}$ is complete. Let $\operatorname{Mor}_{\mathscr{A}}(A, B)$ be a morphism set with more than one element. Let I be a set which has larger cardinality than the set of morphism of A. Finally, let $\prod_{i \in I} B_i = C$ with $B_i = B$ for all $i \in I$. Then the cardinality of $\operatorname{Mor}_{\mathscr{A}}(A, C)$ is larger than the cardinality of the set of all morphisms of $\mathscr{A}$. Thus each morphism set $\operatorname{Mor}_{\mathscr{A}}(A, B)$ can have at most one element. A similar argument holds for a cocomplete small category. Now let us define $A < B$ if and only if $\operatorname{Mor}_{\mathscr{A}}(A, B) \neq \varnothing$, then this is a reflexive and transitive relation on the set of objects of $\mathscr{A}$. Such a category is also called pre-ordered set.

Often a limit is also called an inverse limit, projective limit, infimum, or left root. Correspondingly, a colimit is often called a direct limit, inductive limit, supremum, or right root. We shall use these notations with a somewhat different meaning.

2.6 Special Limits and Colimits

In this section we shall investigate special diagram schemes $\mathscr{A}$ and the limits and colimits they define. Some of these examples are already known from Chapter 1. Let $\mathscr{A}$ be the category

$$\cdot \rightrightarrows \cdot$$

that is, a category with two objects A and B and four morphisms 1_A, 1_B, $f : A \to B$, and $g : A \to B$; let $\mathscr{F} : \mathscr{A} \to \mathscr{C}$ be a covariant functor, then $\varprojlim \mathscr{F} = \operatorname{Ker}(\mathscr{F}f, \mathscr{F}g)$. In fact, let us recall the explicit definition of the limit. A natural transformation $\varphi : \mathscr{K}C \to \mathscr{F}$ is a pair of morphisms $\varphi(A) : C \to \mathscr{F}A$ and $\varphi(B) : C \to \mathscr{F}B$, such that $\mathscr{F}(f)\,\varphi(A) = \varphi(B) = \mathscr{F}(g)\,\varphi(A)$. This is equivalent to giving a morphism $h : C \to \mathscr{F}A$ with the property $\mathscr{F}(f)h = \mathscr{F}(g)h$. The difference kernel of $(\mathscr{F}f, \mathscr{F}g)$ is a morphism $i : \operatorname{Ker}(\mathscr{F}f, \mathscr{F}g) \to \mathscr{F}A$ with the property that to each morphism $h : C \to \mathscr{F}A$ with this property, there is exactly one morphism $h' : C \to \operatorname{Ker}(\mathscr{F}f, \mathscr{F}g)$ with $h = ih'$. This is exactly the definition of the limit of $\mathscr{F}$. Here i is the projection. Dually, $\varinjlim \mathscr{F} = \operatorname{Cok}(\mathscr{F}f, \mathscr{F}g)$.

Let $\mathscr{A}$ be a discrete category, which we may consider as a set I by Section 1.1. Then a diagram $\mathscr{F}$ over $\mathscr{A}$ is a family of objects $\{C_i\}_{i \in I}$ in $\mathscr{C}$. The conditions for the limit $\varprojlim \mathscr{F}$ of $\mathscr{F}$ coincide with the conditions for the product $\prod_{i \in I} C_i$ of the objects C_i. The projections of the product into each single factor coincide with the projections of the limit into the objects $\mathscr{F}(i) = C_i$. Correspondingly, the colimit of $\mathscr{F}$ is the coproduct of the C_i.

Another important example of a special limit is defined by the diagram scheme

that is, by a small category $\mathscr{A}$ with three objects A, B, C, and five morphisms 1_A, 1_B, 1_C, $f : A \to C$, and $g : B \to C$. A natural transformation $\varphi : \mathscr{K} D \to \mathscr{F}$ for an object $D \in \mathscr{C}$ and a diagram $\mathscr{F}$ is completely described by the specification of two morphisms $h : D \to \mathscr{F} A$ and $k : D \to \mathscr{F} B$ with $\mathscr{F}(f)h = \mathscr{F}(g)k$. The limit of $\mathscr{F}$ consists of an object

$$\mathscr{F} A \underset{\mathscr{F} C}{\times} \mathscr{F} B$$

and two morphisms

$$p_A : \mathscr{F} A \underset{\mathscr{F} C}{\times} \mathscr{F} B \to \mathscr{F} A \qquad \text{and} \qquad p_B : \mathscr{F} A \underset{\mathscr{F} C}{\times} \mathscr{F} B \to \mathscr{F} B$$

with $\mathscr{F}(f) p_A = \mathscr{F}(g) p_B$, such that to each triple (D, h, k) with $\mathscr{F}(f)h = \mathscr{F}(g)k$ there is exactly one morphism

$$l : D \to \mathscr{F} A \underset{\mathscr{F} C}{\times} \mathscr{F} B$$

such that the diagram

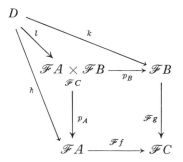

is commutative. This limit will be called *fiber product* of $\mathscr{F} A$ and $\mathscr{F} B$ over $\mathscr{F} C$. Other names are cartesian square and pullback.

Let $\mathscr{A}$ be dual to the diagram used for the definition of the fiber product; thus let $\mathscr{A}$ be of the form

Let $\mathscr{F}$ be a diagram over $\mathscr{A}$ in $\mathscr{C}$. The colimit $\varinjlim \mathscr{F}$ will be called a *cofiber product*. Other names are cocartesian square, pushout, fiber sum, and amalgamated sum.

PROPOSITION 1.　*Let $\mathscr{C}$ be a category with finite products. $\mathscr{C}$ has difference kernels if and only if $\mathscr{C}$ has fiber products.*

Proof.　Let $\mathscr{C}$ have difference kernels. In the diagram

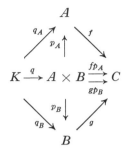

let $(A \times B, p_A, p_B)$ be a product of A and B, and let (K, q) be a difference kernel of (fp_A, gp_B). Furthermore, let $q_A = p_A q$ and $q_B = p_B q$. Then the diagram is commutative, except for the pair of morphisms (fp_A, gp_B). We claim that (K, q_A, q_B) is a fiber product of A and B over C. In fact we have $fq_A = gq_B$. If $h : D \to A$ and $k : D \to B$ is a pair of morphisms of $\mathscr{C}$ with $fh = gk$, then there is exactly one morphism $(h, k) : D \to A \times B$ with $h = p_A(h, k)$ and $k = p_B(h, k)$. Hence, $fp_A(h, k) = gp_B(h, k)$. So there exists exactly one morphism $l : D \to K$ with $ql = (h, k)$, and we have $q_A l = h$ and $q_B l = k$. The diagram extended by $h : D \to A$ and $k : D \to B$ becomes commutative if we add $l : D \to K$ (except for fp_A, gp_B); this implies that l is uniquely determined.

Let $\mathscr{C}$ have fiber products. In the commutative diagram

$$
\begin{array}{ccc}
K & \xrightarrow{\;p_A\;} & A \\
{\scriptstyle p_B}\big\downarrow & & \big\downarrow{\scriptstyle (f,g)} \\
B & \xrightarrow{\;\Delta_B\;} & B \times B
\end{array}
$$

let $B \times B$ be the product of B with itself, Δ_B the diagonal, (f, g) the morphism uniquely determined by two morphisms $f : A \to B$ and $g : A \to B$, and let (K, p_A, p_B) be a fiber product. We claim that (K, p_A) is a difference kernel of the pair of morphisms (f, g). (Distinguish between the pair of morphisms (f, g) and the morphism (f, g)). Now let $q_1 : B \times B \to B$ and $q_2 : B \times B \to B$ be the projections of the product.

Then we have $(f, g)\, p_A = \Delta_B\, p_B$, thus

$$f p_A = q_1(f, g)\, p_A = q_1 \Delta_B p_B = 1_B p_B$$
$$= q_2 \Delta_B p_B = q_2(f, g)\, p_A = g p_A$$

Let $h : D \to A$ with $fh = gh$ be given. Then $fh : D \to B$ and $q_1 \Delta_B fh = 1_B fh = q_1(f, g)h$ and $q_2 \Delta_B fh = 1_B fh = 1_B gg = q_2(f, g)h$, thus $\Delta_B fh = (f, g)h$. Consequently, there exists a unique morphism $k : D \to K$ with $p_B k = h$ and $p_B k = fh(= gh)$. But this is the condition for a difference kernel.

Difference kernels may also be represented in a different form as fiber products. This will be shown by the following corollary.

COROLLARY 1.   *Let $f, g : A \to B$ be morphisms in $\mathscr{C}$. The commutative diagram*

$$
\begin{array}{ccc}
K & \xrightarrow{\;\; p \;\;} & A \\
{\scriptstyle p}\downarrow & & \downarrow{\scriptstyle (1_A, f)} \\
A & \xrightarrow{\;(1_A, g)\;} & A \times B
\end{array}
$$

is a fiber product if and only if (K, p) is a difference kernel of the pair (f, g).

Proof.   The hypothesis that both projections $K \to A$ of the fiber product coincide is no restriction, since if $h, k : C \to A$ are two morphisms with $(1_A, f)h = (1_A, g)k$, then by composition with the projection $A \times B \to A$ we get the equations $h = k$ and $fh = gh$. Thus the claim follows directly from the definition of the fiber product and the difference kernel.

LEMMA 1.   *Let $\mathscr{C}$ have fiber products and a final object. Then $\mathscr{C}$ is a category with finite products.*

Proof.   Let E be a final object in $\mathscr{C}$. Let A and B be objects in $\mathscr{C}$. Then there is exactly one morphism $A \to E$ and exactly one morphism $B \to E$. Assume that the commutative diagram

$$
\begin{array}{ccc}
K & \longrightarrow & A \\
\downarrow & & \downarrow \\
B & \longrightarrow & E
\end{array}
$$

is a fiber product. Then K is a product of A and B. The requirement that the square be commutative is vacuous because there is only one morphism from each object into E.

PROPOSITION 2. *Let $\mathscr{C}$ be a category with (finite) products and difference kernels. Then $\mathscr{C}$ is (finitely) complete.*

Proof. Let $\mathscr{A}$ be a diagram scheme and $\mathscr{F} : \mathscr{A} \to \mathscr{C}$ be a diagram. Let $P = \prod_{A \in \mathscr{A}} \mathscr{F}A$. Let $Q = \prod_{f \in \mathscr{A}} \mathscr{F}R(f)$ where $R(f)$ is the range of f. For each object $\mathscr{F}R(f)$, we get two morphisms from P into $\mathscr{F}R(f)$, namely for $f : A \to A'$ we get the projection $p_{A'} : P \to \mathscr{F}A'$ and the morphism $\mathscr{F}(f)p_A : P \to \mathscr{F}A \to \mathscr{F}A'$. This defines two morphisms $p : P \to Q$ and $q : P \to Q$. Let $K = \mathrm{Ker}(p, q)$. Let $\varphi : \mathscr{K}C \to \mathscr{F}$ be a natural transformation. Then for all $A \in \mathscr{A}$ there are morphisms $\varphi(A) : C \to \mathscr{F}A$ with the property that

$$
\begin{array}{ccc}
C & \xrightarrow{\varphi(A)} & \mathscr{F}A \\
& \searrow{\scriptstyle \varphi(A')} & \downarrow{\scriptstyle \mathscr{F}f} \\
& & \mathscr{F}A'
\end{array}
$$

is commutative for all $f \in \mathscr{A}$. Thus the compositions

$$
C \longrightarrow P \underset{q}{\overset{p}{\rightrightarrows}} Q
$$

are equal, that is, there is exactly one morphism $\varphi^* : C \to K$ such that

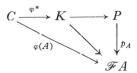

is commutative. Thus, K is a limit of $\mathscr{F}$.

COROLLARY 2. *The categories $\mathbf{S}$ and $\mathbf{Top}$ are complete and cocomplete.*

Proof. By Sections 1.9 and 1.11 both categories have difference kernels and cokernels, products and coproducts. Proposition 2 and the dual of Proposition 2 give the result.

COROLLARY 3. *A category with fiber products and a final object is finitely complete.*

The proof is implied by Proposition 1, Lemma 1, and Proposition 2.

COROLLARY 4. *Let $\mathscr{C}$ be a complete category and let $\mathscr{G} : \mathscr{C} \to \mathscr{D}$ be a functor which preserves difference kernels and products. Then $\mathscr{G}$ preserves limits.*

Proof. By Proposition 2, a limit is composed of two products and a difference kernel. These products and difference kernels in $\mathscr{C}$ are transferred by $\mathscr{G}$ into corresponding products and difference kernels in $\mathscr{D}$. Thus they also form a limit in $\mathscr{D}$ of the diagram which has been transferred by $\mathscr{G}$ into $\mathscr{D}$.

A functor preserving limits [colimits] is called *continuous [cocontinuous]*. In particular, such a functor preserves final and initial objects as limits and colimits respectively of empty diagrams.

A special fiber product is the kernel pair of a morphism. Let $p : B \to C$ be a morphism. An ordered pair of morphisms

$$(f_0 : A \to B, \ f_1 : A \to B)$$

is called a *kernel pair* of p if (1) $pf_0 = pf_1$ and (2) for each ordered pair

$$(h_0 : X \to B, h_1 : X \to B)$$

with $ph_0 = ph_1$, there is exactly one morphism $g : X \to A$ with $h_0 = f_0 g$ and $h_1 = f_1 g$:

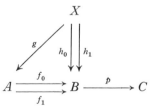

(f_0, f_1) is a kernel pair of p if and only if A is a fiber product of B over C with itself:

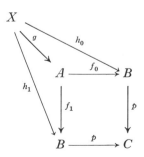

If there are fiber products in $\mathscr{C}$, then there are also kernel pairs of arbitrary morphisms in $\mathscr{C}$.

LEMMA 2. $g : A \to B$ is a monomorphism if and only if $(1_A , 1_A)$ is a kernel pair of g.

Proof.   Let $h_0 , h_1 : X \to A$ be given with $gh_0 = gh_1$. In such a case g is a monomorphism if and only if we always have $h_0 = h_1$. This is true if and only if there is a morphism $f : X \to A$ with $1_A f = h_0$ and $1_A f = h_1$.

COROLLARY 5. *If a functor preserves kernel pairs, then it preserves monomorphisms.*

LEMMA 3. *In the commutative diagram*

$$A \xrightarrow{\ f\ } B \xrightarrow{\ g\ } C$$
$$\Big\downarrow{a} \qquad \Big\downarrow{b} \qquad \Big\downarrow{c}$$
$$A' \xrightarrow{\ f'\ } B' \xrightarrow{\ g'\ } C'$$

let the right square be a fiber product. (A, f, a) is a fiber product of B and A' over B' if and only if (A, gf, a) is a fiber product of C and A' over C'.

Proof.   Let (A, gf, a) be a fiber product. Let $h : D \to B$ and $k : D \to A'$ be morphisms with $bh = f'k$. Then we get for $gh : D \to C$ and for $k : D \to A'$ the equation $cgh = g'f'k$. Thus there is exactly one $x : D \to A$ with $gfx = gh$ and $ax = k$. We show $fx = h$. In fact, then (A, f, a) is a fiber product of B and A' over B'. We have $gh = gh$ and $bh = f'k$. Furthermore, we have $gfx = gh$ and $bfx = f'ax = f'k$. Since the square is a fiber product, the equation $fx = h$ is implied by the uniqueness of the factorization.

Let (A, f, a) be a fiber product. Let $h : D \to C$ and $k : D \to A'$ be morphisms with $ch = g'f'k$. Because of $ch = g'(f'k)$, there is exactly one $x : D \to B$ with $bx = f'k$ and $gx = h$. Because of $bx = f'k$, there is exactly one $y : D \to A$ with $fy = x$ and $ay = k$. Then the uniqueness of y with $gfy = h$ and $ay = k$ follows trivially.

A small category $\mathscr{A}$ is called *filtered* if:

(1)   for any two objects $A, B \in \mathscr{A}$ there is always an object $C \in \mathscr{A}$ together with morphisms $A \to C$ and $B \to C$, and
(2)   for any two morphisms $f, g : A \to B$ there is always a morphism $h : B \to C$ with $hf = hg$.

A small category $\mathscr{A}$ is called *directed* if it is filtered and if each morphism set $\mathrm{Mor}_{\mathscr{A}}(A, B)$ has at most one element. Let $\mathscr{F} : \mathscr{A} \to \mathscr{C}$ be a covariant functor. If $\mathscr{A}$ is filtered, then $\varinjlim \mathscr{F}$ is called a *filtered colimit*. If $\mathscr{A}$ is directed, then $\varinjlim \mathscr{F}$ is called a *direct limit*. Let $\mathscr{F} : \mathscr{A}^0 \to \mathscr{C}$ be a covariant functor. If $\mathscr{A}$ is filtered, then $\varprojlim \mathscr{F}$ is called a *filtered limit*. If $\mathscr{A}$ is directed, then $\varprojlim \mathscr{F}$ is called an *inverse limit*. These special limits and colimits will be very important for abelian categories discussed in Section 4.7

Now we give some examples of finitely complete categories, without proving this property in each particular case: the categories of finite sets, of finite groups, and of unitary noetherian modules over a unitary associative ring. Furthermore, we observe that in **S**, **Gr**, **Ab**, and $_R$**Mod** each subobject appears as a difference kernel. In **Hd** exactly the closed subspaces are difference kernels, in **Top** all subspaces are difference kernels. This may be proved easily with the dual of the following lemma.

LEMMA 4.　*Let $\mathscr{C}$ be a category with kernel pairs and difference cokernels.*

(a) *f is a difference cokernel if and only if f is a difference cokernel of its kernel pair.*

(b) *$h_0 , h_1 : A \to B$ is a kernel pair if and only if it is a kernel pair of its difference cokernel.*

Proof.　We use the diagram

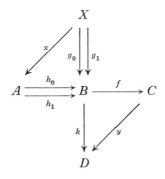

(a)　Let f be a difference cokernel of (g_0 , g_1), and let (h_0 , h_1) be a kernel pair of f. If $kh_0 = kh_1$, then $kg_0 = kg_1$; thus there is exactly one y with $yf = k$.

(b)　Let (h_0 , h_1) be a kernel pair of k and let f be a difference cokernel of (h_0 , h_1). Then there is exactly one y with $k = yf$. If g_0 , g_1 are given with $fg_0 = fg_1$, then $kg_0 = kg_1$, thus there is exactly one x with $h_i x = g_i$ for $i = 0, 1$.

2.7 Diagram Categories

In this section we discuss mainly preservation properties of adjoint functors, limits, and colimits. For this purpose, we need assertions on the behavior of limits and colimits in diagram categories.

THEOREM 1. *Let $\mathscr{A}$ be a diagram scheme and $\mathscr{C}$ be a (finitely) complete category. Then* Funct$(\mathscr{A}, \mathscr{C})$ *is (finitely) complete, and the limits of functors in* Funct$(\mathscr{A}, \mathscr{C})$ *are formed argumentwise.*

Proof. Let $\mathscr{B}$ be another diagram scheme. Let $\mathscr{K} : \mathscr{C} \to$ Funct$(\mathscr{B}, \mathscr{C})$ and $\mathscr{K}' :$ Funct$(\mathscr{A}, \mathscr{C}) \to$ Funct$(\mathscr{B},$ Funct$(\mathscr{A}, \mathscr{C}))$ be constant functors. Let $\mathscr{H} \in$ Funct$(\mathscr{A}, \mathscr{C})$ and $\mathscr{G} \in$ Funct$(\mathscr{A},$ Funct$(\mathscr{B}, \mathscr{C}))$. Let $\mathscr{K}\mathscr{H}$ be the composition of functors, and let $\varphi : \mathscr{K}\mathscr{H} \to \mathscr{G}$ be a natural transformation. Then to each $\varphi(A) \in$ Mor$(\mathscr{K}\mathscr{H}(A), \mathscr{G}(A))$ there is a $\varphi'(A) \in$ Mor$(\mathscr{H}(A), \varprojlim(\mathscr{G}(A)))$ such that the following diagram is commutative:

$$
\begin{array}{ccc}
\text{Mor}(\mathscr{K}\mathscr{H}(A), \mathscr{G}(A)) & \simeq & \text{Mor}(\mathscr{H}(A), \varprojlim(\mathscr{G}(A))) \\
\downarrow{\scriptstyle\text{Mor}(\mathscr{K}\mathscr{H}(A),\mathscr{G}(f))} & & \downarrow{\scriptstyle\text{Mor}(\mathscr{H}(A),\varprojlim(\mathscr{G}(f)))} \\
\text{Mor}(\mathscr{K}\mathscr{H}(A), \mathscr{G}(A')) & \simeq & \text{Mor}(\mathscr{H}(A), \varprojlim(\mathscr{G}(A'))) \\
\uparrow{\scriptstyle\text{Mor}(\mathscr{K}\mathscr{H}(f),\mathscr{G}(A'))} & & \uparrow{\scriptstyle\text{Mor}(\mathscr{H}(f),\varprojlim(\mathscr{G}(A')))} \\
\text{Mor}(\mathscr{K}\mathscr{H}(A'), \mathscr{G}(A')) & \simeq & \text{Mor}(\mathscr{H}(A'), \varprojlim(\mathscr{G}(A')))
\end{array}
$$

where $f : A \to A'$. $\varphi(A') \mathscr{K}\mathscr{H}(f) = \mathscr{G}(f) \varphi(A)$ implies $\varphi'(A')\mathscr{H}(f) = \varprojlim(\mathscr{G}(f)) \varphi'(A)$, that is, $\varphi' : \mathscr{H} \to \varprojlim(\mathscr{G}(-))$ is a natural transformation. So we have Mor$_f(\mathscr{K}\mathscr{H}, \mathscr{G}) \simeq$ Mor$_f(\mathscr{H}, \varprojlim \mathscr{G})$. We define

$$\text{Funct}(\mathscr{A}, \mathscr{K}) : \text{Funct}(\mathscr{A}, \mathscr{C}) \to \text{Funct}(\mathscr{A}, \text{Funct}(\mathscr{B}, \mathscr{C}))$$

by Funct$(\mathscr{A}, \mathscr{K})(\mathscr{H}) = \mathscr{K}\mathscr{H}$ and Funct$(\mathscr{A}, \mathscr{K})(\rho) = \mathscr{K}\rho$ and analogously

$$\text{Funct}(\mathscr{A}, \varprojlim) : \text{Funct}(\mathscr{A}, \text{Funct}(\mathscr{B}, \mathscr{C})) \to \text{Funct}(\mathscr{A}, \mathscr{C})$$

Then Funct$(\mathscr{A}, \mathscr{K})$ is left adjoint to Funct$(\mathscr{A}, \varprojlim)$. If we compose Funct$(\mathscr{A}, \mathscr{K})$ with the isomorphism

$$\text{Funct}(\mathscr{A}, \text{Funct}(\mathscr{B}, \mathscr{C})) \simeq \text{Funct}(\mathscr{B}, \text{Funct}(\mathscr{A}, \mathscr{C}))$$

we get the functor $\mathscr{K}'$, which has a left adjoint functor

$$\varprojlim' : \text{Funct}(\mathscr{B}, \text{Funct}(\mathscr{A}, \mathscr{C})) \to \text{Funct}(\mathscr{A}, \mathscr{C})$$

Here $\varprojlim'(\mathscr{G})(A) = \varprojlim(\mathscr{G}(A))$, which means that the limit is formed argumentwise. Observe that we identified the functor

$$\mathscr{G} \in \mathrm{Funct}(\mathscr{A}, \mathrm{Funct}(\mathscr{B}, \mathscr{C}))$$

with the corresponding functor in $\mathrm{Funct}(\mathscr{B}, \mathrm{Funct}(\mathscr{A}, \mathscr{C}))$.

Dualization of $\mathscr{A}$ and $\mathscr{C}$ implies the dual assertion that, with $\mathscr{C}$, $\mathrm{Funct}(\mathscr{A}, \mathscr{C})$ is also (finitely) cocomplete and that the colimits are formed argumentwise. For this purpose, use $\mathrm{Funct}(\mathscr{A}, \mathscr{C}) \cong \mathrm{Funct}(\mathscr{A}^0, \mathscr{C}^0)^0$ of Section 1.5.

THEOREM 2. *Let $\mathscr{A}$ be a diagram scheme, $\mathscr{F} : \mathscr{A} \to \mathscr{C}$ a diagram in $\mathscr{C}$, and $C \in \mathscr{C}$. If $\varprojlim \mathscr{F}$ or $\varinjlim \mathscr{F}$ exist, then there are, respectively, isomorphisms*

$$\varprojlim \mathrm{Mor}(C, \mathscr{F}) \cong \mathrm{Mor}(C, \varprojlim \mathscr{F})$$

$$\varprojlim \mathrm{Mor}(\mathscr{F}, C) \cong \mathrm{Mor}(\varinjlim \mathscr{F}, C)$$

which are natural in $\mathscr{F}$ and C.

Proof. Let $\mathfrak{F}_1 = \mathrm{Funct}(\mathscr{A}, \mathscr{C})$, $\mathfrak{F}_2 = \mathrm{Funct}(\mathscr{A}, \mathbf{S})$, $\mathscr{F} \in \mathfrak{F}_1$, $C \in \mathscr{C}$, and $X \in \mathbf{S}$. Then

$$\mathrm{Mor}_{\mathfrak{F}_2}(\mathscr{K}X, \mathrm{Mor}_{\mathscr{C}}(\mathscr{F}-, C)) \cong \mathrm{Mor}_{\mathbf{S}}(X, \mathrm{Mor}_{\mathfrak{F}_1}(\mathscr{F}, \mathscr{K}C))$$

natural in $\mathscr{F}$, C, and X. In fact, let $f \in \mathrm{Mor}_{\mathfrak{F}_2}(\mathscr{K}X, \mathrm{Mor}_{\mathscr{C}}(\mathscr{F}-, C))$, then f is uniquely determined by $f(A)(x) : \mathscr{F}A \to C$ for all $x \in X$ and natural in $A \in \mathscr{A}$. We assign $g(x)(A) = f(A)(x) : \mathscr{F}A \to C$ to f. Then $g \in \mathrm{Mor}_{\mathbf{S}}(X, \mathrm{Mor}_{\mathfrak{F}_1}(\mathscr{F}, \mathscr{K}C))$. This application is bijective and natural in $\mathscr{F}$, C, and X. Thus, by changing to the functor which is adjoint to $\mathscr{K}$ we obtain

$$\mathrm{Mor}_{\mathbf{S}}(X, \varprojlim \mathrm{Mor}_{\mathscr{C}}(\mathscr{F}, C)) \cong \mathrm{Mor}_{\mathbf{S}}(X, \mathrm{Mor}_{\mathscr{C}}(\varinjlim \mathscr{F}, C))$$

and thus $\varprojlim \mathrm{Mor}_{\mathscr{C}}(\mathscr{F}, C) \cong \mathrm{Mor}_{\mathscr{C}}(\varinjlim \mathscr{F}, C)$. We obtain the other assertion dually.

Here again the consideration preceeding Section 1.5 on the generalization of notions in $\mathbf{S}$ to arbitrary categories with representable functors are valid. In particular, this theorem generalizes the remark at the end of Section 1.11.

COROLLARY 1. *Let $\mathscr{F} : \mathscr{A} \to \mathscr{C}$ be a diagram. Let $C \in \mathscr{C}$. Then the limit of the diagram $h^C\mathscr{F} : \mathscr{A} \to \mathbf{S}$ is the set $\mathrm{Mor}_f(\mathscr{K}C, \mathscr{F})$.*

Proof. In the proof of Theorem 2 there is an isomorphism

$$\mathrm{Mor}_S(X, \varprojlim \mathrm{Mor}_{\mathscr{C}}(\mathscr{F}, C)) \cong \mathrm{Mor}_S(X, \mathrm{Mor}_f(\mathscr{F}, \mathscr{H} C))$$

which implies $\varprojlim \mathrm{Mor}_{\mathscr{C}}(\mathscr{F}, C) \cong \mathrm{Mor}_f(\mathscr{F}, \mathscr{H} C)$. The assertion of the corollary is dual. Observe that we do not need the existence of $\varinjlim \mathscr{F}$ for this proof.

THEOREM 3. *Left adjoint functors preserve colimits; right adjoint functors preserve limits.*

Proof. Let $\mathscr{F} : \mathscr{C} \to \mathscr{D}$ be left adjoint to $\mathscr{G} : \mathscr{D} \to \mathscr{C}$. Then we have for a diagram $\mathscr{H} : \mathscr{A} \to \mathscr{D}$ and an object $C \in \mathscr{C}$

$$\mathrm{Mor}(C, \mathscr{G} \varprojlim \mathscr{H}) \cong \mathrm{Mor}(\mathscr{F}C, \varprojlim \mathscr{H}) \cong \varprojlim \mathrm{Mor}(\mathscr{F}C, \mathscr{H})$$

$$\cong \varprojlim \mathrm{Mor}(C, \mathscr{G}\mathscr{H}) \cong \mathrm{Mor}(C, \varprojlim \mathscr{G}\mathscr{H})$$

This implies $\mathscr{G} \varprojlim \mathscr{H} \cong \varprojlim \mathscr{G}\mathscr{H}$. One gets the second assertion dually.

LEMMA 1. *Let $\mathscr{F} : \mathscr{A} \times \mathscr{B} \to \mathscr{C}$ be a diagram over the diagram scheme $\mathscr{A} \times \mathscr{B}$. Let there be a limit of $\mathscr{F}(A, -) : \mathscr{B} \to \mathscr{C}$ for all $A \in \mathscr{A}$. There is a limit of $\mathscr{F} : \mathscr{A} \times \mathscr{B} \to \mathscr{C}$ if and only if there is a limit of $\mathscr{F} : \mathscr{A} \to \mathrm{Funct}(\mathscr{B}, \mathscr{C})$. If these limits exist, then we have*

$$\varprojlim_{\mathscr{A}} \varprojlim_{\mathscr{B}} \mathscr{F} \cong \varprojlim_{\mathscr{A} \times \mathscr{B}} \mathscr{F}$$

Proof. To explain over which diagram the limit is to be formed, we wrote the corresponding diagram schemes under the limits. Corresponding functors in $\mathrm{Funct}(\mathscr{A} \times B, \mathscr{C})$, $\mathrm{Funct}(\mathscr{A}, \mathrm{Funct}(\mathscr{B}, \mathscr{C}))$, or $\mathrm{Funct}(\mathscr{B}, \mathrm{Funct}(\mathscr{A}, \mathscr{C}))$ will be denoted by no prime, one prime, or a double prime respectively. Since $\varprojlim_{\mathscr{B}}(\mathscr{F}(A, -))$ exists for all $A \in \mathscr{A}$, $\varprojlim_{\mathscr{B}}(\mathscr{F}'')$ also exists. Then we have

$$\mathrm{Mor}_{\mathscr{C}}(C, \varprojlim_{\mathscr{A} \times \mathscr{B}}(\mathscr{F})) \cong \mathrm{Mor}_f(\mathscr{K}_{\mathscr{A} \times \mathscr{B}}C, \mathscr{F}) \cong \mathrm{Mor}_f((\mathscr{K}_{\mathscr{B}}\mathscr{K}_{\mathscr{A}}C)'', \mathscr{F}'')$$

$$\cong \mathrm{Mor}_f(\mathscr{K}_{\mathscr{A}}C, \varprojlim_{\mathscr{B}} \mathscr{F}'') = \mathrm{Mor}_{\mathscr{C}}(C, \varprojlim_{\mathscr{A}} \varprojlim_{\mathscr{B}} \mathscr{F}'')$$

natural in $C \in \mathscr{C}$. Here $\mathscr{K}_{\mathscr{A} \times \mathscr{B}} : \mathscr{C} \to \mathrm{Funct}(\mathscr{A} \times \mathscr{B}, \mathscr{C})$, $\mathscr{K}_{\mathscr{A}} : \mathscr{C} \to \mathrm{Funct}(\mathscr{A}, \mathscr{C})$, and $\mathscr{K}_{\mathscr{B}} : \mathrm{Funct}(\mathscr{A}, \mathscr{C}) \to \mathrm{Funct}(\mathscr{B}, \mathrm{Funct}(\mathscr{A}, \mathscr{C}))$ are constant functors.

COROLLARY 2. *Limits commute with limits and colimits commute with colimits.*

Proof. Obviously

$$\varprojlim_{\mathscr{A}\times\mathscr{B}} \mathscr{F} \cong \varprojlim_{\mathscr{B}\times\mathscr{A}} \mathscr{F}$$

thus,

$$\varprojlim_{\mathscr{A}} \varprojlim_{\mathscr{B}} \mathscr{F} \cong \varprojlim_{\mathscr{B}} \varprojlim_{\mathscr{A}} \mathscr{F}$$

COROLLARY 3. *The constant functor* $\mathscr{K} : \mathscr{C} \to \mathrm{Funct}(\mathscr{A}, \mathscr{C})$ *preserves limits and colimits.*

Proof. We have

$$\mathrm{Mor}(\mathscr{F}, \mathscr{K} \varprojlim_{\mathscr{B}} \mathscr{G}) \cong \varprojlim_{\mathscr{A}} \mathrm{Mor}(\mathscr{F}, \varprojlim_{\mathscr{B}} \mathscr{G})$$

$$\cong \varprojlim_{\mathscr{B}} \varprojlim_{\mathscr{A}} \mathrm{Mor}(\mathscr{F}, \mathscr{G}) \cong \mathrm{Mor}(\mathscr{F}, \varprojlim_{\mathscr{B}} \mathscr{K}\mathscr{G})$$

where $\mathscr{F} : \mathscr{A} \to \mathscr{C}$ and $\mathscr{G} : \mathscr{B} \to \mathscr{C}$.

LEMMA 2. *Let* $\mathscr{A}$ *be a small category,* $\mathscr{C}$ *an arbitrary category,* $\mathscr{F}, \mathscr{G} : \mathscr{A} \to \mathscr{C}$ *functors, and* $\varphi : \mathscr{F} \to \mathscr{G}$ *a natural transformation. If* φA *is a monomorphism for all* $A \in \mathscr{A}$, *then* φ *is a monomorphism in* $\mathrm{Funct}(\mathscr{A}, \mathscr{C})$. *Let* $\mathscr{C}$ *be finitely complete and* φ *be a monomorphism, then* φA *is a monomorphism for all* $A \in \mathscr{A}$.

Proof. Two natural transformations ψ and ρ coincide if and only if they coincide pointwise ($\psi A = \rho A$). Thus the first assertion is clear. For the second assertion, we consider the commutative diagram in $\mathrm{Funct}(\mathscr{A}, \mathscr{C})$

$$\begin{array}{ccc} \mathscr{F} & \xrightarrow{\mathrm{id}_{\mathscr{F}}} & \mathscr{F} \\ {\scriptstyle \mathrm{id}_{\mathscr{F}}}\downarrow & & \downarrow{\scriptstyle \varphi} \\ \mathscr{F} & \xrightarrow{\varphi} & \mathscr{G} \end{array}$$

which is a fiber product by Section 2.6, Lemma 2. By Theorem 1, this is a fiber product argumentwise for each $A \in \mathscr{A}$. Then again by Section 2.6, Lemma 2 we get that φA is a monomorphism for all $A \in \mathscr{A}$.

COROLLARY 4. *Let $\mathscr{A}$ be a diagram scheme and $\mathscr{C}$ be a finitely complete, locally small category. Then* Funct$(\mathscr{A}, \mathscr{C})$ *is locally small.*

Proof. By Lemma 2, monomorphisms in Funct$(\mathscr{A}, \mathscr{C})$ are formed argumentwise. Similarly, the equivalence of monomorphisms holds argumentwise. In fact, if two natural monomorphisms in Funct$(\mathscr{A}, \mathscr{C})$ are equivalent for each argument $A \in \mathscr{A}$, then the family of uniquely determined isomorphisms of the equivalences defines a natural iso-morphism which induces the equivalence between the two given natural monomorphisms. Now since $\mathscr{A}$ is a small category and since $\mathscr{C}$ is locally small, there can only be a set of subobjects for an object in Funct$(\mathscr{A}, \mathscr{C})$.

COROLLARY 5. *Let*

$$
\begin{array}{ccc}
P & \xrightarrow{p_1} & A \\
{\scriptstyle p_2}\downarrow & & \downarrow{\scriptstyle f} \\
B & \xrightarrow{g} & C
\end{array}
$$

be a fiber product and let f be a monomorphism. Then p_2 is also a mono-morphism.

Proof. The commutative diagram

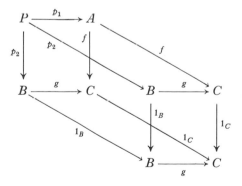

is a morphism between two fiber products. Since f, 1_C, and 1_B are monomorphisms, the corresponding natural transformation is a mono-morphism, thus by Corollary 2 and Section 2.6, Corollary 5 the morphism p_2 is also.

LEMMA 3.

(a) *Right adjoint functors preserve monomorphisms. Left adjoint functors preserve epimorphisms.*

(b) *Let* $\mathscr{F}, \mathscr{G} : \mathscr{A} \to \mathscr{C}$ *be diagrams in* $\mathscr{C}$ *and let* $\varphi : \mathscr{F} \to \mathscr{G}$ *be a morphism of diagrams with monomorphisms* $\varphi A : \mathscr{F} A \to \mathscr{G} A$. *If* $\varprojlim \varphi : \varprojlim \mathscr{F} \to \varprojlim \mathscr{G}$ *exists, then* $\varprojlim \varphi$ *is a monomorphism.*

Proof. (a) is implied by Theorem 3 and Section 2.6, Corollary 5. (b) is implied by Lemma 2, Corollary 2, and Section 2.6, Lemma 2.

THEOREM 4 (Kan). *Let* $\mathscr{A}$ *and* $\mathscr{B}$ *be small categories and let* $\mathscr{C}$ *be a cocomplete category. Let* $\mathscr{F} : \mathscr{B} \to \mathscr{A}$ *be a functor. Then* Funct($\mathscr{F}, \mathscr{C}$) : Funct($\mathscr{A}, \mathscr{C}$) $\to$ Funct($\mathscr{B}, \mathscr{C}$) *has a left adjoint functor.*

Proof. First we introduce the following small category. Let $A \in \mathscr{A}$. Then define $[\mathscr{F}, A]$ with the objects (B, f) with $B \in \mathscr{B}$ and $f : \mathscr{F} B \to A$ in $\mathscr{A}$. A morphism in $[\mathscr{F}, A]$ is a triple $(f, f', u) : (B, f) \to (B', f')$ with $u : B \to B'$ and $f' \mathscr{F} u = f$. A functor $\mathscr{V}(A) : [\mathscr{F}, A] \to \mathscr{B}$ is defined by $\mathscr{V}(A)(B, f) = B$ and $\mathscr{V}(A)(f, f', u) = u$.

Let $g : A \to A'$ be given. We define a functor $[\mathscr{F}, g] : [\mathscr{F}, A] \to [\mathscr{F}, A']$ by $[\mathscr{F}, g](B, f) = (B, gf)$ and $[\mathscr{F}, g](f, f', u) = (gf, gf', u)$. Thus in particular, $\mathscr{V}(A) = \mathscr{V}(A')[\mathscr{F}, g]$.

Define a functor $\mathscr{G} : $ Funct($\mathscr{B}, \mathscr{C}$) $\to$ Funct($\mathscr{A}, \mathscr{C}$) by $\mathscr{G}(\mathscr{H})(A) = \varinjlim \mathscr{H} \mathscr{V}(A)$, $\mathscr{G}(\mathscr{H})(g) = \varinjlim[\mathscr{F}, g] : \varinjlim \mathscr{H} \mathscr{V}(A) \to \varinjlim \mathscr{H} \mathscr{V}(A')$, and $\mathscr{G}(\sigma)(A) = \varinjlim(\sigma \mathscr{V}(A))$. We want to show that $\mathscr{G}$ is left adjoint to Funct($\mathscr{F}, \mathscr{C}$). Let $\mathscr{H} \in$ Funct($\mathscr{B}, \mathscr{C}$) and $\mathscr{L} \in$ Funct($\mathscr{A}, \mathscr{C}$) be given. We show

$$\mathrm{Mor}_f(\mathscr{G}(\mathscr{H}), \mathscr{L}) \cong \mathrm{Mor}_f(\mathscr{H}, \mathscr{L} \mathscr{F})$$

If $\varphi : \mathscr{G}(\mathscr{H}) \to \mathscr{L}$ is a natural transformation, then

$$\varphi(\mathscr{F} B) : \varinjlim \mathscr{H} \mathscr{V}(\mathscr{F} B) \to \mathscr{L} \mathscr{F} B.$$

Since $(B, 1_{\mathscr{F} B}) \in [\mathscr{F}, \mathscr{F} B]$, there is an injection $i : \mathscr{H} B \to \varinjlim \mathscr{H} \mathscr{V}(\mathscr{F} B)$. Set $\psi(B) = \varphi(\mathscr{F} B)i$. This defines a family of morphisms

$$\psi(B) : \mathscr{H} B \to \mathscr{L} \mathscr{F} B.$$

Let $h : B \to B'$ be a morphism in B. Then we get $[\mathscr{F}, \mathscr{F} h] : [\mathscr{F}, \mathscr{F} B] \to [\mathscr{F}, \mathscr{F} B']$, thus $\varinjlim[\mathscr{F}, \mathscr{F} h] : \varinjlim \mathscr{H} \mathscr{V}(\mathscr{F} B) \to \varinjlim \mathscr{H} \mathscr{V}(\mathscr{F} B')$. Since

φ is a natural transformation and because of the properties of the colimit, the diagram

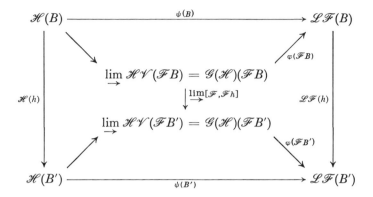

is commutative and thus ψ is a natural transformation.

Let $\psi : \mathscr{H} \to \mathscr{L}\mathscr{F}$ be given. Let $A \in \mathscr{A}$. To each pair $(B, f) \in [\mathscr{F}, A]$ we get a morphism

$$\mathscr{H}(B) \xrightarrow{\psi(B)} \mathscr{L}\mathscr{F}(B) \xrightarrow{\mathscr{L}(f)} \mathscr{L}(A)$$

If $(f, f', u) \subset [\mathscr{F}, A]$, then

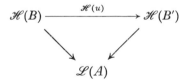

is commutative; thus there is exactly one morphism $\varphi(A) : \varinjlim \mathscr{H}\mathscr{V}(A) \to \mathscr{L}(A)$ such that the diagram

$$
\begin{array}{ccc}
\mathscr{H}B & \xrightarrow{\psi(B)} & \mathscr{L}\mathscr{F}(B) \\
i \downarrow & & \downarrow \mathscr{L}(f) \\
\varinjlim \mathscr{H}\mathscr{V}(A) & \xrightarrow{\varphi(A)} & \mathscr{L}(A)
\end{array}
$$

is commutative. Because of the properties of the colimit, the following diagram with $g : A \to A'$ is also commutative

$$\mathcal{H}(B) \xrightarrow{\psi(B)} \mathcal{L}\mathcal{F}B$$

$$i\downarrow \qquad\qquad \downarrow \mathcal{L}(f)$$

$$\varinjlim \mathcal{H}\mathcal{V}(A) \xrightarrow{\varphi(A)} \mathcal{L}(A)$$

$$\varinjlim[\mathcal{F},g]\downarrow \qquad\qquad \downarrow \mathcal{L}(g)$$

$$\varinjlim \mathcal{H}\mathcal{V}(A') \xrightarrow{\varphi(A')} \mathcal{L}(A')$$

Thus φ is a natural transformation. Because of the uniqueness of φ the application $\varphi \mapsto \psi \mapsto \varphi$ is the identity. Furthermore, one checks easily that $\psi \mapsto \varphi \mapsto \psi$ is the identity. Thus, $\mathrm{Mor}(\mathcal{G}(\mathcal{H}), \mathcal{L}) \cong \mathrm{Mor}(\mathcal{H}, \mathcal{L}\mathcal{F})$.

The given applications imply that this isomorphism is natural in $\mathcal{H}$ and $\mathcal{L}$. This proves the theorem.

COROLLARY 6. *Let $\mathcal{C}$ be cocomplete and $\mathcal{F} : \mathcal{B} \to \mathcal{A}$ be a functor of small categories. Then* $\mathrm{Funct}(\mathcal{F}, \mathcal{C}) : \mathrm{Funct}(\mathcal{A}, \mathcal{C}) \to \mathrm{Funct}(\mathcal{B}, \mathcal{C})$ *preserves limits and colimits.*

Proof. $\mathrm{Funct}(\mathcal{F}, \mathcal{C})$ is a right adjoint functor; consequently it preserves limits. Since in $\mathrm{Funct}(\mathcal{A}, \mathcal{C})$ and in $\mathrm{Funct}(\mathcal{B}, \mathcal{C})$ there exist colimits that are formed argumentwise (Theorem 2), we get for a diagram $\mathcal{H} : \mathcal{D} \to \mathrm{Funct}(\mathcal{A}, \mathcal{C})$

$$\varinjlim \mathrm{Funct}(\mathcal{F}, \mathcal{C})\, \mathcal{H}(B) = \varinjlim \mathcal{H}\mathcal{F}(B) = \mathrm{Funct}(\mathcal{F}, \mathcal{C}) \varinjlim \mathcal{H}(B)$$

COROLLARY 7. *Let $\mathcal{A}$ and $\mathcal{B}$ be small categories and $\mathcal{C}$ a complete category. Let $\mathcal{F} : \mathcal{B} \to \mathcal{A}$ be a functor. Then*

$$\mathrm{Funct}(\mathcal{F}, \mathcal{C}) : \mathrm{Funct}(\mathcal{A}, \mathcal{C}) \to \mathrm{Funct}(\mathcal{B}, \mathcal{C})$$

has a right adjoint functor.

Proof. Dualize $\mathcal{A}$, $\mathcal{B}$, and $\mathcal{C}$.

PROPOSITION 1. *Let $\mathcal{A}$ and $\mathcal{B}$ be small categories and $\mathcal{C}$ be an arbitrary category. Let $\mathcal{F} : \mathcal{B} \to \mathcal{A}$ be a functor, which has a right adjoint functor. Then* $\mathrm{Funct}(\mathcal{F}, \mathcal{C}) : \mathrm{Funct}(\mathcal{A}, \mathcal{C}) \to \mathrm{Funct}(\mathcal{B}, \mathcal{C})$ *has a left adjoint functor.*

Proof. Let $\mathcal{G} : \mathcal{A} \to \mathcal{B}$ be right adjoint to $\mathcal{F}$ and let $\Phi : \mathrm{Id}_{\mathcal{B}} \to \mathcal{G}\mathcal{F}$ and $\Psi : \mathcal{F}\mathcal{G} \to \mathrm{Id}_{\mathcal{A}}$ with $(\mathcal{G}\Psi)(\Phi\mathcal{G}) = \mathrm{id}_{\mathcal{G}}$ and $(\Psi\mathcal{F})(\mathcal{F}\Phi) = \mathrm{id}_{\mathcal{F}}$ be given.

Then we have

$$\text{Funct}(\Phi, \mathscr{C}) : \text{Funct}(\text{Id}_{\mathscr{B}}, \mathscr{C}) \to \text{Funct}(\mathscr{G}\mathscr{F}, \mathscr{C})$$

and

$$\text{Funct}(\Psi, \mathscr{C}) : \text{Funct}(\mathscr{F}\mathscr{G}, \mathscr{C}) \to \text{Funct}(\text{Id}_{\mathscr{A}}, \mathscr{C})$$

with

$$(\text{Funct}(\Psi, \mathscr{C})\,\text{Funct}(\mathscr{G}, \mathscr{C}))(\text{Funct}(\mathscr{G}, \mathscr{C})\,\text{Funct}(\Phi, \mathscr{C})) = \text{id}_{\text{Funct}(\mathscr{G}, \mathscr{C})}$$

$$(\text{Funct}(\mathscr{F}, \mathscr{C})\,\text{Funct}(\Psi, \mathscr{C}))(\text{Funct}(\Phi, \mathscr{C})\,\text{Funct}(\mathscr{F}, \mathscr{C})) = \text{id}_{\text{Funct}(\mathscr{F}, \mathscr{C})}$$

2.8   Constructions with Limits

We want to investigate the behavior of the notions intersection and union introduced in Chapter 1 with respect to limits.

PROPOSITION 1. *Let $\mathscr{C}$ be a category with fiber products. Then $\mathscr{C}$ is a category with finite intersections. If $\mathscr{C}$ is a category with finite intersections and finite products, then $\mathscr{C}$ is finitely complete.*

Proof.   Let $f : A \to C$ and $g : B \to C$ be subobjects of C. We form the fiber product

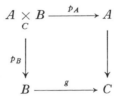

By Section 2.7, Corollary 5, the morphism p_A is a monomorphism. Thus, $fp_A : A \underset{C}{\times} B \to C$ is equivalent to a subobject of C and hence up to equivalence the intersection of A and B.

Given the morphisms $f, g : A \to B$. As in Section 2.6, Corollary 1 the difference kernel of f and g is the fiber product of $(1_A, f) : A \to A \times B$ and $(1_A, g) : A \to A \times B$. Both morphisms are sections with the retraction p_A and hence monomorphisms. This means that we may replace the fiber product by the intersection of the corresponding subobjects. Consequently $\mathscr{C}$ has difference kernels. By Section 2.6, Proposition 2, we get that $\mathscr{C}$ is finitely complete.

PROPOSITION 2. *Let $\mathscr{C}$ be a category with fiber products. Then there exist counterimages in $\mathscr{C}$.*

Proof. Let $f : A \rightarrow C$ be a morphism and $g : B \rightarrow C$ be a subobject of C. Then the fiber product of A and B over C is a counterimage of B under f (up to equivalence of monomorphisms), for $p_A : A \underset{C}{\times} B \rightarrow A$ is a monomorphism by Section 2.7, Corollary 5.

Since we now may interpret counterimages and intersections as limits, we get again the commutativity of counterimages with intersections as in Section 1.13, Theorem 1. In fact, arbitrary intersections are the limit over all occurring monomorphisms.

LEMMA 1. *Let $\mathscr{C}$ be a category with difference kernels and intersections. Given $f, g, h : A \rightarrow B$. Then $\mathrm{Ker}(f, g) \cap \mathrm{Ker}(g, h) \subseteq \mathrm{Ker}(f, h)$.*

Proof. Consider the commutative diagram

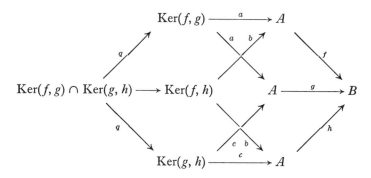

Then $aq = cq'$ implies $faq = gaq = gcq' = hcq' = haq$. Thus aq may be factored uniquely through $\mathrm{Ker}(f, h)$. Since aq is a monomorphism, we get $\mathrm{Ker}(f, g) \cap \mathrm{Ker}(g, h) \subseteq \mathrm{Ker}(f, h)$.

LEMMA 2. *Let $\mathscr{C}$ be a category with fiber products and images. Let $C \subseteq A$, $D \subseteq B$, and $f : A \rightarrow B$ be given. Let $g : C \rightarrow f(C)$ be the morphism induced by f. Then we have $g^{-1}(f(C) \cap D) = C \cap f^{-1}(D)$.*

Proof. In the diagram

$$C \cap f^{-1}(f(C) \cap D) \longrightarrow f^{-1}(f(C) \cap D) \longrightarrow f(C) \cap D$$
$$\downarrow \qquad\qquad\qquad \downarrow \qquad\qquad\qquad \downarrow$$
$$C \longrightarrow A \overset{f}{\longrightarrow} B$$

the outer rectangle is a fiber product because the two inner ones are.

Hence

$$C \cap f^{-1}(f(C) \cap D) \longrightarrow f(C) \cap D$$
$$\downarrow \qquad\qquad \downarrow$$
$$C \xrightarrow{\quad g \quad} f(C)$$

is a fiber product. Consequently

$$C \cap f^{-1}(D) = C \cap f^{-1}f(C) \cap f^{-1}(D)$$
$$= C \cap f^{-1}(f(C) \cap D) = g^{-1}(f(C) \cap D)$$

We shall use these lemmas in Chapter 4.

In $\mathbf{S}$ the difference cokernel $g : B \to C$ of two morphisms h_0, h_1 : $X \to B$ is a set of equivalence classes in B. In the corresponding kernel pair f_0, $f_1 : A \to B$ the set A consists of the pairs of elements in B which are equivalent, or more precisely of the graph R of the equivalence relation in $B \times B$. f_0 and f_1 are, respectively, the projections

$$R \ni (a, b) \mapsto a \in B \qquad \text{and} \qquad R \ni (a, b) \mapsto b \in B$$

In general we define an *equivalence relation* in a category $\mathscr{C}$ as a pair of morphisms f_0, $f_1 : A \to B$ such that for all $X \in \mathscr{C}$, the image of the map

$$(\mathrm{Mor}_\mathscr{C}(X, f_0), \mathrm{Mor}_\mathscr{C}(X, f_1)) : \mathrm{Mor}_\mathscr{C}(X, A) \to \mathrm{Mor}_\mathscr{C}(X, B) \times \mathrm{Mor}_\mathscr{C}(X, B)$$

is an equivalence relation for the set $\mathrm{Mor}_\mathscr{C}(X, B)$. If $(\mathrm{Mor}_\mathscr{C}(X, f_0), \mathrm{Mor}_\mathscr{C}(X, f_1))$ is injective for all $X \in \mathscr{C}$, then the equivalence relation is called a *monomorphic equivalence relation*.

If $\mathscr{C}$ has products, then we may use a morphism $(f_0, f_1) : A \to B \times B$ instead of the pair f_0, $f_1 : A \to B$, because of

$$\mathrm{Mor}_\mathscr{C}(X, B) \times \mathrm{Mor}_\mathscr{C}(X, B) \simeq \mathrm{Mor}_\mathscr{C}(X, B \times B)$$

The pair f_0, $f_1 : A \to B$ is a monomorphic equivalence relation if and only if it is an equivalence relation and the morphism (f_0, f_1) is a mono-morphism.

Let f_0, $f_1 : A \to B$ be a kernel pair of a morphism $p : B \to C$. Let

$$D \xrightarrow{p_1} A$$
$$p_0 \downarrow \qquad \downarrow f_0 \qquad\qquad (1)$$
$$A \xrightarrow{f_1} B$$

be a fiber product. Then we get a commutative diagram

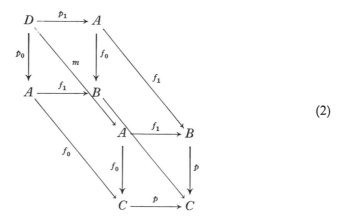

(2)

where m is uniquely determined by $f_0 p_0 : D \to B$ and $f_1 p_1 : D \to B$ with $p f_0 p_0 = p f_1 p_0 = p f_0 p_1 = p f_1 p_1$. Thus

$$f_0 m = f_0 p_0 ; \qquad f_1 m = f_1 p_1 \tag{3}$$

Furthermore, by Section 2.6, Lemma 3, all quadrangles of the diagram are fiber products. In particular

$$D \overset{m}{\underset{p_0}{\rightrightarrows}} A \overset{f_0}{\longrightarrow} B$$

and

$$D \overset{m}{\underset{p_1}{\rightrightarrows}} A \overset{f_1}{\longrightarrow} B$$

are kernel pairs. The diagrams

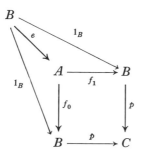   and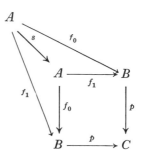

determine in a unique way morphisms $e : B \to A$ and $s : A \to A$ with

$$f_0 e = f_1 e = 1_B \tag{4}$$

and with

$$f_0 s = f_1, \qquad f_1 s = f_0, \qquad \text{and} \qquad s^2 = 1_A \tag{5}$$

This follows from $f_0 s^2 = f_0$ and $f_1 s^2 = f_1$ because the lower squares are fiber products.

Thus we have obtained a diagram

$$D \underset{\underset{p_1}{\longrightarrow}}{\overset{\overset{p_0}{\longrightarrow}}{\overset{m}{\longrightarrow}}} A \underset{\underset{s}{\cup}}{\overset{e}{\longleftarrow}} \underset{\underset{f_1}{\longrightarrow}}{\overset{f_0}{\longrightarrow}} B$$

with the properties (1), (3), (4), and (5). Such a diagram is called a *groupoid* or *preequivalence relation*.

The same construction works also if $f_0, f_1 : A \to B$ is not a kernel pair but a monomorphic equivalence relation. In this case one carries out the construction in **S** for

$$\text{Mor}_\mathscr{C}(X, f_0), \text{Mor}_\mathscr{C}(X, f_1) : \text{Mor}_\mathscr{C}(X, A) \to \text{Mor}_\mathscr{C}(X, B)$$

for all $X \in \mathscr{C}$. In fact, there is a difference cokernel to each equivalence relation in **S**, namely the set of equivalence classes. Since we consider a monomorphic equivalence relation, $\text{Mor}_\mathscr{C}(X, f_0)$, $\text{Mor}_\mathscr{C}(X, f_1)$ is a kernel pair for the difference cokernel. Then it is easy to verify that m_X, e_X, s_X depend naturally on X together with the conditions (2), (3), and (4), so that this defines again a groupoid by the Yoneda lemma. Thus we get part (a) of the following lemma.

LEMMA 3.

(a) *Each kernel pair and each monomorphic equivalence relation is a preequivalence relation.*

(b) *Each preequivalence relation with a monomorphism $(f_0, f_1) : A \to B \times B$ is an equivalence relation.*

Proof. (b) We may identify $\text{Mor}(X, A)$ with the image of $(\text{Mor}(X, f_0), \text{Mor}(X, f_1))$ in $\text{Mor}(X, B \times B) \simeq \text{Mor}(X, B) \times \text{Mor}(X, B)$. For each $b \in \text{Mor}(X, B)$ the pair (b, b) is in $\text{Mor}(X, A)$, since if $eb = (b', b'')$, then $f_0(b', b'') = f_0 eb = b$ and $f_1(b', b'') = f_1 eb = b$, hence $eb = (b, b)$. If $(b, b') \in \text{Mor}(X, A)$, then (b', b) in $\text{Mor}(X, A)$. In fact, $f_0 s(b, b') = f_1(b, b') = b'$ and $f_1 s(b, b') = f_0(b, b') = b$, hence $s(b, b') = (b', b)$.

Finally, with (b, b') and (b', b'') in $\mathrm{Mor}(X, A)$, also (b, b'') in $\mathrm{Mor}(X, A)$. In fact,

$$((b, b'), (b', b'')) \in \mathrm{Mor}(X, D) \simeq \mathrm{Mor}(X, A) \underset{\mathrm{Mor}(X,B)}{\times} \mathrm{Mor}(X, A)$$

holds because $f_0 p_1((b, b'), (b', b'')) = f_0(b', b'') = b'$ and

$$f_1 p_0((b, b'), (b', b'')) = f_1(b, b') = b'.$$

But then $f_0 m((b, b'), (b', b'')) = f_0 p_0((b, b'), (b', b'')) = f_0(b, b') = b$ and $f_1 m((b, b'), (b', b'')) = f_1 p_1((b, b'), (b', b'')) = f_1(b', b'') = b''$, and thus $m((b, b'), (b', b'')) = (b, b'') \in \mathrm{Mor}(X, A)$.

LEMMA 4. *Let* $f_0, f_1 : A \to B$ *be a monomorphic equivalence relation. For the corresponding groupoid, the following diagrams are commutative:*

$$
\begin{array}{ccc}
E & \xrightarrow{\ (1,m)\ } & D \\
{\scriptstyle (m,1)}\downarrow & & \downarrow{\scriptstyle m} \\
D & \xrightarrow{\ m\ } & A
\end{array}
\qquad (i)
$$

$$
\begin{array}{ccc}
A \xrightarrow{\ (ef_0,1_A)\ } D & \qquad & A \xrightarrow{\ (1_A,ef_1)\ } D \\
{\scriptstyle 1_A}\searrow \quad \downarrow{\scriptstyle m} & & {\scriptstyle 1_A}\searrow \quad \downarrow{\scriptstyle m} \\
\qquad A & & \qquad A
\end{array}
\qquad (ii)
$$

$$
\begin{array}{ccccccc}
A & \xrightarrow{\ (1_A,s)\ } & D & \qquad & A & \xrightarrow{\ (s,1_A)\ } & D \\
{\scriptstyle f_0}\downarrow & & \downarrow{\scriptstyle m} & & {\scriptstyle f_1}\downarrow & & \downarrow{\scriptstyle m} \\
B & \xrightarrow{\ e\ } & A & & B & \xrightarrow{\ e\ } & A
\end{array}
\qquad (iii)
$$

Proof. First we define E, $(1, m)$, and $(m, 1)$. Let all squares of the commutative diagram be fiber products.

$$
\begin{array}{ccccc}
E & \xrightarrow{\ q_1\ } & D & \xrightarrow{\ p_1\ } & A \\
{\scriptstyle q_0}\downarrow & & \downarrow{\scriptstyle p_0} & & \downarrow{\scriptstyle f_0} \\
D & \xrightarrow{\ p_1\ } & A & \xrightarrow{\ f_1\ } & B \\
{\scriptstyle p_0}\downarrow & & \downarrow{\scriptstyle f_0} & & \\
A & \xrightarrow{\ f_1\ } & B & &
\end{array}
$$

Then also each rectangle is a fiber product. Define $(1, m)$ by the commutative diagram

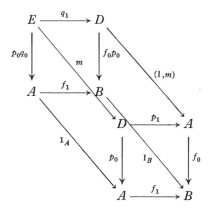

Correspondingly, define $(m, 1)$ by

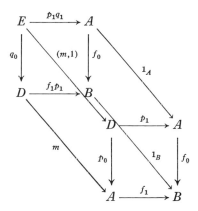

then by (2)

$$f_0 m(1, m) = f_0 p_0(1, m) \quad f_0 p_0 q_0 = f_0 m q_0 = f_0 p_0(m, 1) = f_0 m(m, 1)$$

and

$$f_1 m(1, m) = f_1 p_1(1, m) = f_1 m q_1 = f_1 p_1 q_1 = f_1 p_1(m, 1) = f_1 m(m, 1)$$

Thus $(f_0, f_1) \, m(1, m) = (f_0, f_1) \, m(m, 1)$. Since (f_0, f_1) is a monomorphism, the first diagram in Lemma 4 is commutative. For (ii) we use the commutative diagrams

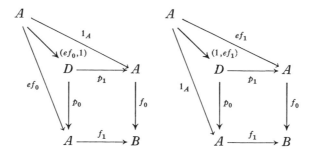

Then

$$f_0 m(ef_0, 1) = f_0 p_0(ef_0, 1) = f_0 ef_0 = f_0 \quad \text{and} \quad f_1 m(ef_0, 1) = f_1 p_1(ef_0 1) = f_1,$$

hence $(f_0, f_1) m(ef_0, 1) = (f_0, f_1)$ implies again $m(ef_0, 1) = 1_A$. Correspondingly, one shows $m(1, ef_1) = 1_A$.

For (iii) we use the commutative diagrams

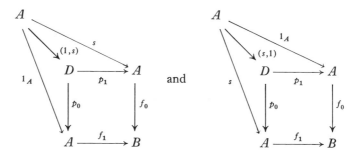

Then $f_0 m(1, s) = f_0 p_0(1, s) = f_0 = f_0 ef_0$ and $f_1 m(1, s) = f_1 p_1(1, s) = f_1 s = f_0 = f_1 ef_0$. Because of $(f_0, f_1) m(1, s) = (f_0 f_1) ef_0$, we also get $m(1, s) = ef_0$. Again one shows $m(s, 1) = ef_1$ correspondingly.

Thus for a monomorphic equivalence relation there is a partially defined composition (on $D \subseteq A \times A$) on A which is associative (i), with neutral elements (ii), and invertible (iii). This is a generalization of Section 1.1, Example 16 to arbitrary categories. Compositions, that is, morphisms from a product $A \times A$ into an object A which have these and similar properties will be dealt with in more detail in Chapter 3. It is because of the properties proved in Lemma 4, that we use the name groupoid.

2.9   The Adjoint Functor Theorem

PROPOSITION 1. *Let $\mathscr{A}$ be a small category. Each functor $\mathscr{F} \in \mathrm{Funct}(\mathscr{A}, \mathscr{S})$ is a colimit of the representable functors over $\mathscr{F}$.*

Proof.   We consider the following category: The objects are the representable functors over $\mathscr{F}$, that is, the pairs (h^A, φ) with a natural transformation $\varphi : h^A \to \mathscr{F}$. The morphisms are commutative diagrams

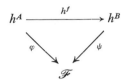

where $f : B \to A$. There is a forgetful functor $(h^A, \varphi) \mapsto h^A$, $(h^f, \varphi, \psi) \mapsto h^f$ from this category into $\mathrm{Funct}(\mathscr{A}, \mathbf{S})$, which we consider as a diagram. This diagram has a colimit by Section 2.7, Theorem 1, which is formed argumentwise and which is denoted by $\varinjlim h^A$. Furthermore, each $\varphi : h^A \to \mathscr{F}$ may be factored through $\varinjlim \overline{h^A}$ as $h^A \to \varinjlim h^A \to \mathscr{F}$. We show that the morphism $\tau(B) : \varinjlim \overline{h^A}(B) \to \mathscr{F}(B)$ is bijective for each $B \in \mathscr{A}$.

Let $x \in \mathscr{F}(B)$. Then by the Yoneda lemma there is an $h^x : h^B \to \mathscr{F}$ with $h^x(1_B) = x$. Thus $\tau(B)$ is surjective.

Let $u, v \in \varinjlim h^A(B)$ with $\tau(B)(u) = \tau(B)(v)$. Then there are $C, D \in \mathscr{A}$ and $y \in h^C(B)$ and $z \in h^D(B)$ with $y \mapsto u$ under $f : h^C(B) \to \varinjlim h^A(B)$ and $z \mapsto v$ under $g : h^D(B) \to \varinjlim h^A(B)$ by the construction of the colimit in $\mathbf{S}$. Let $\varphi : h^C \to \mathscr{F}$ and $\psi : h^D \to \mathscr{F}$ be the corresponding morphisms into $\mathscr{F}$. Then $\varphi(B)(y) = \psi(B)(z)$. Thus by the Yoneda lemma, we get $\varphi h^y = \psi h^z : h^B \to \mathscr{F}$, that is, h^B is over $\mathscr{F}$ with this morphism, and we get $f h^y(B)(1_B) = u$ and $g h^z(B)(1_B) = v$. Hence, $u = v$ and $\tau(B)$ is injective.

If there are no natural transformations $\varphi : h^A \to \mathscr{F}$, then $\mathscr{F}(A) = \varnothing$ for all $A \in \mathscr{C}$. But we also have $\varinjlim h^A(B) = \varnothing$ as a colimit over an empty diagram. Thus we have also in this case $\mathscr{F} \cong \varinjlim h^A$.

COROLLARY 1.   *Let $\mathscr{A}$ be a small, finitely complete, artinian category. Let $\mathscr{F} : \mathscr{A} \to \mathbf{S}$ be a covariant functor which preserves finite limits. Then $\mathscr{F}$ is a direct limit of representable subfunctors.*

Proof.   We show that $\varphi : h^A \to \mathscr{F}$ may be factored through a representable subfunctor of $\mathscr{F}$. Let $f : B \to A$ be minimal in the set of subobjects of A such that there exists a commutative diagram

Then ψ is a natural transformation. It is sufficient to show that $\psi(C) : h^B(C) \to \mathscr{F}(C)$ is injective for all $C \in \mathscr{A}$. Let x, $y \in h^B(C)$ be given with $\psi(C)(x) = \psi(C)(y)$. Let D be a difference kernel of (x, y). Since $\mathscr{F}$ preserves difference kernels, there is a commutative diagram

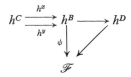

by the Yoneda lemma. Since D is a subobject of A up to equivalence of monomorphisms and because of the minimality of B, we get $D \simeq B$ thus $x = y$. This implies that $\psi : h^B \to \mathscr{F}$ is a subfunctor and that the element which corresponds to $\varphi : h^A \to \mathscr{F}$ in $\mathscr{F}(A)$ is in the image of $\psi(A)$. Consequently $\varinjlim h^B = \mathscr{F}$ if one admits for the h^B only representable subfunctors of $\mathscr{F}$ and if the colimit is directed.

To prove that this colimit is directed let (h^A, φ) and (h^B, ψ) be representable subfunctors of F. Since $\mathscr{F}(A \times B) \simeq \mathscr{F}(A) \times \mathscr{F}(B)$, we get

$$\mathrm{Mor}_f(h^{A \times B}, \mathscr{F}) \simeq \mathrm{Mor}_f(h^A, \mathscr{F}) \times \mathrm{Mor}_f(h^B, \mathscr{F})$$

Thus there is exactly one $\rho : h^{A \times B} \to \mathscr{F}$, such that

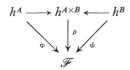

is commutative. ρ may be factored through a representable subfunctor h^C of $\mathscr{F}$.

Let $\mathscr{F} : \mathscr{C} \to \mathscr{D}$ be a functor. Let $D \in \mathscr{D}$. A set $\mathfrak{L}_D$ of objects in $\mathscr{C}$ is called a *solution set* of D with respect to $\mathscr{F}$ if to each $C \in \mathscr{C}$ and to each morphism $D \to \mathscr{F}C$ there is an object $C' \in \mathfrak{L}_D$ and morphisms $f : C' \to C$ and $D \to \mathscr{F}C'$ such that the diagram is commutative. If each $D \in \mathscr{D}$ has a solution set, then we say that $\mathscr{F}$ has solution sets.

COROLLARY 2.   *Let $\mathscr{C}$ be a finitely complete category. Let $\mathscr{F} : \mathscr{C} \to \mathbf{S}$ be a functor which preserves finite limits. Assume that there is a solution set for the one point set $\{\varnothing\} = E$ with respect to $\mathscr{F}$. Then $\mathscr{F}$ is a colimit of representable functors.*

Proof.   Let $\mathfrak{L} = \mathfrak{L}_E$ be the solution set of E. Let $\mathscr{L}$ be the full subcategory of $\mathscr{C}$ with the set of objects $\mathfrak{L}$. By Proposition 1, the restriction of $\mathscr{F}$ to $\mathscr{L}$ is a colimit of representable functors on $\mathscr{L}$, that is $\varinjlim h^A(B) = \mathscr{F}(B)$ for $A, B \in \mathscr{L}$. We want to prove that this equation holds for all $B \in \mathscr{C}$ where the left side is argumentwise a colimit.

First we reformulate the condition about the solution set. For each $C \in \mathscr{C}$ and for each $x \in \mathscr{F}(C)$, there is an $A \in \mathscr{L}$ and an $f : A \to C$ and a $y \in \mathscr{F}A$ with $\mathscr{F}f(y) = x$, expressed differently: for each $C \in \mathscr{C}$ and for each $h^x : h^C \to \mathscr{F}$, there is an $A \in \mathscr{L}$ and an $f : A \to C$ and an $h^y : h^A \to \mathscr{F}$ with $h^x = h^y h^f$. This is a consequence of the Yoneda lemma.

Since all the h^A are over $\mathscr{F}$ and since $\varinjlim h^A(-)$ is a functor, we get a natural transformation $\tau : \varinjlim h^A(-) \to \mathscr{F}$ through which the natural transformations $h^A \to \mathscr{F}$ may be factored. Furthermore, $\tau(B)$ is an isomorphism for all $B \in \mathscr{L}$. We want to prove this for all $B \in \mathscr{C}$. Let $x \in \mathscr{F}B$. Then there is an $A' \in \mathscr{L}$, a morphism $A' \to B$, and a $y \in \mathscr{F}A'$ which is mapped onto x by $\mathscr{F}A' \to \mathscr{F}B$. Since the diagram

$$\begin{array}{ccc} \varinjlim h^A(A') & \longrightarrow & \varinjlim h^A(B) \\ \downarrow & & \downarrow \\ \mathscr{F}A' & \longrightarrow & \mathscr{F}B \end{array}$$

is commutative and since $\varinjlim h^A(A') = \mathscr{F}A'$, the morphism $\varinjlim h^A(B) \to \mathscr{F}B$ is an epimorphism.

Let $x, y \in \varinjlim h^A(B)$ be such that they have the same image in $\mathscr{F}B$. Then there are $A', A'' \in \mathscr{L}$ with $h^{A'}(B) \ni u \mapsto x \in \varinjlim h^A(B)$ and $h^{A''}(B) \ni v \mapsto y \in \varinjlim h^A(B)$ and the images of u and v in $\mathscr{F}B$ coincide. Thus,

$$\begin{array}{ccc} h^B & \xrightarrow{\ h^u\ } & h^{A'} \\ {\scriptstyle h^v}\downarrow & & \downarrow \\ h^{A''} & \longrightarrow & \mathscr{F} \end{array}$$

is commutative. Let C be a fiber product of $u : A' \to B$ and $v : A'' \to B$. Then $\mathscr{F}C$ is a fiber product of $\mathscr{F}u$ and $\mathscr{F}v$. Consequently, the diagram may be completed in two steps to the commutative diagram

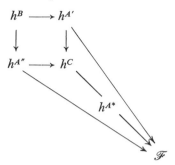

where $h^{A^*} \to \mathscr{F}$ is the factorization of $h^C \to \mathscr{F}$ with $A^* \in \mathscr{L}$, which exists by the solution set condition. Thus the images of u and v are already equal in $h^{A^*}(B)$ and consequently also in $\varinjlim h^A(B)$. Hence, $\tau(B)$ is an isomorphism.

We observe that $\mathscr{F}C = \varnothing$ for all $C \in \mathscr{C}$ if and only if the solution set for E is empty. In fact, the colimit over an empty diagram is an initial object. If $\mathscr{C}$ is empty, then the assertion of the corollary is empty, since then $\mathscr{F}$ is a colimit over an empty diagram of representable functors, that is, an initial object in $\text{Funct}(\mathscr{C}, \mathbf{S})$.

COROLLARY 3 (Kan). *Let $\mathscr{A}$ be a small category, $\mathscr{C}$ a cocomplete category, and $\mathscr{F} : \mathscr{A} \to \mathscr{C}$ a functor. Then there is a functor*

$$\mathscr{G} : \text{Funct}(\mathscr{A}^0, \mathbf{S}) \to \mathscr{C}$$

which is uniquely determined up to an isomorphism such that

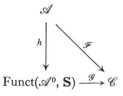

is commutative up to an isomorphism, that is, $\mathscr{G}h \cong \mathscr{F}$, and such that $\mathscr{G}$ preserves colimits. $\mathscr{G}$ is left adjoint to the functor

$$\text{Mor}_{\mathscr{C}}(\mathscr{F}-, -) : \mathscr{C} \to \text{Funct}(\mathscr{A}^0, \mathbf{S})$$

with $\text{Mor}_{\mathscr{C}}(\mathscr{F}-, -)(C)(A) = \text{Mor}_{\mathscr{C}}(\mathscr{F}A, C)$ and an analogous formula for the morphisms.

Proof. By the required properties of $\mathscr{G}$ we get for a functor $\mathscr{H} \in \mathrm{Funct}(\mathscr{A}^0, \mathbf{S})$ with $\mathscr{H} = \varinjlim h_A$ (by Proposition 1)

$$\mathscr{G}(\mathscr{H}) = \mathscr{G}(\varinjlim h_A) \cong \varinjlim \mathscr{G}h_A \cong \varinjlim \mathscr{F}A$$

But $\mathscr{G}(H) = \varinjlim \mathscr{F}A$ defines a functor with the required properties, as is easy to check. Then

$$\mathrm{Mor}_\mathscr{C}(\mathscr{G}(\mathscr{H}), C) = \mathrm{Mor}_\mathscr{C}(\varinjlim \mathscr{F}A, C) \cong \varprojlim \mathrm{Mor}_\mathscr{C}(\mathscr{F}A, C) = \varprojlim h_C\mathscr{F}(A)$$

$$\cong \varprojlim \mathrm{Mor}_f(h_A, h_C\mathscr{F}) \cong \mathrm{Mor}_f(\varinjlim h_A, h_C\mathscr{F})$$

$$= \mathrm{Mor}_f(\mathscr{H}, \mathrm{Mor}_C(\mathscr{F}-, -)(C))$$

shows the adjointness of $\mathscr{G}$ and $\mathrm{Mor}_\mathscr{C}(\mathscr{F}-, -)$.

THEOREM 1 (representable functor theorem). *Let $\mathscr{C}$ be a complete nonempty category. A functor $\mathscr{F} : \mathscr{C} \to \mathbf{S}$ is representable if and only if*

(1) *$\mathscr{F}$ preserves limits*
(2) *there is a solution set for $\{\varnothing\} = E$ with respect to $\mathscr{F}$.*

Proof. Since $\mathscr{F}$ preserves empty limits, $\mathscr{F}$ preserves final objects. Thus there is a $C \in \mathscr{C}$ with $\mathscr{F}C \neq \varnothing$.

By the preceeding corollary we know that $\mathscr{F}$ is a colimit of the representable functors over $\mathscr{F}$ where the representing objects are in the solution set $\mathfrak{L}$. Let $\mathscr{V} : \mathscr{A} \to \mathscr{C}$ be the functor which defines the diagram of the representing objects. Let $B = \varprojlim \mathscr{V}$ and $\sigma : \mathscr{K}B \to \mathscr{V}$ be the natural transformation of the projections. By the Yoneda lemma, a diagram

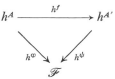

is commutative if and only if $\mathscr{F}f(\psi) = \varphi$.

Let $f : A' \to A$ be a morphism in the diagram defined by $\mathscr{V}$. Let $\sigma(A) : B \to A$ and $\sigma(A') : B \to A'$ be the corresponding projection morphisms. Then we get two commutative diagrams

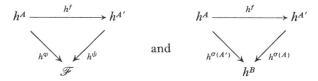

Since $\mathscr{F}$ is (argumentwise) a colimit of these representable functors, there is exactly one morphism $\eta : \mathscr{F} \to h^B$ with $\eta h^\varphi = h^{\sigma(A)}$. We want to show that there is also exactly one natural transformation $h^\rho : h^B \to \mathscr{F}$ with $h^\rho h^{\sigma(A)} = h^\varphi$. Since $\mathscr{F}$ preserves limits, $\mathscr{F}B$ is a limit in the commutative diagram

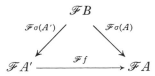

For the elements $\varphi \in \mathscr{F}A$ and $\psi \in \mathscr{F}A'$ used above, we get $\mathscr{F}f(\psi) = \varphi$. Thus there is exactly one $\rho \in \mathscr{F}B$ with $\mathscr{F}\sigma(A)(\rho) = \varphi$. Consequently, there is also exactly one $h^\rho : h^B \to \mathscr{F}$ with $h^\rho h^{\sigma(A)} = h^\varphi$. We only used that $\mathscr{F}$ preserves limits, which is also true for h^B. Thus h^ρ and η are inverse to each other and $\mathscr{F}$ is representable. Conversely, if $\mathscr{F} \cong h^B$, then (2) is satisfied by B. (1) holds because of Theorem 2 of Section 2.7.

THEOREM 2 (adjoint functor theorem). *Let $\mathscr{C}$ be a complete, nonempty category. Let $\mathscr{F} : \mathscr{C} \to \mathscr{D}$ be a covariant functor. $\mathscr{F}$ has a left adjoint functor if and only if*

(1) *$\mathscr{F}$ preserves limits, and*
(2) *$\mathscr{F}$ has solution sets.*

Proof. By Section 2.1, Proposition 2 $\mathscr{F}$ has a left adjoint functor if and only if $\mathrm{Mor}_{\mathscr{D}}(C, \mathscr{F}-)$ is representable for all $D \in \mathscr{D}$. But for a fixed $D \in \mathscr{D}$ conditions (1) and (2) coincide with conditions (1) and (2) of Theorem 1 if we consider the reformulation of the solution set of E in Corollary 2. Thus, Theorem 1 implies this theorem.

2.10 Generators and Cogenerators

For further applications of the adjoint functor theorem, we want to introduce special objects in the categories under consideration. A family $\{G_i\}_{i \in I}$ of objects (with a set I) in a category $\mathscr{C}$ is called a *set of generators* if for each pair of different morphisms $f, g : A \to B$ in $\mathscr{C}$ there is a G_i and a morphism $h : G_i \to A$ with $fh \neq gh$. If the sets $\mathrm{Mor}_{\mathscr{C}}(G_i, A)$ are nonempty for all $i \in I$ and all $A \in \mathscr{C}$ then this definition is equivalent to the condition that the functor

$$\prod_{i \in I} \mathrm{Mor}_{\mathscr{C}}(G_i, -) : \mathscr{C} \to \mathbf{S}$$

is faithful. If the set of generators consists of exactly one element G, then G is called a *generator*. G is a generator if and only if $\mathrm{Mor}_\mathscr{C}(G, -)$ is faithful functor. If $\mathscr{C}$ is a cocomplete category with a set of generators $\{G_i\}_{i \in I}$ and if all the sets $\mathrm{Mor}_\mathscr{C}(G_i, A)$ are nonempty, then by $\prod \mathrm{Mor}_\mathscr{C}(G_i, -) \cong \mathrm{Mor}_\mathscr{C}(\amalg G_i, -)$ the coproduct of the G_i is a generator.

LEMMA 1. *Let $\mathscr{C}$ be a category with a generator. Then the difference subobjects of each object form a set.*

Proof. Let B and B' be two proper difference subobjects of A. In the diagram

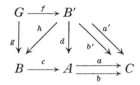

let (B, c) be a difference kernel of (a, b). Let $a' = ad$ and $b' = bd$. Now let $d \cdot \mathrm{Mor}_C(G, B') = c \cdot \mathrm{Mor}_C(G, B)$ as subsets of $\mathrm{Mor}_C(G, A)$. For each $f : G \to B'$, there is a $g : G \to B$ with $cg = df$; hence $a'f = adf = acg = bcg = bdf = b'f$. This is true for each choice of $f \in \mathrm{Mor}_\mathscr{C}(G, B')$; hence $a' = b'$. Consequently, there is exactly one $h : B' \to B$ with $ch = d$. Analogously, one shows the unique existence of a morphism $k : B \to B'$ with $dk = c$. Thus c and d are equivalent monomorphisms defining the same difference subobject. Hence, the set of difference subobject has a smaller cardinality than the power set of $\mathrm{Mor}_\mathscr{C}(G, A)$, for different subobjects (B, c) and (B', d) must lead to different sets $d \cdot \mathrm{Mor}_C(G, B') \neq c \cdot \mathrm{Mor}_C(G, B)$.

LEMMA 2. *Let $\mathscr{C}$ be a category with coproducts. An object G in $\mathscr{C}$ is a generator if and only if to each object A in $\mathscr{C}$ there is an epimorphism $f : \amalg G \to A$.*

Proof. Here we also admit a coproduct with an empty index set, which is an initial object. Let $\mathrm{Mor}_\mathscr{C}(G, A) = I$. We form a coproduct of G with itself over the index set I. We define $f : \amalg G \to A$ as the morphism with ith component $i \in \mathrm{Mor}_\mathscr{C}(G, A)$. Then f is an epimorphism if G is a generator. Conversely, if for each A there is an epimorphism f, then different morphisms $g, h : A \to B$ stay different after the composition with f. But then for some injection $G \to \amalg G$ the composed morphisms must be different from each other.

LEMMA 3.   *Let $\mathscr{C}$ be a balanced category with finite intersections and a set of generators. Then $\mathscr{C}$ is locally small.*

Proof.   As in Lemma 1 we shall show that different subobjects B and B' of A define different subsets of $\mathrm{Mor}_{\mathscr{C}}(G_i , A)$ for some i, where $\{G_i\}$ is a set of generators. Assume B and B' different. Since $\mathscr{C}$ is balanced, not both morphisms $B \cap B' \to B$ and $B \cap B' \to B'$ can be epimorphisms because in this case both would be isomorphisms compatible with the morphisms into A thus $B = B'$ as subobjects. Suppose $B \cap B' \to B$ is not an epimorphism. Then there exist two different morphisms $f, g : B \to C$, such that

$$(B \cap B' \to B \xrightarrow{f} C) = (B \cap B' \to B \xrightarrow{g} C)$$

Let $h : G_i \to B$ be given with $fh \neq gh$. Then h cannot be factored through $B \cap B'$. Since $B \cap B'$ is a fiber product, there is also no morphism $G_i \to B'$ with

$$(G_i \to B' \to A) = (G_i \xrightarrow{h} B \to A)$$

Thus the maps defined by $B' \to A$ and $B \to A$ map $\mathrm{Mor}_{\mathscr{C}}(G_i , B')$ and $\mathrm{Mor}_{\mathscr{C}}(G_i , B)$ onto different subsets of $\mathrm{Mor}_{\mathscr{C}}(G_i , A)$ respectively.

LEMMA 4.   *Let $\mathscr{A}$ be a small category. Then $\mathrm{Funct}(\mathscr{A}, \mathbf{S})$ has a set of generators.*

Proof.   We show that $\{h^A \mid A \in \mathscr{A}\}$ is a set of generators. Let $\varphi, \psi \colon \mathscr{F} \to \mathscr{G}$ be two different morphisms in $\mathrm{Funct}(\mathscr{A}, \mathbf{S})$. Then there is at least one $A \in \mathscr{A}$ with $\varphi(A) \neq \psi(A)$. Thus by the Yoneda lemma, $\mathrm{Mor}_f(h^A, \varphi) \neq \mathrm{Mor}_f(h^A, \psi)$, so there exists a $\rho \in \mathrm{Mor}_f(h^A, \mathscr{F})$ with $\varphi\rho \neq \psi\rho$.

A *cogenerator* is defined dually. In $\mathbf{S}$ each nonempty set is a generator and each set with at least two elements is a generator. In $\mathbf{Top}$ each discrete, nonempty topological space is a generator and each topological space X with at least two elements and $\{\varnothing , X\}$ as the set of open sets is a cogenerator. One also says that X has the coarsest topology. In $\mathbf{S}^*$ each set with at least two elements is a generator and a cogenerator. In $\mathbf{Top}^*$ each discrete topological space with at least two elements is a generator and each topological space with the coarsest topology and at least two elements is a cogenerator. We shall show more about the categories $\mathbf{Ab}$, $_R\mathbf{Mod}$, $\mathbf{Gr}$, and $\mathbf{Ri}$ in Chapters 3 and 4.

2.11 Special Cases of the Adjoint Functor Theorem

LEMMA. *Let $\mathscr{C}$ be a complete, locally small category and let the functor $\mathscr{F} : \mathscr{C} \to \mathbf{S}$ preserve limits. For each element $x \in \mathscr{F}C$, there exists a minimal subobject $C' \subseteq C$ with an element $y \in \mathscr{F}C'$ which is mapped onto x by the induced morphism $\mathscr{F}C' \to \mathscr{F}C$.*

Proof. Since $\mathscr{F}$ preserves limits, the induced morphisms $\mathscr{F}C' \to \mathscr{F}C$ are monomorphisms by Section 2.6, Corollary 5. Thus the element $y \in \mathscr{F}C'$ is uniquely determined. We consider the category of the subobjects B of C for which there exists a (uniquely determined) $y \in \mathscr{F}B$ which is mapped onto x by $\mathscr{F}B \to \mathscr{F}C$. The limit (intersection) C' of these subobjects has the same property because $\mathscr{F}$ preserves limits, and because the existence of $y \in \mathscr{F}C'$ with this property is equivalent to the property that there exists a map $\{\varnothing\} \to \mathscr{F}C'$ which together with the map $\mathscr{F}C' \to \mathscr{F}C$ has the element x as an image. But this holds for the objects B in the above defined diagram.

THEOREM 1. *Let $\mathscr{C}$ be a complete, locally small category with a cogenerator G. A functor $\mathscr{F} : \mathscr{C} \to \mathbf{S}$ is representable if and only if $\mathscr{F}$ preserves limits.*

Proof. To use Section 2.9, Theorem 1 we have to define a solution set for E. Let $x \in \mathscr{F}C$ and let C coincide with the minimal subobject C' as constructed in the lemma. Let $y \in \mathscr{F}G$. If there is an $f : C \to G$ with $\mathscr{F}f(x) = y$, then f is uniquely determined. In fact, if two morphisms have this property, then let $D \to C$ be the difference kernel of these two morphisms. Since $\mathscr{F}$ preserves difference kernels, there is an $x' \subset \mathscr{F}D$ which is mapped onto y by $\mathscr{F}D \to \mathscr{F}G$. Since C is minimal (in the sense of the lemma), we get $D = C$, that is, both morphisms coincide. Thus we may consider $\mathrm{Mor}_{\mathscr{C}}(C, G)$ as a subset of $\mathscr{F}G$. By the dual of Section 2.10, Lemma 2, $C \to \prod G$ is a monomorphism, where the product is formed over the index set $\mathrm{Mor}_{\mathscr{C}}(C, G)$ and where the components of this morphism are all morphisms of $\mathrm{Mor}_{\mathscr{C}}(C, G)$. Then also $C \to \prod G$ is a monomorphism where the product is formed over the index set $\mathscr{F}G$ and where we use for the additional factors of the product arbitrary morphisms of $\mathrm{Mor}_{\mathscr{C}}(C, G)$ as additional components. Thus C is a subobject of $\prod_{\mathscr{F}G} G = D$ up to equivalence of monomorphisms. This holds for all such minimal objects C. Since $\mathscr{C}$ is locally small, these objects form a set, a solution set for E with respect to $\mathscr{F}$.

THEOREM 2. *Let $\mathscr{C}$ be a complete, locally small category with a cogenerator. Let $\mathscr{F} : \mathscr{C} \to \mathscr{D}$ be a covariant functor. $\mathscr{F}$ has a left adjoint functor if and only if $\mathscr{F}$ preserves limits.*

Proof. This is shown in a way similar to the proof that Theorem 1 implies Theorem 2 in Section 2.9.

COROLLARY. *Let $\mathscr{C}$ be a complete, locally small category with a cogenerator. Then $\mathscr{C}$ is cocomplete.*

Proof. Let $\mathscr{A}$ be a diagram scheme. The constant functor $\mathscr{K} : \mathscr{C} \to$ Funct$(\mathscr{A}, \mathscr{C})$ preserves limits. By Theorem 2, $\mathscr{K}$ has a left adjoint functor $\varinjlim$. This holds for all diagram schemes $\mathscr{A}$.

We now discuss an example for Theorem 2, where we refer the reader to textbooks on topology for the particular notions and theorems. The full subcategory of compact hausdorff spaces in **Top** is a reflexive subcategory of the full subcategory of normal hausdorff spaces in **Top**. Urysohn's lemma guarantees that the interval $[0, 1]$ is a cogenerator. The closed subspaces of compact hausdorff spaces are again compact and represent the difference subobjects. By the theorem of Tychonoff, the products are also compact. Thus there is a left adjoint functor for the embedding functor. This left adjoint functor is called the Stone–Čech compactification.

THEOREM 3. *Let $\mathscr{C}$ be a full reflexive subcategory of a cocomplete category $\mathscr{D}$. Then $\mathscr{C}$ is cocomplete.*

Proof. Let $\mathscr{E} : \mathscr{C} \to \mathscr{D}$ be the embedding. Let $\mathscr{A}$ be a diagram scheme and $\mathscr{F} : \mathscr{A} \to \mathscr{C}$ be a diagram. Let $\mathscr{R} : \mathscr{D} \to \mathscr{C}$ be the reflector for $\mathscr{E}$. Since $\mathscr{E}$ is full and faithful, we get $\mathrm{Mor}_f(\mathscr{F}, \mathscr{F}') \cong \mathrm{Mor}_f(\mathscr{E}\mathscr{F}, \mathscr{E}\mathscr{F}')$ for $\mathscr{F}, \mathscr{F}' \in$ Funct$(\mathscr{A}, \mathscr{C})$ which is natural in $\mathscr{F}$ and $\mathscr{F}'$. This may be shown similarly to the isomorphism $\mathrm{Mor}_f(\mathscr{K}\mathscr{H}, \mathscr{G}) \cong \mathrm{Mor}_f(\mathscr{H}, \varprojlim \mathscr{G})$ in Section 2.7, Theorem 1. Then the isomorphisms

$$\mathrm{Mor}_f(\mathscr{F}, \mathscr{K}C) \cong \mathrm{Mor}_f(\mathscr{E}\mathscr{F}, \mathscr{E}\mathscr{K}C) \cong \mathrm{Mor}_f(\mathscr{E}\mathscr{F}, \mathscr{K}\mathscr{E}C)$$

$$\cong \mathrm{Mor}_{\mathscr{D}}(\varinjlim \mathscr{E}\mathscr{F}, \mathscr{E}C) \cong \mathrm{Mor}_{\mathscr{C}}(\mathscr{R} \varinjlim \mathscr{E}\mathscr{F}, C)$$

are natural in $\mathscr{F}$ and C. Thus $\mathscr{C}$ has colimits.

THEOREM 4. *Let $\mathscr{C}$ be a full subcategory of a complete, locally small and locally cosmall category $\mathscr{D}$. Let $\mathscr{C}$ be closed with respect to products and subobjects in $\mathscr{D}$. Then $\mathscr{C}$ is a reflexive subcategory of $\mathscr{D}$.*

Proof. Since $\mathscr{C}$ is closed with respect to forming products and subobjects in $\mathscr{D}$, in particular with respect to difference subobjects, $\mathscr{C}$ is also closed with respect to forming limits in $\mathscr{D}$ (of diagrams in $\mathscr{C}$). Thus $\mathscr{C}$ is complete and the embedding functor preserves limits. Thus we have to find only a solution set. Since the embedding functor preserves limits, it preserves subobjects. Hence $\mathscr{C}$ is locally small. Given a morphism $D \to C$. Since the functor $\mathrm{Mor}_{\mathscr{D}}(D, -) : \mathscr{C} \to \mathbf{S}$ preserves limits, it preserves, by Lemma 1, a minimal subobject C' of C which may be factored through $D \to C$. Let $f, g : C' \to D'$ in $\mathscr{D}$ be given such that $fh = gh$, where $h : D \to C'$ is the factorization morphism. Then h may be factored through the difference kernel of (f, g). Since C' was minimal, we get $f = g$ and that h is an epimorphism. Consequently, the set of quotient objects of D is a solution set.

Observe that we used in the proof only that $\mathscr{C}$ is closed with respect to forming difference subobjects instead of all subobjects. This, however, is often more difficult to check if one does not know exactly what the difference subobjects are.

Some examples are that the full subcategory of commutative rings is a reflexive subcategory of **Ri**. Similarly, the full subcategory of hausdorff spaces in **Top** is reflexive. We also observe that the full subcategory of integral domains is not reflexive in **Ri**, for if it were it would have to be closed with respect to forming products in **Ri**. But the product of $\mathbb{Z}$ with itself is not an integral domain.

2.12 Full and Faithful Functors

LEMMA 1. *Let $\mathscr{F} : \mathscr{C} \to \mathscr{D}$ be a faithful functor. Then $\mathscr{F}$ reflects monomorphisms and epimorphisms.*

Proof. Given $f, g, h \in \mathscr{C}$ with $fg = fh$. Then $\mathscr{F}f\mathscr{F}g = \mathscr{F}f\mathscr{F}h$. If $\mathscr{F}f$ is a monomorphism, then $\mathscr{F}g = \mathscr{F}h$. Since $\mathscr{F}$ is faithful we get $g = h$. By dualizing, we get the assertion for epimorphisms.

PROPOSITION 1. *Let $\mathscr{F} : \mathscr{C} \to \mathscr{D}$ be a full and faithful functor. Then $\mathscr{F}$ reflects limits and colimits.*

Proof. Let $\mathscr{G} : \mathscr{A} \to \mathscr{C}$ be given. $\mathscr{G}$ has a limit if and only if the functor $\mathrm{Mor}_f(\mathscr{K}-, \mathscr{G}) : \mathscr{C}^0 \to \mathbf{S}$ is representable. Given $C \in \mathscr{C}$ with $\mathrm{Mor}_f(\mathscr{K}-, \mathscr{F}\mathscr{G}) \cong \mathrm{Mor}_{\mathscr{D}}(-, \mathscr{F}C)$. Then $\mathrm{Mor}_f(\mathscr{F}\mathscr{K}-, \mathscr{F}\mathscr{G}) \cong \mathrm{Mor}_D(\mathscr{F}-, \mathscr{F}C)$ as functors from $\mathscr{C}^0$ into $\mathbf{S}$. Since $\mathscr{F}$ is full and faithful, we get $\mathrm{Mor}_f(\mathscr{K}-, \mathscr{G}) \cong \mathrm{Mor}_{\mathscr{C}}(-, C)$. Dually, one shows that $\mathscr{F}$ reflects colimits.

PROPOSITION 2. *Let $\mathscr{A}$ be a small category. The covariant representation functor $h : \mathscr{A} \to \text{Funct}(\mathscr{A}^0, \mathbf{S})$ reflects limits and colimits and preserves limits.*

Proof. We know from Section 1.15 that h is full and faithful. Thus Proposition 1 holds. The last assertion is implied by Section 2.7, Theorem 2.

Observe that h does not necessarily preserve colimits. In fact, let $\mathscr{A}$ be a skeleton of the full subcategory of the finitely generated abelian groups in **Ab**. Then $\mathscr{A}$ is small. We may assume that $\mathbb{Z}$ and $\mathbb{Z}/n\mathbb{Z}$ are in $\mathscr{A}$ for some $n > 1$. Then $\mathbb{Z}/n\mathbb{Z}$ is a cokernel of $n : \mathbb{Z} \to \mathbb{Z}$, the multiplication with n. But $\text{Mor}_{\mathscr{A}}(-, \mathbb{Z}/n\mathbb{Z})$ is not a cokernel of $\text{Mor}_{\mathscr{A}}(-, n) :$ $\text{Mor}_{\mathscr{A}}(-, \mathbb{Z}) \to \text{Mor}_{\mathscr{A}}(-, \mathbb{Z})$ because this does not hold argumentwise, for example for the argument $\mathbb{Z}/n\mathbb{Z}$.

PROPOSITION 3. *Let $\mathscr{F} : \mathscr{C} \to \mathscr{D}$ be left adjoint to $\mathscr{G} : \mathscr{D} \to \mathscr{C}$. Let $\psi : \text{Mor}_{\mathscr{C}}(-, \mathscr{G}-) \cong \text{Mor}_{\mathscr{D}}(\mathscr{F}-, -)$ be the corresponding natural isomorphism and let $\Psi : \mathscr{F}\mathscr{G} \to \text{Id}_{\mathscr{D}}$ be the natural transformation constructed in Section 2.1. Then the following are equivalent:*

(1) *$\mathscr{G}$ is faithful.*

(2) *$\mathscr{G}$ reflects epimorphisms.*

(3) *If $g : C \to \mathscr{G}D$ is an epimorphism, then also $\psi(g)$ is an epimorphism.*

(4) *$\Psi D : \mathscr{F}\mathscr{G}D \to D$ is an epimorphism for all $D \in \mathscr{D}$.*

Proof. That (1) $\Rightarrow$ (2) is implied by the lemma. (2) $\Rightarrow$ (3): By the remark after Section 2.2, Theorem 1, $\mathscr{G}g^* = \mathscr{G}(\psi(g))$ is an epimorphism if g is an epimorphism. Then by (2), $\psi(g)$ is also an epimorphism. (3) $\Rightarrow$ (4) holds if one sets for g the identity $1_{\mathscr{G}D}$. (4) $\Rightarrow$ (1): The map $\mathscr{G} : \text{Mor}_{\mathscr{D}}(D, D') \to \text{Mor}_{\mathscr{C}}(\mathscr{G}D, \mathscr{G}D')$ is by definition of $\Psi : \mathscr{F}\mathscr{G} \to \text{Id}_{\mathscr{D}}$ composed by $\text{Mor}_{\mathscr{D}}(D, D') \to \text{Mor}_{\mathscr{D}}(\mathscr{F}\mathscr{G}D, D') \cong \text{Mor}_{\mathscr{C}}(\mathscr{G}D, \mathscr{G}D')$. If ΨD is an epimorphism, then this map is injective.

LEMMA 2. *With the notations of Proposition 3, $\mathscr{G}$ is full if and only if the morphisms $\Psi D : \mathscr{F}\mathscr{G}D \to D$ are sections.*

Proof. We use Section 1.10, Lemma 3 and the fact that the map $\mathscr{G} : \text{Mor}_{\mathscr{D}}(D, D') \to \text{Mor}_{\mathscr{C}}(\mathscr{G}D, \mathscr{G}D')$ is composed of

$$\text{Mor}_{\mathscr{D}}(D, D') \to \text{Mor}_{\mathscr{D}}(\mathscr{F}\mathscr{G}D, D') \cong \text{Mor}_{\mathscr{C}}(\mathscr{G}D, \mathscr{G}D')$$

COROLLARY. *With the notations of Proposition 3, $\mathcal{G}$ is full and faithful if and only if the morphisms $\Psi D : \mathcal{FG}D \to D$ are isomorphisms.*

Proof. This corollary is implied by Proposition 3 and Lemma 2 because the isomorphism between $\mathrm{Mor}_{\mathscr{D}}(D, D')$ and $\mathrm{Mor}_{\mathscr{D}}(\mathcal{FG}D, D')$ for all D' (natural) implies the isomorphism between D and $\mathcal{FG}D$.

PROPOSITION 4. *With the notations of Proposition 3, let $\mathcal{G}$ be full and faithful. Let $\mathcal{H} : \mathcal{A} \to \mathscr{D}$ be a diagram. Let $\mathscr{C}$ be a limit or a colimit of $\mathcal{GH}$. Then $\mathcal{F}C$ is a limit or, respectively, a colimit of $\mathcal{H}$. If $\mathscr{C}$ is (finitely) complete or cocomplete, then $\mathscr{D}$ is also (finitely) complete or cocomplete respectively.*

Proof. Since in the case of the colimit, $\mathrm{Mor}_{\mathscr{C}}(C, -) \cong \mathrm{Mor}_f(\mathcal{GH}, \mathcal{H}-)$, we get

$$\mathrm{Mor}_{\mathscr{D}}(\mathcal{F}C, -) \cong \mathrm{Mor}_{\mathscr{C}}(C, \mathcal{G}-) \cong \mathrm{Mor}_f(\mathcal{GH}, \mathcal{GH}-) \cong \mathrm{Mor}_f(\mathcal{H}, \mathcal{H}-)$$

We prove the second assertion in the inversely connected category $\mathcal{V}_{\mathcal{H}}'(\mathrm{Funct}(\mathcal{A}, \mathscr{C}), \mathscr{C})$, where we get a commutative diagram

$$
\begin{array}{ccccc}
C & \xrightarrow{\Phi C} & \mathcal{GF}C & \xrightarrow{\rho} & C \\
\downarrow & & \downarrow & & \downarrow \\
\mathcal{GH} & \xrightarrow{\Phi\mathcal{GH}} & \mathcal{GFGH} & \xrightarrow{\mathcal{G}\Psi\mathcal{H}} & \mathcal{GH}
\end{array}
$$

The morphism $(\mathcal{G}\Psi\mathcal{H})(\Phi\mathcal{GH})$ is the identity. Since C is a limit, there is a uniquely determined morphism ρ, and $\rho(\Phi C)$ is also the identity. Thus ρ is a retraction. Since $\Phi : \mathrm{Id}_{\mathscr{C}} \to \mathcal{GF}$ is a natural transformation, and since $\mathcal{GF}\Phi = \Phi\mathcal{GF}$ by $(\mathcal{G}\Psi\mathcal{F})(\mathcal{GF}\Phi) = (\mathcal{G}\Psi\mathcal{F})(\Phi\mathcal{GF})$, the square

$$
\begin{array}{ccc}
\mathcal{GF}C & \xrightarrow{\rho} & C \\
\scriptstyle{\mathcal{GF}(\Phi C)}\downarrow & & \downarrow\scriptstyle{\Phi C} \\
\mathcal{GFGF}C & \xrightarrow{\mathcal{GF}\rho} & \mathcal{GF}C
\end{array}
$$

is commutative. Since $(\mathcal{GF}\rho)(\mathcal{GF}(\Phi C))$ is the identity, ρ is an isomorphism, hence also ΦC. Since $\mathcal{G}\Psi\mathcal{H}$ is an isomorphism, also $\Phi\mathcal{GH}$ is an isomorphism. Thus $\mathcal{GF}C$ is a limit of $\mathcal{GFGH}$. $\mathcal{G}$, being full and faithful, reflects limits. Thus $\mathcal{F}C$ is a limit of $\mathcal{FGH}$. This proves the second assertion of the proposition.

Problems

2.1. Let $\mathscr{G} : \mathbf{Gr} \to \mathbf{S}$ be the forgetful functor which assigns to each group the under-lying set. Formulate the universal problem in $\mathscr{V}_{\mathscr{G}}(\mathbf{S}, \mathbf{Gr})$ for $A \in \mathbf{S}$ and determine whether a universal solution exists. Does $\mathscr{G}$ have a left adjoint functor? Formulate the universal problem in $\mathscr{V}_{\mathscr{G}}(\mathbf{Gr}, \mathbf{S})$. How does the universal solution change if one replaces $\mathbf{Gr}$ by $\mathbf{Ab}$?

2.2. If

$$
\begin{array}{ccc}
A & \xrightarrow{\;f\;} & B \\
{\scriptstyle f}\downarrow & & \downarrow{\scriptstyle g} \\
B & \xrightarrow{\;g\;} & C
\end{array}
$$

is a fiber product, then f is a monomorphism.

2.3. A full faithful functor $\mathscr{F}$ defines an equivalence with the image of $\mathscr{F}$.

2.4. If $\mathscr{F} : \mathscr{C} \to \mathbf{S}$ has a left adjoint functor, then $\mathscr{F}$ is representable.

2.5. Prove (without using Section 2.8, Lemma 3) that each kernel pair is a mono-morphic equivalence relation.

2.6. (Ehrbar) Let $\mathscr{Q}$ and $\mathscr{S}$ be subcategories of a category $\mathscr{C}$. We say that $\mathscr{Q}$ and $\mathscr{S}$ *decompose* the category $\mathscr{C}$ if all objects and all isomorphisms of $\mathscr{C}$ are in $\mathscr{Q}$ as well as in $\mathscr{S}$, if there is a $\mathscr{Q}$-$\mathscr{S}$-decomposition for each $f \in \mathscr{C}$, that is, if to each $f \in \mathscr{C}$ there is a pair $(q, s) \in \mathscr{Q} \times \mathscr{S}$ with $f = sq$, and if to any two $\mathscr{Q}$-$\mathscr{S}$-decompositions (q, s) and (q', s') of the same morphism $f \in \mathscr{C}$ there is exactly one $h \in \mathscr{C}$ with $hq = q'$ and $s = s'h$.

Show that h is an isomorphism.

If $bq = sa$ with $q \in \mathscr{Q}$ and $s \in \mathscr{S}$, then there is exactly one morphism $d \in \mathscr{C}$ such that the diagram

is commutative.

Let $f \in \mathscr{C}$ and $A \in \mathscr{C}$. f is called an *epimorphic relative* to A if $\mathrm{Mor}_{\mathscr{C}}(f, A)$ is an injective map.

Let $\mathscr{C}$ be a category with nonempty products and assume that $\mathscr{C}$ is decomposed by the subcategories $\mathscr{Q}$ and $\mathscr{S}$. Let $\mathfrak{A}$ be a class of objects in $\mathscr{C}$ with the property that all $q \in \mathscr{Q}$ are epimorphic relative to all $A \in \mathfrak{A}$. Let $\mathfrak{A}^*$ be the full subcategory of $\mathscr{C}$ with the objects $A^* \in \mathscr{C}$ for which there is a family $\{A_i\}_{i \in I} \subseteq A$ and a morphism $s : A^* \to \prod_{i \in I} A_i$ with $s \in \mathscr{S}$. $\mathfrak{A}^*$ is a reflexive subcategory of $\mathscr{C}$ if and only if to each object $B \in \mathscr{C}$ there exists a nonempty set L of morphisms $f \in \mathscr{C}$ with B the domain of f and with the range of f in $\mathfrak{A}^*$ and with the property that to each $g \in \mathscr{C}$ with B domain of g and the range of g in $\mathfrak{A}$ there is an $f \in L$ and an $h \in \mathscr{C}$ with $g = hf$. (Hint: Since $\mathscr{S}$ contains products of morphisms, $\mathfrak{A}^*$ contains products. Furthermore, all $q \in \mathscr{Q}$ are epimorphic relative to all $A^* \in \mathfrak{A}^*$. If L is as above, and if $h : B \to \prod_{f \in L} R(f)$ (with $R(f)$ the range of f) is the morphism with $p_f h = f$ for all $f \in L$, and if (q, s) is a $\mathscr{Q}$-$\mathscr{S}$-decomposition of f, then q is the adjunction $\Phi(B)$ with $\Phi : \mathrm{Id}_{\mathscr{C}} \to \mathscr{R}$ where $\mathscr{R}$ is the reflector we wanted to find (Section 2.1, Theorem 1 and 2 and Section 2.4).)

$\mathscr{C} = \mathbf{Top}$, $\mathscr{D}$ the category of continuous, dense maps in $\mathscr{C}$, and $\mathscr{S}$ the category of injective, closed, continuous maps define the Stone–Čech compactification with $\mathfrak{A} = \{[0, 1]\}$.

2.7. Use the construction in the proof of Section 2.6, Proposition 2 to show

(a)   that for a diagram $\mathscr{F} : \mathscr{A} \to \mathbf{S}$ the limit of $\mathscr{F}$ is

$$\varprojlim \mathscr{A} = \left\{ (x_A)_{A \in \mathscr{A}} \in \prod_{A \in \mathscr{A}} \mathscr{F}A \mid (\mathscr{F}f)(x_A) = x_B \quad \text{for all} \quad f : A \to B \text{ in } \mathscr{A} \right\}$$

(b)   that for a diagram $\mathscr{F} : \mathscr{A} \to \mathbf{S}$ the colimit of $\mathscr{F}$ is

$$\varinjlim \mathscr{F} = \left\{ \text{equivalence classes in } \bigcup_{A \in \mathscr{A}} \mathscr{F}A \text{ (disjoint union) with} \right.$$

$$\left. x_A \sim (\mathscr{F}f)(x_B) \quad \text{for all} \quad f : A \to B \text{ in } \mathscr{F}; \quad x_A \in \mathscr{F}A; \quad x_B \in \mathscr{F}B \right\}$$

(c)   that for a directed diagram scheme $\mathscr{A}$ and a diagram $\mathscr{F} : \mathscr{A} \to \mathbf{S}$ with $\mathscr{F}f$ surjective for all $f \in \mathscr{A}$ the direct limit is

$$\varinjlim \mathscr{F} = \left\{ (x_A)_{A \in \mathscr{A}} \in \prod_{A \subset \mathscr{A}} \mathscr{F}A \mid (\mathscr{F}f)(x_A) = x_B \quad \text{for all} \quad f : A \to B \text{ in } \mathscr{A} \right\}$$

3

Universal Algebra

The theory of equationally defined algebras is one of the nicest applications of the theory of categories and functors. Many of the well-known universal constructions, for example, group-ring, symmetric and exterior algebras, and their properties can be treated simultaneously. The introduction into this theory in the first two sections originates from the dissertation of Lawvere. The method of Section 3.3 leads to Linton's notion of a varietal category, which, however, will not be explicitely formulated. In the fourth section we shall use the techniques of monads or—as they are called in Zürich—triples. Theorem 4 in the last section is essentially a result of Hilton.

3.1 Algebraic Theories

Let $\mathbf{N}$ be the full subcategory of $\mathbf{S}$ with finite sets as objects, where for each finite cardinal there is exactly one set of this cardinality in $\mathbf{N}$. In particular, let $\varnothing$ be in $\mathbf{N}$. We denote the objects of $\mathbf{N}$ by small Latin letters ($n \in \mathbf{N}$). In special cases we shall also use the cardinals of the corresponding sets as objects of $\mathbf{N}$ ($0, 1, 2, 3,... \in \mathbf{N}$).

Let $n \in \mathbf{N}$. Then n is an n-fold coproduct (disjoint union) of 1 with itself. $0 \ (= \varnothing)$ is an initial object in $\mathbf{N}$ (empty union). Consequently, we get $\mathrm{Mor}_{\mathbf{N}}(m, n) \cong \mathrm{Mor}_{\mathbf{N}}(1, n)^m$ (m-fold product). Since each morphism $1 \to n$ is an injection into the coproduct n, all morphisms in $\mathbf{N}$ are m-tuples of injections into coproducts. $\mathbf{N}$ is a category with finite co-products.

Let $\mathbf{N}^0$ be the dual category of $\mathbf{N}$. The objects will be denoted just as in $\mathbf{N}$. Each object $n \in \mathbf{N}^0$ is an n-fold product of 1 with itself. 0 is a final object. Each morphism is an n-tuple of projections from products. In particular, we identify $\mathrm{Mor}_{\mathbf{N}^0}(m, n) = \mathrm{Mor}_{\mathbf{N}^0}(m, 1)^n$ (n-fold product). $\mathbf{N}^0$ is a category with finite products.

A covariant functor $\mathsf{A} \colon \mathbf{N}^0 \to \mathfrak{A}$ which is bijective on the object classes

120

and which preserves finite products is called an *algebraic theory*. In particular, A preserves the final object.

Since A is bijective on the objects, we denote the corresponding objects in $\mathfrak{A}$ and in $\mathbf{N}^0$ with the same signs, that is, with small Latin letters or the corresponding cardinals. $p_n^i : n \to 1$ denotes the ith projection from n to 1 in $\mathbf{N}^0$ as well as in $\mathfrak{A}$. We shall often talk about an algebraic theory $\mathfrak{A}$ without explicitly giving the corresponding functor A since this functor may be easily found from the notation used.

Let $A : \mathbf{N}^0 \to \mathfrak{A}$ and $B : \mathbf{N}^0 \to \mathfrak{B}$ be algebraic theories. A morphism of algebraic theories is a functor $\mathscr{G} : \mathfrak{A} \to \mathfrak{B}$ such that $\mathscr{G}A = B$ holds. Thus the algebraic theories form a category **Alt**.

An algebraic theory $A : \mathbf{N}^0 \to \mathfrak{A}$ is called *consistent* if A is faithful.

Let $\mathscr{N}$ be a discrete category with a countable set of objects denoted by 0, 1, 2, 3,... . Let $\mathfrak{B} : \mathbf{Alt} \to \mathrm{Funct}(\mathscr{N}, \mathbf{S})$ be a functor defined by

$$\mathfrak{B}(A, \mathfrak{A})(n) = \mathrm{Mor}_{\mathfrak{A}}(n, 1)$$

$$\mathfrak{B}(\mathscr{G})(n) = (\mathscr{G} : \mathrm{Mor}_{\mathfrak{A}}(n, 1) \to \mathrm{Mor}_{\mathfrak{B}}(n, 1))$$

THEOREM. *$\mathfrak{B}$ has a left adjoint functor $\mathfrak{F} : \mathrm{Funct}(\mathscr{N}, \mathbf{S}) \to \mathbf{Alt}$.*

Proof. We construct $\mathfrak{F}$ explicitly. Given $H : \mathscr{N} \to \mathbf{S}$. We construct sets $M(r, s)$ for $r, s \in \mathscr{N}$ in the following way. First let

$$M_1(r, 0) = \{\omega_r\}$$

$$M_1(r, 1) = H(r) \cup \mathrm{Mor}_{\mathbf{N}^0}(r, 1) \qquad \text{with a disjoint union}$$

$$M_1(r, s) = M_1(r, 1)^s \qquad \text{for } s > 1$$

We denote the s-tuples also by $(\sigma_1, ..., \sigma_s)$. Then define

$$M_1'(r, s) = \{[\sigma, \tau] \mid \sigma \in M_1(t, s), \quad \tau \in M_1(r, t), \quad t \in \mathscr{N}\} \cup M_1(r, s)$$

In contrast to the s-tuples in $M_1(r, s)$ we write the pairs $[\sigma, \tau]$ with brackets.

If the sets $M_{i-1}(r, s)$ and $M'_{i-1}(r, s)$ are already known, then let

$$M_i(r, 0) = M'_{i-1}(r, 0)$$

$$M_i(r, 1) = M'_{i-1}(r, 1)$$

$$M_i(r, s) = M_i(r, 1)^s \cup M'_{i-1}(r, s) \qquad \text{for } s > 1$$

$$M_i'(r, s) = \{[\sigma, \tau] \mid \sigma \in M_i(t, s), \quad \tau \in M_i(r, t), \quad t \in \mathscr{N}\} \cup M_i(r, s)$$

Then

$$\{w_r\} \subseteq M_1(r, 0) \subseteq M_1'(r, 0) \subseteq M_2(r, 0) \subseteq M_2'(r, 0) \subseteq \cdots$$

$$H(r) \cup \mathrm{Mor}_{N^0}(r, 1) \subseteq M_1(r, 1) \subseteq M_1'(r, 1) \subseteq M_2(r, 1) \subseteq M_2'(r, 1) \subseteq \cdots$$

$$M_1(r, s) \subseteq M_1'(r, s) \subseteq M_2(r, s) \subseteq M_2'(r, s) \subseteq \cdots$$

hold. So we define $M(r, s) = \bigcup M_i(r, s)$.
The following assertions hold:

(a) $\{w_r\} \subseteq M(r, 0)$ for all $r \geqslant 0$.

(b) $H(r) \cup \mathrm{Mor}_{N^0}(r, 1) \subseteq M(r, 1)$.

(c)   If $\sigma_i \in M(r, 1)$ for $i = 1, \dots, s$ with $s > 1$, then the s-tuple $(\sigma_1, \dots, \sigma_s) \in M(r, s)$ for all $r \geqslant 0$.

(d)   If $\sigma \in M(t, s)$ and $\tau \in M(r, t)$, then $[\sigma, \tau] \in M(r, s)$ for all r, s, $t \geqslant 0$.

On the sets $M(r, s)$ let R be the equivalence relation induced by the following conditions:

(1)   If $\sigma, \tau \in M(r, 0)$, then $(\sigma, \tau) \in R$.

(2)   If $\sigma_j \in M(r, 1)$ for $j = 1, \dots, s$, then $([p_s{}^i, (\sigma_1, \dots, \sigma_s)], \sigma_i) \in R$ for $i = 1, \dots, s$.

(3)   If $\sigma \in M(r, s)$, then $(([p_s{}^1, \sigma], \dots, [p_s{}^s, \sigma]), \sigma) \in R$.

(4)   If $\sigma \in M(r, s)$, then

$$([[(p_s{}^1, \dots, p_s{}^s), \sigma], \sigma) \in R \quad \text{and} \quad ([\sigma, (p_r{}^1, \dots, p_r{}^r)], \sigma) \in R.$$

(5)   If $\sigma \in M(r, s)$, $\tau \in M(s, t)$, and $\rho \in M(t, u)$, then

$$([[\rho, \tau], \sigma], [\rho, [\tau, \sigma]]) \in R.$$

(6)   If $\sigma_i, \tau_i \in M(r, 1)$ and $(\sigma_i, \tau_i) \in R$ for $i = 1, \dots, s$, then

$$((\sigma_1, \dots, \sigma_s), (\tau_1, \dots, \tau_s)) \in R.$$

(7)   If $\sigma, \sigma' \in M(r, t)$ and $\tau, \tau' \in M(t, s)$ and $(\sigma, \sigma'), (\tau, \tau') \in R$, then $([\tau, \sigma], [\tau', \sigma']) \in R$.

Observe that two elements are equivalent only if they are in the same set $M(r, s)$. Thus we define $\mathrm{Mor}_{\mathfrak{F}_H}(r, s) = M(r, s)/R$ as the set of equivalence classes defined by R. Let $\psi \in \mathrm{Mor}_{\mathfrak{F}H}(r, s)$ and $\varphi \in \mathrm{Mor}_{\mathfrak{F}H}(s, t)$ with the representatives $\tau \in M_i(r, s)$ and $\sigma \in M_i(s, t)$ which is possible by a sufficiently large choice of i. Then let the composition $\varphi\psi$ of φ with ψ be the equivalence class of $[\sigma, \tau] \in M_{i+1}(r, t) \subseteq M(r, t)$. By (7), this class is independent of the choice of the representatives of φ and ψ. By (5), this composition is associative. By (4), the equivalence class of $(p_r{}^1,..., p_r{}^r)$ is the identity for the composition. Thus $\mathfrak{F}H$ is a category with the objects $0, 1, 2,...$, and the morphism sets $\mathrm{Mor}_{\mathfrak{F}H}(r, s)$.

0 is a final object in $\mathfrak{F}H$ by (1). Conditions (2), (3), and (6) imply $\mathrm{Mor}_{\mathfrak{F}H}(r, s) \cong \mathrm{Mor}_{\mathfrak{F}H}(r, 1)^s$. In fact, (6) implies that for morphisms $\varphi_i \in \mathrm{Mor}_{\mathfrak{F}H}(r, 1)$ with representatives $\sigma_i \in M(r, 1)$ for $i = 1,..., s$ the morphism $(\varphi_1,..., \varphi_s) \in \mathrm{Mor}_{\mathfrak{F}H}(r, s)$ with the representative $(\sigma_1,..., \sigma_s) \in M(r, s)$ is independent of the choice of the representatives σ_i. (2) implies the existence of a factorization morphism φ such that $p_n{}^i\varphi = \varphi_i$, namely $\varphi = (\varphi_1,..., \varphi_s)$ and (3) implies the uniqueness of such a factorization morphism. Thus the object $s \in \mathfrak{F}H$ is an s-fold product of 1 with itself.

Obviously $s \mapsto s$ and $p_j{}^i \mapsto p_j{}^i$ induces a product-preserving functor $\mathbf{N}^0 \to \mathfrak{F}H$, called the *free algebraic theory generated by H*.

Let $H, H' \in \mathrm{Funct}(\mathcal{N}, \mathbf{S})$ and let $f : H \to H'$ be a natural transformation. Since $\mathcal{N}$ is discrete, the maps $f(r) : H(r) \to H'(r)$ may be chosen arbitrarily. Define $\mathfrak{F}f$ by

$$\mathfrak{F}f(\varphi) = f(\varphi) \qquad \text{for} \quad \varphi \in H(n)$$

$$\mathfrak{F}f(p_r{}^i) = p_r{}^i \qquad \text{for} \quad p_r{}^i \in \mathrm{Mor}_{\mathbf{N}^0}(r, 1)$$

$$\mathfrak{F}f(\varphi_1,..., \varphi_s) = (\mathfrak{F}f(\varphi_1),..., \mathfrak{F}f(\varphi_s))$$

$$\mathfrak{F}f(\varphi\psi) = \mathfrak{F}f(\varphi)\,\mathfrak{F}f(\psi)$$

Then $\mathfrak{F}f$ maps the equivalence relation R into R'. Hence, $\mathfrak{F}f$ is a morphism of free algebraic theories $\mathfrak{F}f : \mathfrak{F}H \to \mathfrak{F}H'$. One easily verifies $\mathfrak{F}(fg) = \mathfrak{F}(f)\,\mathfrak{F}(g)$ and $\mathfrak{F}1_H = \mathrm{Id}_{\mathfrak{F}H}$. Thus $\mathfrak{F} : \mathrm{Funct}(\mathcal{N}, \mathbf{S}) \to \mathbf{Alt}$ is a functor. It remains to show that

$$\mathrm{Mor}_{\mathbf{Alt}}(\mathfrak{F}H, (\mathbf{A}, \mathfrak{A})) \cong \mathrm{Mor}_f(H, \mathfrak{B}(\mathbf{A}, \mathfrak{A}))$$

holds naturally in H and $(\mathbf{A}, \mathfrak{A})$. Let $f : H \to \mathfrak{B}(\mathbf{A}, \mathfrak{A})$ be given, that is, for each r let $f(r) : H(r) \to \mathrm{Mor}_{\mathfrak{A}}(r, 1)$ be given. We define a morphism $g : \mathfrak{F}H \to (\mathbf{A}, \mathfrak{A})$ of algebraic theories in the following way.

First let

$$g(\omega_r) \in \mathrm{Mor}_{\mathfrak{A}}(r, 0) \qquad \text{for} \qquad \omega_r \in M(r, 0)$$

$$g(\sigma) = f(\sigma) \qquad \text{for all} \quad \sigma \in H(r)$$

$$g(p_j{}^i) = p_j{}^i$$

$$g((\sigma_1, ..., \sigma_s)) = x \in \mathrm{Mor}_{\mathfrak{A}}(r, s) \qquad \text{for all} \quad \sigma_i \in M(r, 1), \quad i = 1, ..., s,$$

$$\text{and all} \quad r \in \mathcal{N}$$

where x corresponds to the element $(g(\sigma_1), ..., g(\sigma_s))$ under $\mathrm{Mor}_{\mathfrak{A}}(r, s) \cong \mathrm{Mor}_{\mathfrak{A}}(r, 1)^s$, and

$$g([\sigma, \tau]) = g(\sigma) g(\tau)$$

for all $\sigma \in M(t, s)$, $\tau \in M(r, t)$ and all $r, s, t \in \mathcal{N}$.

Thus $g : M(r, s) \to \mathrm{Mor}_{\mathfrak{A}}(r, s)$ is defined. Since $\mathfrak{A}$ is an algebraic theory, R-equivalent elements in $M(r, s)$ are mapped into the same morphisms in $\mathrm{Mor}_{\mathfrak{A}}(r, s)$. Thus we get a functor $g : \mathfrak{F}H \to (A, \mathfrak{A})$ which is a morphism of algebraic theories because of $g(p_j{}^i) = p_j{}^i$. If, conversely, $g : \mathfrak{F}H \to (A, \mathfrak{A})$ is given, then we get a family of maps $f(r) : H(r) \to \mathrm{Mor}_{\mathfrak{F}H}(r, 1) \to \mathrm{Mor}_{\mathfrak{A}}(r, 1)$. These two applications are inverse to each other and compatible with the composition with morphisms $H \to H'$ and $(A, \mathfrak{A}) \to (B, \mathfrak{B})$, hence natural in H and $(A, \mathfrak{A})$.

Let two morphisms of free algebraic theories $p_1, p_2 : \mathfrak{F}L \to \mathfrak{F}H$ be given. If one extends the equivalence relation R which we used for the construction of $\mathfrak{F}H$ by the condition

(8)   If $\varphi \in \mathrm{Mor}_{\mathfrak{F}L}(r, s)$, then $(p_1(\varphi), p_2(\varphi)) \in R$

then the equivalence classes for this new equivalence relation form again an algebraic theory. This may be seen in the same way as in the construction of free algebraic theories.

Conversely, let $\mathfrak{A}$ be an algebraic theory and $\Psi : \mathfrak{F}\mathfrak{B}(\mathfrak{A}) \to \mathfrak{A}$ be the adjunction morphism of Section 2.1, Theorem 1.

$$L(n) = \{(\varphi, \psi) \mid \varphi, \psi \in \mathrm{Mor}_{\mathfrak{F}\mathfrak{B}(\mathfrak{A})}(n, 1), \quad \Psi(\varphi) = \Psi(\psi)\}$$

and

$$q_1 : L(n) \ni (\varphi, \psi) \mapsto \varphi \in \mathrm{Mor}_{\mathfrak{F}\mathfrak{B}(\mathfrak{A})}(n, 1)$$

$$q_2 : L(n) \ni (\varphi, \psi) \mapsto \psi \in \mathrm{Mor}_{\mathfrak{F}\mathfrak{B}(\mathfrak{A})}(n, 1)$$

define morphisms $q_i : L \to \mathfrak{B}\mathfrak{F}\mathfrak{B}(\mathfrak{A})$. Since $\mathfrak{F}$ is left adjoint to $\mathfrak{B}$, we get morphisms $p_i : \mathfrak{F}L \to \mathfrak{F}\mathfrak{B}(\mathfrak{A})$. Since $\mathfrak{B}(\Psi)\, q_1 = \mathfrak{B}(\Psi)\, q_2$ holds for

$$L \xrightarrow{\ q_i\ } \mathfrak{B}\mathfrak{F}\mathfrak{B}(\mathfrak{A}) \xrightarrow{\ \mathfrak{B}(\Psi)\ } \mathfrak{B}(\mathfrak{A})$$

the equation $\Psi p_1 = \Psi p_2$ holds for

$$\mathfrak{F}L \xrightarrow{\ p_i\ } \mathfrak{F}\mathfrak{B}(\mathfrak{A}) \xrightarrow{\ \Psi\ } \mathfrak{A}$$

Because $\mathrm{Mor}_{\mathfrak{A}}(r, s) \cong \mathrm{Mor}_{\mathfrak{A}}(r, 1)^s$, the functor Ψ is surjective on the morphism sets. If $\Psi(\varphi) = \Psi(\psi)$, then

$$\varphi, \psi \in \mathrm{Mor}_{\mathfrak{F}\mathfrak{B}(\mathfrak{A})}(r, s) \cong \mathrm{Mor}_{\mathfrak{F}\mathfrak{B}(\mathfrak{A})}(r, 1)^s$$

and hence $p_s{}^i\Psi(\varphi) = p_s{}^i\Psi(\psi)$. But then $p_s{}^i\varphi,\ p_s{}^i\psi \in \mathrm{Mor}_{\mathfrak{F}\mathfrak{B}(\mathfrak{A})}(r, 1)$ with $\Psi(p_s{}^i\varphi) = \Psi(p_s{}^i\psi)$. Consequently, $p_s{}^i\varphi$ and $p_s{}^i\psi$ are equivalent for $i = 1,...,s$ with respect to the equivalence relation extended by (8). Also φ and ψ are equivalent by (2) and (6). Thus this new equivalence relation defines an algebraic theory isomorphic to $\mathfrak{A}$.

Thus each algebraic theory may be represented by giving H, $L \in \mathrm{Funct}(\mathcal{N}, \mathbf{S})$, and two morphisms $q_1,\ q_2 : L \to \mathfrak{B}\mathfrak{F}H$ (instead of $p_1,\ p_2 : \mathfrak{F}L \to \mathfrak{F}H$). One may choose $L(n)$ as above as pairs of elements in $\mathfrak{B}\mathfrak{F}H(n)$, such that $q_1(n)$ and $q_2(n)$ may be defined as projections onto the particular components. In the following we shall always proceed in this way.

The elements of $H(n)$ are called *n-ary operations*, the elements of $L(n)$ *identities of nth order*. Obviously one can use different n-ary operations and identities of nth order for the representation of the same algebraic theory. Thus also the elements of $\mathfrak{B}\mathfrak{A}(n)$ are called n-ary operations.

Example

An important example is the following representation. The represented algebraic theory is called the *algebraic theory of groups*.

n	$H(n)$	$L(n)$
0	$\{e\}$	$\varnothing$
1	$\{s\}$	$\{(m(1_1, s); e0_1), (m(1_1, e0_1); 1_1)\}$
2	$\{m\}$	$\varnothing$
3	$\varnothing$	$\{(m(m(p_3{}^1, p_3{}^2), p_3{}^3); m(p_3{}^1, m(p_3{}^2, p_3{}^3)))\}$

$$H(n) = L(n) = \varnothing \qquad \text{for} \quad n \geqslant 4$$

Explicitly this scheme for the algebraic theory of groups means that there exist morphisms $e : 0 \to 1$, $s : 1 \to 1$, and $m : 2 \to 1$ such that the following diagrams are commutative:

$$
\begin{array}{ccc}
1 & \xrightarrow{\ (1_1, s)\ } & 1 \times 1 \\
{\scriptstyle 0_1}\downarrow & & \downarrow{\scriptstyle m} \\
0 & \xrightarrow{\quad e \quad} & 1
\end{array}
$$

$$
\begin{array}{ccc}
1 & \xrightarrow{\ (1_1, e0_1)\ } & 1 \times 1 \\
& {\scriptstyle 1_1}\searrow & \downarrow{\scriptstyle m} \\
& & 1
\end{array}
$$

$$
\begin{array}{ccc}
1 \times 1 \times 1 & \xrightarrow{\ m \times 1_1\ } & 1 \times 1 \\
{\scriptstyle 1_1 \times m}\downarrow & & \downarrow{\scriptstyle m} \\
1 \times 1 & \xrightarrow{\quad m \quad} & 1
\end{array}
$$

where $0_1 : 1 \to 0$ is the morphism from 1 into the final object 0 and where $1_1 \times m = (p_3^1, m(p_3^2, p_3^3))$ and $m \times 1_1 = (m(p_3^1, p_3^2), p_3^3)$.

If one interprets e as the neutral element, s as forming inverses, and m as multiplication, then the diagrams represent the group axioms.

3.2 Algebraic Categories

Let $\mathfrak{A}$ be an algebraic theory. A product-preserving functor $A : \mathfrak{A} \to \mathbf{S}$ is called an $\mathfrak{A}$-*algebra*. A natural transformation $f : A \to B$ between two $\mathfrak{A}$-algebras A and B is called an $\mathfrak{A}$-*algebra homomorphism* or simply an $\mathfrak{A}$-*homomorphism*. The full subcategory of $\mathrm{Funct}(\mathfrak{A}, \mathbf{S})$ of product-preserving functors is denoted by $\mathrm{Funct}_\pi(\mathfrak{A}, \mathbf{S})$ and is called the *algebraic category* for the algebraic theory $\mathfrak{A}$. An $\mathfrak{A}$-algebra A is called *canonical* if $A(n) = A(1) \times \cdots \times A(1)$, where the right product is the set of n-tuples with elements of $A(1)$, and if $A(p_n{}^i)(x_1, \ldots, x_n) = x_i$ for all n and i.

Let the algebraic theory $\mathfrak{A}$ be represented by H and L, and let A be a canonical $\mathfrak{A}$-algebra. Then A induces a product-preserving functor $B : \mathfrak{F}H \to \mathfrak{A} \to \mathbf{S}$ which is a canonical $\mathfrak{F}H$-algebra. Let φ be an n-ary operation of $H(n)$, and let $A(1) = B(1) = X$. Then the map

$$B(\varphi) : X \times \cdots \times X \to X$$

is an n-ary operation on the set X in the sense of algebra. Let $(\varphi, \psi) \in L(n)$ be an identity of nth order. Then the two operations $B(\varphi)$ and $B(\psi)$ coincide on the set X, though the n-ary operations φ and ψ in $\mathfrak{F}H$ may be different. Thus an identity (or equation) for the operations on the set X is given. The $\mathfrak{A}$-algebra A is called an *equationally defined algebra*.

If $\mathfrak{A}$ is the algebraic theory of groups and A a canonical $\mathfrak{A}$-algebra, then A is a group. The maps

$$A(e) : \{\varnothing\} \to A(1), \quad A(s) : A(1) \to A(1), \qquad \text{and} \quad A(m) : A(1) \times A(1) \to A(1)$$

interpreted as neutral element, inverse map, and multiplication respectively make the following diagrams commutative

$$
\begin{array}{ccc}
A(1) & \xrightarrow{(1_{A(1)},A(s))} & A(1) \times A(1) \\
{\scriptstyle A(0_1)}\downarrow & & \downarrow{\scriptstyle A(m)} \\
\{\varnothing\} & \xrightarrow{\quad A(e) \quad} & A(1)
\end{array}
$$

$$
\begin{array}{ccc}
A(1) & \xrightarrow{(1_{A(1)},A(e0_1))} & A(1) \times A(1) \\
 & {\scriptstyle 1_{A(1)}}\searrow \qquad & \downarrow{\scriptstyle A(m)} \\
 & & A(1)
\end{array}
$$

$$
\begin{array}{ccc}
A(1) \times A(1) \times A(1) & \xrightarrow{A(m) \times 1_{A(1)}} & A(1) \times A(1) \\
{\scriptstyle 1_{A(1)} \times A(m)}\downarrow & & \downarrow{\scriptstyle A(m)} \\
A(1) \times A(1) & \xrightarrow{\quad A(m) \quad} & A(1)
\end{array}
$$

since A is a functor. Hence $A(1)$ is a group. Conversely, if G is a group with the multiplication $\mu: G \times G \to G$, the neutral element $\epsilon: \{\varnothing\} \to G$, and the inverse $\sigma: G \to G$, then we define $A(n) = G \times \cdots \times G$ (n times), $A(m) = \mu$, $A(e) = \epsilon$, and $A(s) = \sigma$. If we represent the algebraic theory $\mathfrak{A}$ of groups as in Section 3.1, then these data suffice to define uniquely a canonical $\mathfrak{F}H$-algebra $A: \mathfrak{F}H \to \mathbf{S}$. Since G is a group, all the identities of L hold for this $\mathfrak{F}H$-algebra. So this defines, in fact, a canonical $\mathfrak{A}$-algebra. This implies the following lemma.

LEMMA 1.   *There is a bijection between the class of all groups and the class of all canonical $\mathfrak{A}$-algebras, where $\mathfrak{A}$ is the algebraic theory of groups.*

Let $f : A \to B$ be an $\mathfrak{A}$-homomorphism of canonical $\mathfrak{A}$-algebras. Let $\varphi : n \to 1$ be an n-ary operation in $\mathfrak{A}$. Then the following diagram is commutative:

$$
\begin{array}{ccc}
A(1) \times \cdots \times A(1) & \xrightarrow{\ f(1) \times \cdots \times f(1)\ } & B(1) \times \cdots \times B(1) \\
{\scriptstyle A(\varphi)} \downarrow & & \downarrow {\scriptstyle B(\varphi)} \\
A(1) & \xrightarrow[\ \ \ \ \ \ \ \ \ \ f(1)\ \ \ \ \ \ \ \ \ \ ]{} & B(1)
\end{array}
$$

In fact, one easily verifies with the operations $p_n^{\,1},\ldots, p_n^{\,n}$ that $f(n) = f(1) \times \cdots \times f(1)$. If f is a map from $A(1)$ to $B(1)$ such that the above diagram is commutative for all n and all n-ary operations φ, then f is an $\mathfrak{A}$-homomorphism. Thus the $\mathfrak{A}$-homomorphisms are homomorphisms in the sense of algebra, compatible with the operations. So it suffices to give a map $f : A(1) \to B(1)$ compatible with the n-ary operations in $H(n)$ for all n, if one defines $f(n) = f \times \cdots \times f$. Then f is already an $\mathfrak{A}$-homomorphism. This follows directly from the definition of $\mathfrak{F}H$.

For the example of the algebraic theory of groups, this means that the group homomorphisms may be bijectively mapped onto the $\mathfrak{A}$-homomorphisms of the corresponding $\mathfrak{A}$-algebras and, consequently, that the category of groups is isomorphic to the full subcategory of the canonical $\mathfrak{A}$-algebras of $\mathrm{Funct}_\pi(\mathfrak{A}, \mathbf{S})$.

LEMMA 2. *Let $\mathfrak{A}$ be an algebraic theory. Then each $\mathfrak{A}$-algebra A is isomorphic to a canonical $\mathfrak{A}$-algebra B in $\mathrm{Funct}_\pi(\mathfrak{A}, \mathbf{S})$.*

Proof. Let $B(1) := A(1)$ and $B(n) := B(1) \times \cdots \times B(1)$. Let $B(p_n^{\,i})$ be the projection onto the ith component of the n-tuples in $B(1) \times \cdots \times B(1)$. Then $B(n)$ is an n-fold product of $B(1)$ with itself. Thus there exist uniquely determined isomorphisms $A(n) \cong B(n)$, such that for all projections the diagram

$$
\begin{array}{ccc}
A(n) & \cong & B(n) \\
{\scriptstyle A(p_n^{\,i})} \downarrow & & \downarrow {\scriptstyle B(p_n^{\,i})} \\
A(1) & = & B(1)
\end{array}
$$

is commutative. Let $\varphi : n \to 1$ be an arbitrary n-ary operation in $\mathfrak{A}$. Then $B(\varphi)$ is uniquely determined by the commutativity of

$$
\begin{array}{ccc}
A(n) & \cong & B(n) \\
{\scriptstyle A(\varphi)} \downarrow & & \downarrow {\scriptstyle B(\varphi)} \\
A(1) & = & B(1)
\end{array}
$$

It is easy to verify that B is a canonical $\mathfrak{A}$-algebra, which then by construction is isomorphic to A.

Using Section 2.1, Proposition 3 we obtain the following corollary.

COROLLARY 1. *Let A be the algebraic theory of groups. Then $\mathrm{Funct}_\pi(A, \mathbf{S})$ is equivalent to the category of groups. The full subcategory of canonical $\mathfrak{A}$-algebras is isomorphic to the category of groups.*

Thus far we have discussed only the example of groups in detail. But similar considerations hold for each category of equationally defined algebras in the sense of (universal) algebra, in particular the categories $\mathbf{S}$, $\mathbf{S}^*$, $\mathbf{Ab}$, $_R\mathbf{Mod}$, and $\mathbf{Ri}$. For $\mathbf{Ri}$ choose for a representation of the corresponding algebraic theory the

$$0\text{-ary operations:} \quad 0, 1$$

$$1\text{-ary operation:} \quad -$$

$$2\text{-ary operations:} \quad +, \cdot$$

The identities are, apart from the group properties with respect to $+$, the associativity and the distributivity of the multiplication, the commutativity of the addition, and the property of 1 as the neutral element of the multiplication. The reader can construct the corresponding diagrams easily.

$\mathbf{S}$ is defined by $H = \varnothing$ and $L = \varnothing$. Thus the corresponding algebraic theory is $\mathbf{N}^0$.

Another interesting example is $_R\mathbf{Mod}$. Here the operations are e, s, and m for the group property and, in addition, all elements of R considered as unary operations. Hence this is an example where $H(1)$ may be infinite. The identities arise as in the above example for rings from the defining equations for R-modules.

Let $\mathrm{Funct}_\pi(\mathfrak{A}, \mathbf{S})$ be an algebraic category. The evaluation on $1 \in \mathfrak{A}$ defines a functor $\mathfrak{B} : \mathrm{Funct}_\pi(\mathfrak{A}, \mathbf{S}) \to \mathbf{S}$ with $\mathfrak{B}(A) = A(1)$ and $\mathfrak{B}(f) = f(1)$. This functor will be called the *forgetful functor*. The set $\mathfrak{B}(A) = A(1)$ is called the *underlying set* of the $\mathfrak{A}$-algebra A.

THEOREM. *Let $\mathfrak{A}$ be an algebraic theory. The algebraic category $\mathrm{Funct}_\pi(\mathfrak{A}, \mathbf{S})$ is complete, the limits are formed argumentwise, and the forgetful functor into the category of sets preserves limits and is faithful.*

Proof. By Section 2.7, Theorem 1 $\mathrm{Funct}(\mathfrak{A}, \mathbf{S})$ is complete and the limits are formed argumentwise. Since limits commute with products, a limit of product-preserving functors is again product preserving. Since the forgetful functor is the evaluation on $1 \in A$ and since limits are formed argumentwise, $\mathfrak{B}$ preserves limits. Let f, $g : A \to B$ be two $\mathfrak{A}$-homomorphisms and let $f(1) = g(1)$, then $f(n) = g(n)$ for all $n \in \mathfrak{A}$, since all diagrams

$$
\begin{array}{ccc}
A(n) & \xrightarrow{\,f(n)\,} & B(n) \\
{\scriptstyle A(p_n{}^i)}\Big\downarrow & & \Big\downarrow{\scriptstyle B(p_n{}^i)} \\
A(1) & \xrightarrow{\,g(1)\,} & B(1)
\end{array}
$$

are commutative. Consequently, $\mathfrak{B}$ is faithful.

COROLLARY 2. *Let $f : A \to B$ be an $\mathfrak{A}$-homomorphism of $\mathfrak{A}$-algebras. f is a monomorphism in $\mathrm{Funct}_\pi(\mathfrak{A}, \mathbf{S})$ if and only if $f(1)$ is injective.*

Proof. $\mathfrak{B}$, being faithful, reflects monomorphisms (Section 2.12, Lemma 1). $\mathfrak{B}$, preserving limits, preserves monomorphisms (Section 2.6, Corollary 5).

A subobject $f : A \to B$ is called a *subalgebra*. The corollary implies that $\mathrm{Funct}_\pi(\mathfrak{A}, \mathbf{S})$ is locally small since $\mathfrak{B}$ is faithful and $\mathbf{S}$ is locally small.

The Theorem and Corollary 2 are generalizations of some assertions we made in Chapter 1 for $\mathbf{S}$, $\mathbf{S}^*$, $\mathbf{Gr}$, $\mathbf{Ab}$, $\mathbf{Ri}$, and $_R\mathbf{Mod}$.

The example $\mathbb{Z} \to \mathbb{P}$ in $\mathbf{Ri}$ of Section 1.5 shows that epimorphisms in $\mathrm{Funct}_\pi(\mathfrak{A}, \mathbf{S})$ are not necessarily surjective maps (after the application of the forgetful functor). So the example in Section 1.5, which shows that in $\mathbf{Gr}$ (and also in $\mathbf{Ab}$) the epimorphisms are exactly the surjective maps, becomes all the more interesting.

3.3   Free Algebras

Let $\mathbf{A} : \mathbf{N}^0 \to \mathfrak{A}$ be an algebraic theory. We construct a product-preserving functor $\mathbf{A}_\infty : \mathbf{S}^0 \to \mathfrak{A}_\infty$ which is bijective on the object classes, and a full faithful functor $\mathscr{I}_\infty : \mathfrak{A} \to \mathfrak{A}_\infty$ such that the diagram

$$
\begin{array}{ccc}
\mathbf{N}^0 & \xrightarrow{\;\mathbf{A}\;} & \mathfrak{A} \\
\Big\downarrow & & \Big\downarrow{\scriptstyle \mathscr{I}_\infty} \\
\mathbf{S}^0 & \xrightarrow{\;\mathbf{A}_\infty\;} & \mathfrak{A}_\infty
\end{array}
$$

is commutative where $\mathbf{N}^0 \to \mathbf{S}^0$ is the natural embedding. We may identify the objects of $\mathfrak{A}_\infty$ with the objects in $\mathbf{S}^0$. For two sets X and Y, we define $\text{Mor}_{\mathfrak{A}_\infty}(X, Y) = \text{Mor}_{\mathfrak{A}_\infty}(X, 1)^Y$. Then $\mathbf{A}_\infty$ will become a product-preserving functor.

For the definition of $\text{Mor}_{\mathfrak{A}_\infty}(X, 1)$ let X^* be the set of triples (f, n, g) where $f : X \to n$ is a morphism in $\mathbf{S}^0$ and where $g : n \to 1$ is a morphism in $\mathfrak{A}$. Here n is a finite set in $\mathbf{N}^0$. We call two elements (f, n, g) and (f', n', g') in X^* equivalent if there is a finite set n'' in $\mathbf{N}^0$ and if there are morphisms $X \to n''$, $n'' \to n'$, and $n'' \to n$ in $\mathbf{S}^0$ such that the diagrams

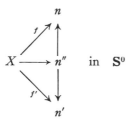

in $\mathbf{S}^0$

and

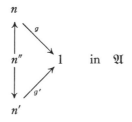

in $\mathfrak{A}$

are commutative.

This relation is an equivalence relation. We only have to show the transitivity. Let $(f, n, g) \sim (f', n', g')$ and $(f', n', g') \sim (f'', n'', g'')$ and let n^* and n^{**} be elements which induce the equivalences. Let m be the fiber product of $n^* \to n'$ with $n^{**} \to n'$. Then the diagram

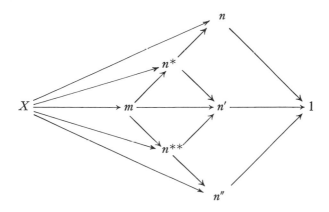

is commutative. (Compare the morphisms in the corresponding categories.) Let $\mathrm{Mor}_{\mathfrak{A}_\infty}(X, 1)$ be the set of equivalence classes.

LEMMA 1. $\mathfrak{A}_\infty$ *is a category.*

Proof.   Let (f, n, g) be a representative of an element in $\mathrm{Mor}_{\mathfrak{A}_\infty}(X, 1)$. Then f^0 is a map from n into X in the category **S**. Let n' be the image of n under this map. Then we may decompose $f : X \to n$ as follows $X \xrightarrow{f'} n' \to n$. Obviously then (f', n', gh) is equivalent to (f, n, g). Furthermore, n' is (up to equivalence of monomorphisms) a finite subset of X. Such a representative will be called reduced.

Let $((f_i, n_i, g_i)_{i \in Y}) : X \to Y$ and $(f', n', g') : Y \to 1$ be reduced representatives of morphisms in $\mathfrak{A}_\infty$. Let $r = \sum_{i \in n'} n_i$ (disjoint union or coproduct in **N**). Then by the product property of r in $\mathbf{S}^0$, the following morphisms are defined: $f : X \to r$ by the f_i and $g : r \to n'$ by the g_i. Then let the composition of the given morphisms be $(f, r, g'g)$. This composition still depends on the choice of the representatives. Let (f'', n'', g'') be reduced and equivalent to (f', n', g'). Without loss of generality we may assume that $n' \subseteq n'' \subseteq Y$ in **S** and that $hf'' = f'$ and $g'h = g''$ for $h : n'' \to n'$ in $\mathbf{S}^0$. Let $r' = \sum_{i \in n''} n_i$, then

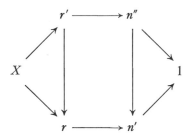

is commutative. Similarly one shows that the composition does not depend on the choice of the representatives of the (f_i, n_i, g_i).

Let $p_x : X \to 1$ be the projections from X into 1 in $\mathbf{S}^0$. Then $((p_x, 1, 1_1)_{x \in X})$ is the identity on X in $\mathfrak{A}_\infty$. In fact, given $(f, n, g) : X \to 1$, then $(f, n, g)((p_x, 1, 1_1)_{x \in X}) = (f, n, g)$. Given $((f_i, n_i, g_i)_{i \in X}) : Y \to X$, then $(p_x, 1, 1_1)((f_i, n_i, g_i)_{i \in X}) = (f_x, n_x, g_x)$.

To prove the associativity let $((f_y, n_y, g_y)_{y \in Y}) : X \to Y$,

$$((f_z, n_z, g_z)_{z \in Z}) : Y \to Z, \quad \text{and} \quad (f, n, g) : Z \to 1$$

be reduced representatives of morphisms in $\mathfrak{A}_\infty$. It is easy to see that

$$\sum_{z \in n} \sum_{y \in n_z} n_y = \sum_{y \in r} n_y \quad \text{with} \quad r = \sum_{z \in n} n_z$$

implies that the composition is associative.

COROLLARY. *There exists a product-preserving functor* $A_\infty : S^0 \to \mathfrak{A}_\infty$ *which is bijective on the classes of objects and a full faithful functor* $\mathscr{I}_\infty : \mathfrak{A} \to \mathfrak{A}_\infty$ *such that*

$$
\begin{array}{ccc}
N^0 & \xrightarrow{\ A\ } & \mathfrak{A} \\[4pt]
\downarrow & & \downarrow{\scriptstyle \mathscr{I}_\infty} \\[4pt]
S^0 & \xrightarrow{\ A_\infty\ } & \mathfrak{A}_\infty
\end{array}
$$

is commutative.

Proof. It suffices to define A_∞ on the projections $p_x : X \to 1$. Let $A_\infty(p_x) = (p_x, 1, 1_1)$. Then it is clear that A_∞ preserves products. Let $\mathscr{I}_\infty(n) = n$ and $\mathscr{I}_\infty(g) = (1_n, n, g)$ for $g : n \to 1$ in $\mathfrak{A}$. Since we have $(1_n, n, g) \sim (g, 1, 1_1)$ for $g : n \to 1$ in N^0, the square is commutative.

We still have to show that $\mathscr{I}_\infty$ is full and faithful. Given $f, g : n \to 1$ in $\mathfrak{A}$. Let $(1_n, n, f) \sim (1_n, n, g)$ in $\mathfrak{A}_\infty$. Then there exist n' and $l : n \to n'$ with a commutative diagram

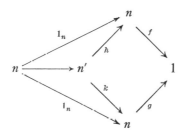

Hence $hl = 1_n$ and $kl = 1_n$. Furthermore, $fh = gk$. By composition with l we then get $f = g$. Thus $\mathscr{I}_\infty$ is faithful. Now let $n' \xrightarrow{f} n \xrightarrow{g} 1$ in $\mathfrak{A}_\infty$ be given. Then $(f, n, g) \sim (1_{n'}, n', gf)$ and $\mathscr{I}_\infty(gf) = (1_{n'}, n', gf)$. Hence $\mathscr{I}_\infty$ is full and faithful.

LEMMA 2. *Let* $A : \mathfrak{A} \to S$ *be a product-preserving functor. Then there exists up to an isomorphism exactly one product-preserving functor* $A' : \mathfrak{A}_\infty \to S$ *with* $A'\mathscr{I}_\infty = A$.

Proof. In order that $A'\mathscr{I}_\infty = A$ and that A' preserves products, we must have $A'(X) \cong A'(1)^X$ and $A'(1) = A(1)$. Furthermore, $A'(p_x, 1, 1_1) \cong A(1)^{p_x}$ and $A'(1_n, n, g) = A(g)$ must hold. By composition $A'(f, n, g) \cong A(g) A(1)^f$ must hold. With these definitions, A' is a product-preserving functor and, in fact, $A'\mathscr{I}_\infty = A$ holds.

LEMMA 3. *Let A, $B : \mathfrak{A} \to \mathbf{S}$ be product-preserving functors and A', B' be the extensions to $\mathfrak{A}_\infty$ as constructed in Lemma 2. Let $\varphi : A \to B$ be a natural transformation. Then there is exactly one natural transformation $\varphi' : A' \to B'$ with $\varphi' \mathscr{I}_\infty = \varphi$.*

Proof. We define $\varphi'(X) \cong \varphi(1)^X : A(1)^X \to B(1)^X$. Obviously this is the only possibility for a definition of φ' because the functors A' and B' preserve products. At the same time it is clear that φ' behaves naturally with respect to all projections between the products. But φ' is natural also with respect to the morphisms in $\mathfrak{A}$, since we only have to consider the restriction $\varphi' \mathscr{I}_\infty = \varphi$.

THEOREM 1. *Let $\mathfrak{A}$ be an algebraic theory. The forgetful functor $\mathscr{V} : \mathrm{Funct}_\pi(\mathfrak{A}, \mathbf{S}) \to \mathbf{S}$ is monadic.*

Proof. We define a functor $\mathscr{F} : \mathbf{S} \to \mathrm{Funct}_\pi(\mathfrak{A}, \mathbf{S})$ by $\mathscr{F}(X)(-) = \mathrm{Mor}_{\mathfrak{A}_\infty}(X, -)$. Then

$$\mathrm{Mor}_{\mathbf{S}}(X, \mathscr{V}A) \cong \mathrm{Mor}_{\mathbf{S}}(X, A(1)) \cong A(1)^X \cong A'(X)$$

$$\cong \mathrm{Mor}_f(\mathrm{Mor}_{A_\infty}(X, -), A') = \mathrm{Mor}_f(\mathscr{F}(X), A)$$

holds naturally for $X \in \mathbf{S}$ and $A \in \mathrm{Funct}_\pi(\mathfrak{A}, \mathbf{S})$ where we used the last two lemmas.

Now we use Section 2.3, Theorem 2. Let f_0, $f_1 : A \to B$ be a $\mathscr{V}$-contractible pair in $\mathrm{Funct}_\pi(\mathfrak{A}, \mathbf{S})$. Since there are difference cokernels in $\mathbf{S}$ we get a commutative diagram in $\mathbf{S}$:

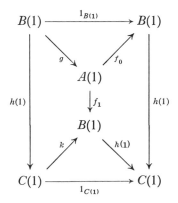

where we wrote f_i instead of $f_i(1)$. If we form the n-fold product of all objects and morphisms of this diagram, we get again a corresponding diagram. In particular

$$A(n) \underset{f_1(n)}{\overset{f_0(n)}{\rightrightarrows}} B(n) \xrightarrow{(h(1))^n} C(1)^n$$

is a difference cokernel. Given $\varphi : n \to 1$ we get a commutative diagram

$$
\begin{array}{ccc}
A(n) \rightrightarrows B(n) \longrightarrow C(1)^n \\
\downarrow{\scriptstyle A(\varphi)} \quad \downarrow{\scriptstyle B(\varphi)} \quad \downarrow{\scriptstyle C(\varphi)} \\
A(1) \rightrightarrows B(1) \longrightarrow C(1)
\end{array}
$$

where $C(\varphi)$ is uniquely determined by the property of the difference cokernel. Thus $C : \mathfrak{A} \to \mathbf{S}$ with $C(n) := C(1)^n$ is a product-preserving functor and $h : B \to C$ a natural transformation which is uniquely determined by $h(1) : B(1) \to C(1)$. Since $C(n)$ is a difference cokernel for all $n \in \mathfrak{A}$, C is a difference cokernel of (f_0, f_1) in $\mathrm{Funct}_\pi(\mathfrak{A}, \mathbf{S})$.

This theorem shows that the $\mathfrak{A}$-algebras and $\mathfrak{A}$-homomorphisms are exactly the $\mathscr{V}\mathscr{F}$-algebras and $\mathscr{V}\mathscr{F}$-homomorphisms in the sense of Section 2.3. Thus the free $\mathscr{V}\mathscr{F}$-algebras are also called *free $\mathfrak{A}$-algebras*. $\mathscr{F}(X)$ is called *free $\mathfrak{A}$-algebra freely generated by the set X*.

PROPOSITION. *Let $\mathscr{H}$ be the monad defined by $\mathscr{V}$ and $\mathscr{F}$. Then there exists an isomorphism between $(\mathbf{S}_{\mathscr{H}})^0$ (in the sense of Section 2.3) and $\mathfrak{A}_\infty$ such that*

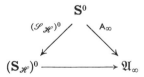

is commutative.

Proof. The correspondence for the objects is clear because $(\mathscr{S}_{\mathscr{H}})^0$ and A_∞ are bijective for the object classes. For the morphisms

$$\mathrm{Mor}_{\mathfrak{A}_\infty}(X, Y) \cong \mathrm{Mor}_f(\mathrm{Mor}_{\mathfrak{A}_\infty}(Y, -), \mathrm{Mor}_{\mathfrak{A}_\infty}(X, -))$$

holds naturally in the objects X and Y in $\mathfrak{A}_\infty$ by the Yoneda lemma. By definition, the morphisms between the objects X and Y in $\mathbf{S}_{\mathscr{H}}$ are exactly the morphisms of the $\mathscr{H}$-algebras $(\mathscr{H}X, \mu X)$ and $(\mathscr{H}Y, \mu Y)$ and hence the morphisms of the free $\mathfrak{A}$-algebras $\mathscr{F}(X) = \mathrm{Mor}_{\mathfrak{A}_\infty}(X, -)$ and $\mathscr{F}(Y) = \mathrm{Mor}_{\mathfrak{A}_\infty}(Y, -)$. By definition

$$\mathrm{Mor}_{\mathbf{S}\mathscr{H}}(Y, X) \cong \mathrm{Mor}_f(\mathrm{Mor}_{\mathfrak{A}_\infty}(Y, -), \mathrm{Mor}_{\mathfrak{A}_\infty}(X, -))$$

is natural in the $\mathfrak{A}_\infty$-objects ($= \mathbf{S}_{\mathscr{H}}$-objects). Hence $\mathrm{Mor}_{\mathfrak{A}_\infty}(X, Y) \cong \mathrm{Mor}_{\mathscr{C}^0}(X, Y)$ with $\mathscr{C} = \mathbf{S}_{\mathscr{H}}$. Let $f : X \to X'$ and $g : Y' \to Y$ be morphisms in $\mathfrak{A}_\infty$ and let f' and g' be the corresponding morphisms in $(\mathbf{S}_{\mathscr{H}})^0$, then the Yoneda lemma implies that

$$
\begin{array}{ccc}
\mathrm{Mor}_{\mathfrak{A}_\infty}(X', Y') & \cong & \mathrm{Mor}_{\mathscr{C}^0}(X', Y') \\
{\scriptstyle \mathrm{Mor}_{\mathfrak{A}_\infty}(f,g)} \downarrow & & \downarrow {\scriptstyle \mathrm{Mor}_{\mathscr{C}^0}(f',g')} \\
\mathrm{Mor}_{\mathfrak{A}_\infty}(X, Y) & \cong & \mathrm{Mor}_{\mathscr{C}^0}(X, Y)
\end{array}
$$

is commutative. So the compositions under this application of morphisms coincide.

This clarifies the significance of the construction of Kleisli in Section 2.3, Theorem 1. Conversely, we now have a method at hand to reconstruct the algebraic theory from an algebraic category $\mathrm{Funct}_\pi(\mathfrak{A}, \mathbf{S})$ and the corresponding forgetful functor. One has to restrict $(\mathscr{S}_{\mathscr{H}})^0 : \mathbf{S}^0 \to (\mathbf{S}_{\mathscr{H}})^0$ only to the full subcategory $\mathbf{N}^0$ of $\mathbf{S}^0$.
With these means we can also show the significance of consistent algebraic theories.

THEOREM 2. *Let* $\mathsf{A} : \mathbf{N}^0 \to \mathfrak{A}$ *be an algebraic theory,* $\mathrm{Funct}_\pi(\mathfrak{A}, \mathbf{S})$ *the corresponding algebraic theory and* $\mathscr{H}$ *the monad defined by the monadic forgetful functor* $\mathscr{V} : \mathrm{Funct}_\pi(\mathfrak{A}, \mathbf{S}) \to \mathbf{S}$. *Then the following are equivalent*:

(1) $\mathsf{A} : \mathbf{N}^0 \to \mathfrak{A}$ *is consistent.*
(2)   *There exists an* $\mathfrak{A}$*-algebra* A *whose underlying set has more than one element.*
(3)   *The natural transformation* $\epsilon : \mathrm{Id}_\mathbf{S} \to \mathscr{H}$ *is argumentwise a monomorphism.*
(4) $\mathscr{H} : \mathbf{S} \to \mathbf{S}$ *is faithful.*

Proof.   (1) $\Rightarrow$ (2): Since A is faithful, $\mathrm{Mor}_{\mathfrak{A}}(n, 1)$ has at least n elements, the projections. But $\mathrm{Mor}_{\mathfrak{A}}(n, -)$ is the free algebra generated by n.
(2) $\Rightarrow$ (3): Let (A, α) be an $\mathscr{H}$-algebra and let A have more than one element. Let X be an arbitrary set. Then there is an injective map $i : X \to A^X$. Since $\alpha\epsilon(A) : A \to \mathscr{H}A \to A$ is the identity on A the map $\epsilon(A)$ is injective and hence also $\epsilon(A)i$. Since ϵ is a natural transformation we get $\epsilon(A)i = H(i)\,\epsilon(X)$. Thus $\epsilon(X) : X \to \mathscr{H}(X)$ is a monomorphism.

(3) ⇒ (4): Let f, $g : X \to Y$ be two maps in **S** with $\mathscr{H}f = \mathscr{H}g$. Since $\epsilon(Y)$ is a monomorphism and $\epsilon(Y)f = \mathscr{H}f\epsilon(X)$, we get $f = g$. Hence, $\mathscr{H}$ is faithful.

(4) ⇒ (1): $\mathscr{S}_{\mathscr{H}}$ is faithful because $\mathscr{H}$ is (Section 2.3, Corollary). So $(\mathscr{S}_{\mathscr{H}})^0$ restricted to $\mathbf{N}^0$ is faithful and consequently **A** also is.

3.4   Algebraic Functors

Let $\mathfrak{A}$ be an algebraic theory, $\mathscr{V} : \mathrm{Funct}_\pi(\mathfrak{A}, \mathbf{S}) \to \mathbf{S}$ the corresponding forgetful functor, and $\mathscr{H}$ the corresponding monad.

LEMMA 1.   *Let $f : (A, \alpha) \to (B, \beta)$ be a morphism of $\mathscr{H}$-algebras. Then on the set $f(A) = C$ there exists exactly one $\mathscr{H}$-algebra structure $\gamma : \mathscr{H}C \to C$, such that the factorization morphisms $g : A \to C$ and $h : C \to B$ of f are morphisms of $\mathscr{H}$-algebras.*

Proof.   We use the following commutative diagram:

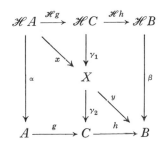

where $hg = f$, g is a surjective map, and h is an injective map, that is the factorization of f through the image of f. Since g is a retraction and h is a section (in **S**), $\mathscr{H}g$ and $\mathscr{H}h$ is a factorization of $\mathscr{H}f$ through the image of $\mathscr{H}f$. Let x and y be the factorization of $\beta\mathscr{H}f = f\alpha$ through the image. Then there are maps γ_1 and γ_2 making the above diagram commutative. But $\gamma = \gamma_2\gamma_1$ is the only morphism making both squares in the diagram commutative, since h is a monomorphism and $\mathscr{H}g$ is an epimorphism. If one uses the fact that g, $\mathscr{H}g$, and $\mathscr{H}\mathscr{H}g$ are retractions, then the axioms for an algebra are easy to verify.

COROLLARY 1. $\mathrm{Funct}_\pi(\mathfrak{A}, \mathbf{S})$ *has epimorphic images. The resulting epimorphisms are surjective on the underlying sets.*

Proof. The corollary is implied by Lemma 1 of this section, Corollary 2 of Section 3.2, and Section 3.3, Theorem 1.

Although $\text{Funct}_\pi(\mathfrak{A}, \mathbf{S})$ has epimorphic images, the example of **Ri** shows that $\text{Funct}_\pi(\mathfrak{A}, \mathbf{S})$ is not balanced in general. On the other hand, a bijective morphism of $\mathscr{H}$-algebras is an isomorphism because $\mathscr{H}$ preserves isomorphisms.

Let (A, α) be an $\mathscr{H}$-algebra and X a subset of A. This defines a morphism $\mathscr{S}^{\mathscr{H}}(X) \to (A, \alpha)$. Let (B, β) be the image of this morphism. Then $X \subseteq B \subseteq A$ and (B, β) is the smallest subalgebra of (A, α) containing X. In fact, there is an $\mathscr{H}$-homomorphism from $\mathscr{S}^{\mathscr{H}}(X)$ into each subalgebra of (A, α) containing X. (B, β) is called the *subalgebra of (A, α) generated by X*. An $\mathscr{H}$-algebra (A, α) is *generated* by the set X if $X \subseteq A$ and if (A, α) coincides with the subalgebra of (A, α) generated by X. If X is finite, then (A, α) is said to be *finitely generated*.

LEMMA 2. *There is only a set of nonisomorphic $\mathscr{H}$-algebras generated by X.*

Proof. Let $X \subseteq A$ and $f : \mathscr{H}X \to A$ be a surjective map. Then on A there is at most one $\mathscr{H}$-algebra structure $\alpha : \mathscr{H}A \to A$ such that $f : \mathscr{S}^{\mathscr{H}}(X) \to (A, \alpha)$ is a homomorphism of algebras. In fact, in the diagram

$$
\begin{array}{ccc}
\mathscr{H}\mathscr{H}X & \xrightarrow{\;\mathscr{H}f\;} & \mathscr{H}A \\
{\scriptstyle \mu(X)}\big\downarrow & & \big\downarrow{\scriptstyle \alpha} \\
\mathscr{H}X & \xrightarrow{\;f\;} & A
\end{array}
$$

$\mathscr{H}f$ is a surjective map. There is an $\mathscr{H}$-algebra structure on A if and only if (A, α) is generated by X. Since there is only a set of nonisomorphic surjective maps with domain $\mathscr{H}X$ the lemma is proved.

COROLLARY 2. *There is only a set of nonisomorphic $\mathscr{H}$-algebras generated by epimorphic images of X.*

Proof. X has only a set of nonisomorphic epimorphic images.

Let $\mathscr{G} : \mathfrak{A} \to \mathfrak{B}$ be a morphism of algebraic theories. By composition $\mathscr{G}$ induces a functor

$$\text{Funct}_\pi(\mathscr{G}, \mathbf{S}) : \text{Funct}_\pi(\mathfrak{B}, \mathbf{S}) \to \text{Funct}_\pi(\mathfrak{A}, \mathbf{S})$$

called the *algebraic functor*. Furthermore, the diagram

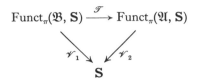

$$\text{Funct}_\pi(\mathfrak{B}, \mathbf{S}) \xrightarrow{\ \mathscr{T}\ } \text{Funct}_\pi(\mathfrak{A}, \mathbf{S})$$

is commutative, where $\mathscr{T} = \text{Funct}_\pi(\mathscr{G}, \mathbf{S})$ and where the $\mathscr{V}_i$ are the forgetful functors.

LEMMA 3. *Let $A \in \text{Funct}_\pi(\mathfrak{A}, \mathbf{S})$ and $B \in \text{Funct}_\pi(\mathfrak{B}, \mathbf{S})$. Let $f : A \to \mathscr{T}B$ be an $\mathfrak{A}$-homomorphism. Then there exists a minimal B-subalgebra B' of B such that there is an $\mathfrak{A}$-homomorphism $g : A \to \mathscr{T}B'$ making the diagram*

$$A \xrightarrow{\ g\ } \mathscr{T}B'$$
$$\mathscr{T}B$$

commutative.

Proof. Let $\mathscr{A} = \text{Funct}_\pi(\mathfrak{A}, \mathbf{S})$. The functor $\text{Mor}_\mathscr{A}(A, \mathscr{T}-)$: $\text{Funct}_\pi(\mathfrak{B}, \mathbf{S}) \to \mathbf{S}$ preserves limits and $\text{Funct}_\pi(\mathfrak{B}, \mathbf{S})$ is locally small and complete. By the Lemma of Section 2.11, to each $f : A \to \mathscr{T}B$ there is a minimal subobject $B' \subseteq B$ and a morphism $g : A \to \mathscr{T}B'$ such that the diagram becomes commutative.

THEOREM 1. *Each algebraic functor is monadic.*

Proof. Let $\mathscr{T}$, $\mathscr{V}_1$, and $\mathscr{V}_2$ be as in Lemma 3. Let f_0, $f_1 : A \to B$ in $\text{Funct}_\pi(\mathfrak{B}, \mathbf{S})$ be $\mathscr{T}$-contractible. Then f_0, f_1 is $\mathscr{V}_1$-contractible too because of $\mathscr{V}_1 = \mathscr{V}_2 \mathscr{T}$. There exists a difference cokernel $g : \mathscr{T}B \to C$ of $\mathscr{T}f_0$, $\mathscr{T}f_1$ in $\text{Funct}_\pi(\mathfrak{A}, \mathbf{S})$ if and only if there exists a difference cokernel $h : \mathscr{V}_1 \to X$ of $\mathscr{V}_2 \mathscr{T}f_0$, $\mathscr{V}_2 \mathscr{T}f_1$ in $\mathbf{S}$. Then there exists also a difference cokernel $k : B \to D$ of f_0, f_1 in $\text{Funct}_\pi(\mathfrak{B}, \mathbf{S})$ and $\mathscr{V}_2 \mathscr{T}k = \mathscr{V}_1 k = h = \mathscr{V}_2 g$. Since $\mathscr{V}_2$ generates the difference cokernels under consideration, we get $\mathscr{T}k = g$. k is uniquely determined by $\mathscr{V}_2 g = h$ since $\mathscr{V}_1$ is monadic. Hence $\mathscr{T}$ generates difference cokernels of $\mathscr{T}$-contractible pairs.

By Section 2.3, Lemma 5 the functor $\mathscr{V}_2$ generates isomorphisms. There is a uniquely determined morphism $f : \mathscr{T} \varprojlim \mathscr{D} \to \varprojlim \mathscr{T}\mathscr{D}$ in $\text{Funct}_\pi(\mathfrak{A}, \mathbf{S})$ for a diagram $\mathscr{D}$ in $\text{Funct}_\pi(\mathfrak{B}, \mathbf{S})$ which is determined by the universal property of the limit. But $\mathscr{V}_2 f$ is an isomorphism since $\mathscr{V}_1 = \mathscr{V}_2 \mathscr{T}$ preserves limits. Hence f is an isomorphism. Consequently, $\mathscr{T}$ preserves limits.

By Section 2.9, Theorem 2, it is sufficient to find solution sets for $\mathscr{T}$. Let $A \in \mathrm{Funct}_\pi(\mathfrak{A}, \mathbf{S})$ and $f : A \to \mathscr{T} B$ be an $\mathfrak{A}$-homomorphism. By Lemma 3, the set given in Corollary 2 is a solution set of A with respect to $\mathscr{T}$.

THEOREM 2. *Let $\mathfrak{A}$ be an algebraic theory. Then the functor* $\mathrm{Funct}_\pi(\mathfrak{A}, \mathbf{S}) \to \mathrm{Funct}(\mathfrak{A}, \mathbf{S})$ *defined by the embedding is monadic.*

Proof. It is sufficient to show that $\mathrm{Funct}_\pi(\mathfrak{A}, \mathbf{S})$ is a reflexive subcategory of $\mathrm{Funct}(\mathfrak{A}, \mathbf{S})$ (Section 2.4, Theorem 2). By the construction of the limits in both categories (argumentwise) the embedding preserves limits. Let $A \in \mathrm{Funct}(\mathfrak{A}, \mathbf{S})$ and $B \in \mathrm{Funct}_\pi(\mathfrak{A}, \mathbf{S})$. Let $f : A \to B$ be a natural transformation. Let $B' \subseteq B$ be the $\mathfrak{A}$-subalgebra of B generated by $f(A(1))$. Let $\varphi : n \to 1$ be an n-ary operation in $\mathfrak{A}$. Then the following diagram is commutative:

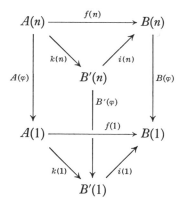

Here $k(n)$ is uniquely defined by the fact that $B'(n)$ is an n-fold product of $B'(1)$ with itself. For $\varphi = p_n{}^i$ the diagram is commutative by definition. In the general case we only have to prove the commutativity $B'(\varphi)\, k(n) = k(1)\, A(\varphi)$. But this holds because $i(1)$ is an injective morphism. Thus, by Corollary 2 a solution set is given.

COROLLARY 3. $\mathrm{Funct}_\pi(\mathfrak{A}, \mathbf{S})$ *is cocomplete.*

Proof. Section 2.11, Theorem 3 and the dual of Section 2.7, Theorem 1 imply the corollary.

Let $\mathscr{T} : \mathscr{C} \to \mathscr{D}$ be a functor. A morphism $f : A \to B$ is called a *relatively split epimorphism* if f is an epimorphism and $\mathscr{T}f$ is a retraction. Dually, one defines a *relatively split monomorphism*. An object $P \in \mathscr{C}$ is said to be *relatively projective (relatively injective)* if for all relatively split epimorphisms (monomorphisms) f in $\mathscr{C}$ the map $\mathrm{Mor}_{\mathscr{C}}(P, f)$ $(\mathrm{Mor}_{\mathscr{C}}(f, P))$ is surjective. If $\mathscr{T}$ is the identity functor, then all objects are relatively projective and relatively injective (Section 1.10, Lemma 3). If $\mathscr{T}$ has a left adjoint functor $\mathscr{S}$, then $\mathscr{S}D$ is relatively projective for all $D \in \mathscr{D}$. In fact, $\mathrm{Mor}_{\mathscr{C}}(\mathscr{S}D, f) \cong \mathrm{Mor}_{\mathscr{D}}(D, \mathscr{T}f)$ is surjective.

Let $\mathscr{T}$ be an algebraic functor with the left adjoint functor $\mathscr{S}$. We say that the objects $\mathscr{S}D$ are *relatively free*. Then each relatively free object is relatively projective. Since $\mathscr{V} : \mathrm{Funct}_\pi(\mathfrak{A}, \mathbf{S}) \to \mathbf{S}$ is also an algebraic functor, namely the functor induced by $\mathbf{A} : \mathbf{N}^0 \to \mathfrak{A}$, each free $\mathfrak{A}$-algebra is relatively projective with respect to the surjective $\mathfrak{A}$-homomorphisms. In this case we say the relatively projective objects are also $\mathfrak{A}$-projective.

THEOREM 3. *Let $\mathfrak{A}$ be an algebraic theory. Then there exists a finitely generated, $\mathfrak{A}$-projective generator in $\mathrm{Funct}_\pi(\mathfrak{A}, \mathbf{S})$.*

Proof. The free $\mathfrak{A}$-algebra $\mathrm{Mor}_{\mathfrak{A}}(1, -)$ has this property. The only thing to show is that $\mathrm{Mor}_{\mathfrak{A}}(1, -)$ is a generator. This assertion follows from $\mathrm{Mor}_f(\mathrm{Mor}_{\mathfrak{A}}(1, -), A) \cong \mathscr{V}(A)$ and from the fact that $\mathscr{V}$ is faithful.

Let (A, α) be an $\mathfrak{A}$-algebra. A *congruence* on (A, α) is a kernel pair $x, y : \mathfrak{p} \to A$ in $\mathbf{S}$ such that $(x, y) : \mathfrak{p} \to A \times A$ defines a subalgebra $(\mathfrak{p}, \pi)$ of $(A, \alpha) \times (A, \alpha)$. Clearly, $(x, y) : \mathfrak{p} \to A \times A$ is injective since $(x, y)h = (x, y)k$ implies $xh = xk$ and $yh = yk$ and thus $h = k$ by the uniqueness of the factorization morphism. Furthermore, π is uniquely determined by the algebra structure on $A \times A$.

LEMMA 4. *Let (A, α) be an $\mathfrak{A}$-algebra. $x, y : \mathfrak{p} \to A$ is a congruence on (A, α) if and only if there is an algebra structure $\pi : \mathscr{H}\mathfrak{p} \to \mathfrak{p}$ on $\mathfrak{p}$ such that $x, y : (\mathfrak{p}, \pi) \to (A, \alpha)$ is a kernel pair in $\mathrm{Funct}_\pi(A, \mathbf{S})$.*

Proof. Let x, y be a kernel pair in $\mathrm{Funct}_\pi(\mathfrak{A}, \mathbf{S})$. Since $\mathscr{V} : \mathrm{Funct}_\pi(\mathfrak{A}, \mathbf{S}) \to \mathbf{S}$ preserves limits x, y is a kernel pair in $\mathbf{S}$. Furthermore, $(x, y) : (\mathfrak{p}, \pi) \to (A, \alpha) \times (A, \alpha)$ is a subalgebra since $\mathrm{Funct}_\pi(\mathfrak{A}, \mathbf{S})$ is complete.

Now let $x, y : \mathfrak{p} \to A$ be a congruence. Since (x, y) is an $\mathfrak{A}$-homomorphism, also $x = p_1(x, y)$ and $y = p_2(x, y)$ are $\mathfrak{A}$-homomorphisms. Now let $h : A \to C$ be a difference cokernel for x, y in $\mathbf{S}$. Then there is a $k : C \to A$ with $hk = 1_C$. Then $h1_A = h = hkh$ for the pair of morphisms 1_A, $kh : A \to A$. Thus there exists exactly one $g : A \to B$ with $xg = 1_A$ and $yg = kh$ and hence $ygx = khx = khy = ygy$. So

x, $y : (\mathfrak{p}, \pi) \to (A, \alpha)$ is a $\mathscr{V}$-contractible pair. Consequently, there is an $\mathfrak{A}$-algebra structure on C such that (C, γ) is a difference cokernel of x, y in $\mathrm{Funct}_\pi(\mathfrak{A}, \mathbf{S})$ (Section 2.3, Lemma 4 and Section 3.3, Theorem 1). By Section 2.6, Lemma 4, a kernel pair in $\mathrm{Funct}_\pi(\mathfrak{A}, \mathbf{S})$ of $(A, \alpha) \to (C, \gamma)$ has $\mathfrak{p}$ as underlying set up to an isomorphism. However, the $\mathfrak{A}$-algebra structure on $\mathfrak{p}$ is uniquely determined by the injective morphism $(x, y) : \mathfrak{p} \to A \times A$. Hence x, $y : (\mathfrak{p}, \pi) \to (A, \alpha)$ is a kernel pair in $\mathrm{Funct}_\pi(\mathfrak{A}, \mathbf{S})$.

We denote the difference cokernel of a congruence x, $y : (\mathfrak{p}, \pi) \to (A, \alpha)$ by $(A/\mathfrak{p}, \alpha')$ or simply by $A/\mathfrak{p}$ since the corresponding $\mathfrak{A}$-algebra structure is uniquely determined. $A^2 = A \times A$ and A with the morphisms p_1, $p_2 : A \times A \to A$ and 1_A, $1_A : A \to A$ are always congruences on (A, α).

COROLLARY 4.   *An $\mathfrak{A}$-homomorphism $f : (A, \alpha) \to (C, \gamma)$ is a difference cokernel in $\mathrm{Funct}_\pi(\mathfrak{A}, \mathbf{S})$ if and only if $f : A \to C$ is surjective.*

Proof.   The proof of Lemma 4 implies that differences cokernels are surjective maps. Now let $f : (A, \alpha) \to (C, \gamma)$ be an $\mathfrak{A}$-homomorphism with a surjective map $f : A \to C$. Let x, $y : (\mathfrak{p}, \pi) \to (A, \alpha)$ be a kernel pair of f. Then x, $y : \mathfrak{p} \to A$ is a kernel pair of f in $\mathbf{S}$. Since $f : A \to C$ is a difference cokernel for x, y in $\mathbf{S}$ we get that $f : (A, \alpha) \to (B, \beta)$ is a difference cokernel for x, y in $\mathrm{Funct}_\pi(\mathfrak{A}, \mathbf{S})$ as in the proof of Lemma 4.

THEOREM 4 (homomorphism theorem).   *Let x, $y : \mathfrak{p} \to A$ and x', $y' : \mathfrak{p}' \to A$ be congruences on (A, α). Let $\varphi : \mathfrak{p} \to \mathfrak{p}'$ be given with $x'\varphi = x$ and $y'\varphi = y$ ($\mathfrak{p} \subseteq \mathfrak{p}'$). Let $g : (A, \alpha) \to A/\mathfrak{p}$ be a difference cokernel of x, y and $h : (A, \alpha) \to A/\mathfrak{p}'$ be a difference cokernel of x', y'. Then there is exactly one $\mathfrak{A}$-homomorphism $f : A/\mathfrak{p} \to A/\mathfrak{p}'$ such that*

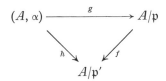

is commutative and f is surjective (as a set map).

Proof.   We have $(x', y')\varphi = (x, y)$ in $\mathbf{S}$. Since (x', y') is injective $(x', y')\, \varphi\pi = (x', y')\, \pi'\mathscr{H}\varphi$ implies $\varphi\pi = \pi'\mathscr{H}\varphi$, that is, φ is an $\mathfrak{A}$-homomorphism. Then the existence of f follows from the properties of the difference cokernels. f is surjective because h is surjective.

COROLLARY 5. *Let $f : (A, \alpha) \to (B, \beta)$ be an $\mathfrak{A}$-homomorphism and let $x, y : (\mathfrak{p}, \pi) \to (A, \alpha)$ be a kernel pair of f. Then $A/\mathfrak{p} \cong \operatorname{Im}(f)$ as $\mathfrak{A}$-algebras.*

Proof. The morphism $(A, \alpha) \to \operatorname{Im}(f)$ is surjective (Corollary 1) hence, a difference cokernel of its kernel pair (Corollary 4 and Section 2.6, Lemma 4). Since the kernel pairs of $(A, \alpha) \to \operatorname{Im}(f)$ and $f : (A, \alpha) \to (B, \beta)$ coincide on the underlying sets, they coincide in $\operatorname{Funct}_\pi(A, \mathbf{S})$. This implies the assertion.

LEMMA 5. *Let A be a fiber product of B and B' over C and let D be a fiber product of E and E' over F. Let a morphism of diagrams $(B, B', C) \to (E, E', F)$ be given such that $C \to F$ is a monomorphism. Then $B \times B' \to E \times E'$ and $D \to E \times E'$ are uniquely defined and A is a fiber product of $B \times B'$ and D over $E \times E'$.*

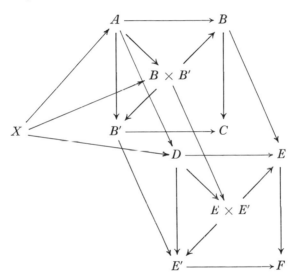

Proof. Given $X \to B \times B'$ and $X \to D$ with $(X \to B \times B' \to E \times E') = (X \to D \to E \times E')$; then

$$(X \to B \times B' \to B \to C \to F) = (X \to B \times B' \to B' \to C \to F).$$

Since $C \to F$ is a monomorphism, we get $(X \to B \times B' \to B \to C) = (X \to B \times B' \to B' \to C)$. Thus there exists exactly one morphism $X \to A$ with $(X \to A \to B \times B') = (X \to B \times B')$. $(X \to E \to F) = (X \to E' \to F)$ implies that there is exactly one morphism $X \to D$ with $(X \to D \to E) = (X \to E)$ and $(X \to D \to E') = (X \to E')$. But both the original morphism $X \to D$ and $X \to A \to D$ have this property.

Thus $(X \twoheadrightarrow D) = (X \to A \to D)$ and A is a fiber product of $B \times B'$ and D over $E \times E'$.

THEOREM 5 (first isomorphism theorem). *Let (A, α) be an $\mathfrak{A}$-algebra. Let $i : (B, \beta) \to (A, \alpha)$ be an $\mathfrak{A}$-subalgebra and let x, $y : (\mathfrak{p}, \pi) \to (A, \alpha)$ be a congruence on A. Let $h : (A, \alpha) \to A/\mathfrak{p}$ be a difference cokernel of x, y. Let $\mathfrak{p}(B) = h^{-1}(hi(B))$ in $\mathbf{S}$. Then*

(1) $\mathfrak{p}(B)$ *is a subalgebra of (A, α);*
(2) $\mathfrak{p} \cap B^2$ *is a congruence on B;*
(3) $B/\mathfrak{p} \cap B^2 \cong \mathfrak{p}(B)/\mathfrak{p}$ *as $\mathfrak{A}$-algebras.*

Proof. $hi(B)$ is an $\mathfrak{A}$-algebra as the image of hi (Lemma 1 and Corollary 1). $\mathfrak{p}(B) = h^{-1}(hi(B))$ is an $\mathfrak{A}$-algebra as a limit of $\mathfrak{A}$-algebras (Section 3.2, Theorem). $\mathfrak{p} \cap B^2 = \mathfrak{p} \cap (B \times B)$ is a kernel pair of $hi : (B, \beta) \to (A, \alpha) \to A/\mathfrak{p}$, for

$$
\begin{array}{ccccc}
(\mathfrak{p} \cap B^2, \pi') & \underset{y'}{\overset{x'}{\rightrightarrows}} & (B, \beta) & \overset{hi}{\longrightarrow} & A/\mathfrak{p} \\
\downarrow & & \downarrow{\scriptstyle i} & & \downarrow \\
(\mathfrak{p}, \pi) & \underset{y}{\overset{x}{\rightrightarrows}} & (A, \alpha) & \overset{h}{\longrightarrow} & A/\mathfrak{p}
\end{array}
$$

is a special case of Lemma 5. Similarly, $\mathfrak{p} \cap \mathfrak{p}(B^2)$ is a kernel pair of $\mathfrak{p}(B) \to (A, \alpha) \to A/\mathfrak{p}$. Thus,

$$ B/\mathfrak{p} \cap B^2 \cong hi(B) \cong h(h^{-1}(hi(B)) \cong \mathfrak{p}(B)/\mathfrak{p} \cap \mathfrak{p}(B)^2 $$

If $a \in \mathfrak{p}(B)$ and if a is $\mathfrak{p}$-equivalent to b, then also $b \in \mathfrak{p}(B)$, since a and b are mapped onto the same element in $A/\mathfrak{p}$. Thus, $\mathfrak{p}(B)$ is saturated with respect to $\mathfrak{p}$. So we write $\mathfrak{p}(B)/\mathfrak{p}$ instead of $\mathfrak{p}(B)/\mathfrak{p} \cap \mathfrak{p}(B)^2$.

THEOREM 6 (second isomorphism theorem).   *Let $\mathfrak{q} \subseteq \mathfrak{p} (\subseteq A \times A)$ be congruences on A. Let $\mathfrak{p}/\mathfrak{q}$ be the image of $\mathfrak{p} \to A \times A \to A/\mathfrak{q} \times A/\mathfrak{q}$. Then $\mathfrak{p}/\mathfrak{q}$ is a congruence on $A/\mathfrak{q}$ and*

$$ A/\mathfrak{p} \cong (A/\mathfrak{q})/(\mathfrak{p}/\mathfrak{q}) $$

Proof.   Let $\mathfrak{r}$ be the kernel pair of $A/\mathfrak{q} \to A/\mathfrak{p}$. Then $A/\mathfrak{p} \cong (A/\mathfrak{q})/\mathfrak{r}$ by Corollary 4 and Theorem 4. $A \to A/\mathfrak{p}$ and $A/\mathfrak{q} \to A/\mathfrak{p}$ induce a morphism of kernel pairs $\mathfrak{p} \to \mathfrak{r}$. By Lemma 5,

$$
\begin{array}{ccc}
\mathfrak{p} & \longrightarrow & A \times A \\
\downarrow & & \downarrow{\scriptstyle g} \\
\mathfrak{r} & \overset{f}{\longrightarrow} & A/\mathfrak{q} \times A/\mathfrak{q}
\end{array}
$$

is a fiber product in $\text{Funct}_\pi(\mathfrak{A}, \mathbf{S})$ and in $\mathbf{S}$. Since the set-theoretic fiber product is $\{(a, b) \in \mathfrak{r} \times A \times A \mid f(a) = g(b)\}$ and since g is surjective, $\mathfrak{p} \to \mathfrak{r}$ is also surjective. Hence, $\mathfrak{p} \to \mathfrak{r} \to A/\mathfrak{q} \times A/\mathfrak{q}$ is a decomposition of $\mathfrak{p} \to A \times A \to A/\mathfrak{q} \times A/\mathfrak{q}$ through the image, thus $\mathfrak{r} = \mathfrak{p}/\mathfrak{q}$.

3.5 Examples of Algebraic Theories and Functors

We know already some examples of algebraic categories namely $\mathbf{S}$, $\mathbf{S}^*$, $\mathbf{Gr}$, $\mathbf{Ab}$, $_R\mathbf{Mod}$ and $\mathbf{Ri}$. To give more examples in a convenient manner we shall partly use the usual symbols $(+, \cdot, [,], \text{etc.})$ for the definition of the operations, and we shall represent the identities as equations between the elements of $\text{Mor}_\mathfrak{A}(n, 1)$. The reader will easily translate these data into the general formalism, if he compares them with the example of the algebraic theory of groups.

Examples

1. *M-(multiplicative) object*: The algebraic theory of M-objects is defined by

    (1)   a multiplication $\mu : 2 \to 1$
    (2)   without identities

2. *Semigroup*:

    (1) $\mu : 2 \to 1$ with $\mu(x, y) = xy$
    (2) $(xy)z = x(yz)$

3. *Monoid*:

    (1) $\mu : 2 \to 1$; $e : 0 \to 1$ with $\mu(x, y) = xy$; $e(\omega_1) = 0$
    (2) $0x = x = x0$; $(xy)z = x(yz)$

4. *H-(Hopf)object*:

    (1) $\mu : 2 \to 1$; $e : 0 \to 1$ with $\mu(x, y) = xy$; $e(\omega_1) = 0$
    (2) $0x = x = x0$

5. *Quasigroup*:

    (1) $\alpha : 2 \to 1$; $\beta : 2 \to 1$; $\gamma : 2 \to 1$ with
          $\alpha(x, y) = xy$; $\beta(x, y) = x/y$; $\gamma(x, y) = x\backslash y$
    (2) $(x/y)y = x$; $x(x\backslash y) = y$; $x\backslash(xy) = y$; $(xy)/y = x$

These equations mean that the equation $xy = z$ is uniquely solvable with respect to each of the three elements.

6. *Loop*:

    (1)   Quasigroup together with $e : 0 \to 1$ and $e(\omega_1) = 0$

    (2) $0x = x = x0$

Here the operations and the identities of the quasigroup shall hold.

7. *Group*:

    (1) $\mu : 2 \to 1$; $s : 1 \to 1$; $e : 0 \to 1$ with $\mu(x, y) = xy$;
       $s(x) = x^{-1}$; $e(\omega_1) = 1$

    (2) $1x = x$; $x^{-1}x = 1$; $(xy)z = x(yz)$

8. *Ring*:

    (1)   Group (μ, s, e) together with $v : 2 \to 1$ with
       $\mu(x, y) = x + y$; $s(x) = -x$; $e(\omega_1) = 0$; $v(x, y) = xy$

    (2) $x + y = y + x$; $x(y + z) = (xy) + (xz)$; $(x + y)z = (xz) + (yz)$

9. *Unitary ring*:

    (1)   Ring together with $e' : 0 \to 1$ with $e'(\omega_1) = 1$

    (2) $1x = x = x1$

10. *Associative ring*:

    (1)   Ring together with

    (2) $(xy)z = x(yz)$

11. *Commutative ring*:

    (1)   Ring together with

    (2) $xy = yx$

12. *Anticommutative ring*:

    (1)   Ring together with

    (2) $xx = 0$

This identity implies $xy = -yx$. The converse does not hold in general.

13. *Radical ring*:

    (1)   Associative ring together with $g : 1 \to 1$ with $g(x) = x'$

    (2) $x + x' + xx' = x + x' + x'x = 0$

14. *Lie ring*:

    (1)   Anticommutative ring (where we write $v(x, y) = [x, y]$
       instead of $v(x, y) = xy$)

    (2) $[x, [y, z]] + [y, [z, x]] + [z, [x, y]] = 0$

15. *Jordan ring*:
    (1)   Commutative ring together with
    (2) $((xx)y)x = (xx)(yx)$

16. *Alternative ring*:
    (1)   Ring together with
    (2) $(xx)y = x(xy); \quad x(yy) = (xy)y$

17. *R-module* (for an associative ring):
    (1)   Commutative group together with $r : 1 \to 1$ for all $r \in R$
    (2) $(r + r')m = rm + r'm; \quad r(m + m') = rm + rm';$
        $r(r'm) = (rr')m$

18. *Unitary R-module* (for a unitary, associative ring R):
    (1)   *R*-module together with
    (2) $1m = m$

19. *Lie module* (for a Lie ring R):
    (1)   Commutative group together with $r : 1 \to 1$ for all $r \in R$
    (2) $(r + r')m = (rm) + (r'm); \quad [r, r']m = (r(r'm)) - (r'(rm));$
        $r(m + m') = (rm) + (rm')$

20. *Jordan module* (for a Jordan ring R):
    (1)   Commutative group together with $r : 1 \to 1$ for all $r \in R$
    (2) $(r + r')m = (rm) + (r'm); \quad r(m + m') = (rm) + (rm');$
        $r(r'((rm) + (rm))) = (rr')((rm) + (rm)); \quad r((rr)m) = (rr)(rm)$

21. *S-right-module* (for an associative ring S)
    like an S-module, but $(ss')m = s'(sm)$ holds instead of $(ss')m = s(s'm)$

22. *R-S-bimodule*:
    (1)   *R*-module and *S*-module with the same commutative group
        with
    (2) $r(sm) = s(rm)$ for all $r \in R$ and $s \in S$

23. *k-algebra* (with an associative, commutative, unitary ring k):
    (1)   Ring together with $r : 1 \to 1$ for all $r \in k$
    (2) $(r + r')x = (rx) + (r'x); \; r(x + y) = (rx) + (ry); \; (rr')x =$
        $r(r'x); \quad 1x = x; \quad r(xy) = (rx)y = x(ry)$

24. *k-Lie-algebra*, *k-Jordan-algebra*, and *alternative k-algebra* arise from
    Example 23 if we replace "ring" by "Lie ring," "Jordan ring," or
    "alternative ring," respectively.

25. *Nilalgegra of degree n:*
   (1) k-algebra together with
   (2) $x^n = 0$

26. *Nilpotent algebra of degree n:*
   (1) k-algebra together with
   (2) $x_1(x_2 (\cdots x_n) \cdots) = 0$

It is interesting to know which algebraic structures are not equationally defined. In special cases it is easy to find properties of algebraic categories which do not hold in these cases. For example, the fields (with unitary ring homomorphisms) do not form an algebraic category because not each set-theoretic product of two fields can be considered as a field again (Section 3.2, Theorem). For the same reason, integral domains (with unitary ring homomorphisms) do not form an algebraic category (example of Section 2.12). The divisible abelian groups do not form an algebraic category because the monomorphisms are not always injective maps (Section 3.2, Corollary 2 and Section 1.5, Example 1).

Morphisms of algebraic theories always define algebraic functors. Many universal constructions in algebra are left adjoint functors of algebraic functors. Most morphisms of algebraic theories are defined by adding operations and (or) identities, as we found already in the examples of algebraic theories. In the following examples we shall not give special explanations if we use the above mentioned construction.

Examples

27. $\mathfrak{A}$ (= algebraic theory of groups) → $\mathfrak{B}$ (= algebraic theory of commutative groups) induces an algebraic functor

$$\text{Funct}_\pi(\mathfrak{B}, \mathbf{S}) \to \text{Funct}_\pi(\mathfrak{A}, \mathbf{S})$$

The left adjoint functor is called the *commutator factor group.*

28. $\mathfrak{A}$ (= k-module) → $\mathfrak{B}$ (= associative, unitary k-algebra) defines (as in Example 27) the functor *tensor algebra.*

29. $\mathfrak{A}$ (= k-module) → $\mathfrak{B}$ (= associative, commutative, unitary k-algebra) defines the functor *symmetric algebra.*

30. $\mathfrak{A}$ (= k-module) → $\mathfrak{B}$ (= associative, anticommutative k-algebra) defines the functor *exterior algebra.*

31. $\mathfrak{A}$ (= associative ring) → $\mathfrak{B}$ (= associative, unitary ring) defines the functor *adjunction of a unit.*

32. $\mathfrak{A}$ ($= k$-Lie-algebra) $\to \mathfrak{B}$ ($=$ unitary, associative k-algebra), where the Lie-multiplication [,] is mapped into the operation $xy - yx$ with the associative multiplication, defines the functor *universal enveloping algebra of a Lie algebra.*

33. $\mathfrak{A}$ ($= k$-Jordan-algebra) $\to \mathfrak{B}$ ($=$ unitary, associative k-algebra), where the Jordan multiplication is mapped into the operation $xy + yx$ with the associative multiplication, defines the functor *universal enveloping algebra of a Jordan-algebra.*

34. $\mathfrak{A}$ ($=$ monoid) $\to \mathfrak{B}$ ($=$ unitary, associative ring) defines the functor *monoid ring.*

35. Let $f : k \to k'$ be a unitary ring homomorphism of commutative, unitary, associative rings.
$\mathfrak{A}$ ($= k$-module or k-algebra) $\to \mathfrak{B}$ ($= k'$-module or k'-algebra respectively) defines the functor *base (-ring) extension.*

36. $\mathfrak{A}$ ($= \mathbf{N}^0$) $\to \mathfrak{B}$ ($=$ unitary, associative (commutative) k-algebra) defines the functor *(commutative) polynomial algebra.*

3.6 Algebras in Arbitrary Categories

Let $\mathscr{C}$ be an arbitrary category and $\mathfrak{A}$ an algebraic theory. An $\mathfrak{A}$-*object* in $\mathscr{C}$ is an object $A \in \mathscr{C}$ together with a functor $\mathscr{A} : \mathscr{C}^0 \to \text{Funct}_\pi(\mathfrak{A}, \mathbf{S})$, such that

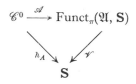

$$\mathscr{C}^0 \xrightarrow{\mathscr{A}} \text{Funct}_\pi(\mathfrak{A}, \mathbf{S})$$

is commutative with $h_A = \text{Mor}_\mathscr{C}(-, A)$. This means that each set $\text{Mor}_\mathscr{C}(C, A)$ carries the structure of an $\mathfrak{A}$-algebra and that each morphism $f : C \to C'$ induces an $\mathfrak{A}$-homomorphism $\text{Mor}_\mathscr{C}(C', A) \to \text{Mor}_\mathscr{C}(C, A)$. Here we meet again the common principle (see Section 1.5): Generalize notions from the category $\mathbf{S}$ to the category $\mathscr{C}$ with the help of the bifunctor $\text{Mor}_\mathscr{C}(-, -)$ in the covariant argument.

One wants to carry out many computations and definitions for $\mathfrak{A}$-objects as for $\mathfrak{A}$-algebras. But $\mathfrak{A}$-objects $(A, \mathscr{A})$ have no elements in general. As a substitute we have the elements of the $\mathfrak{A}$-algebras $\text{Mor}_\mathscr{C}(C, A)$, often denoted by $A(C)$ (or better $\mathscr{A}(C)$). Then one has to check in addition that the computations and definitions behave naturally with respect to C.

An $\mathfrak{A}$-morphism $f : (A, \mathscr{A}) \to (B, \mathscr{B})$ is a natural transformation $f : A \to B$. This defines a natural transformation $\mathscr{V}f : h_A \to h_B$, which again defines a morphism $f^* : A \to B$ by the Yoneda lemma. The category of $\mathfrak{A}$-objects and $\mathfrak{A}$-morphisms will be denoted by $\mathscr{C}^{(\mathfrak{A})}$ and will be called *category of $\mathfrak{A}$-objects* in $\mathscr{C}$.

If $\mathscr{G} : \mathfrak{A} \to \mathfrak{B}$ is a morphism of algebraic theories, then this induces a functor $\mathscr{C}^{(\mathscr{G})} : \mathscr{C}^{(\mathfrak{B})} \to \mathscr{C}^{(\mathfrak{A})}$.

THEOREM 1.   *Let $\mathscr{C}$ be a category with finite products. Then there is an equivalence $\mathscr{C}^{(\mathfrak{A})} \simeq \mathrm{Funct}_\pi(\mathfrak{A}, \mathscr{C})$ such that, for all morphisms $\mathscr{G} : \mathfrak{B} \to \mathfrak{A}$ of algebraic theories, the diagram*

$$\begin{array}{ccc} \mathscr{C}^{(\mathfrak{A})} & \simeq & \mathrm{Funkt}_\pi(\mathfrak{A}, \mathscr{C}) \\ {\scriptstyle \mathscr{C}^{(\mathscr{G})}} \downarrow & & \downarrow {\scriptstyle \mathrm{Funkt}_\pi(\mathscr{G},\mathscr{C})} \\ \mathscr{C}^{(\mathfrak{B})} & \simeq & \mathrm{Funkt}_\pi(\mathfrak{B}, \mathscr{C}) \end{array}$$

is commutative.

Proof.   Let $(A, \mathscr{A})$ be an $\mathfrak{A}$-object. Then we can regard $\mathscr{A}$ as a bifunctor $\mathscr{A} : \mathscr{C}^0 \times \mathbf{S}$ with

$$\mathscr{A}(C, n) \simeq \mathscr{A}(C, 1)^n = \mathrm{Mor}_\mathscr{C}(C, A)^n \simeq \mathrm{Mor}_\mathscr{C}(C, A^n)$$

and

$$\mathscr{A}(C, \varphi) \simeq \mathrm{Mor}_\mathscr{C}(C, A^\varphi) : \mathrm{Mor}_\mathscr{C}(C, A^m) \to \mathrm{Mor}_\mathscr{C}(C, A^n)$$

where $A^\varphi : A^m \to A^n$ exists by the Yoneda lemma.

Let $f : (A, \mathscr{A}) \to (B, \mathscr{B})$ be an $\mathfrak{A}$-morphism and let $f^* : A \to B$ be induced by f. Then, $f(C, n) \simeq \mathrm{Mor}_\mathscr{C}(C, (f^*)^n)$. These applications define a functor $\mathscr{C}^{(\mathfrak{A})} \to \mathrm{Funct}_\pi(\mathfrak{A}, \mathscr{C})$.

Let $\mathscr{X} \in \mathrm{Funct}_\pi(\mathfrak{A}, \mathscr{C})$. Then $A = \mathscr{X}(1)$ and $\mathscr{A}(C, n) = \mathrm{Mor}_\mathscr{C}(C, A^n)$ define an object in $\mathscr{C}^{(\mathfrak{A})}$. In fact, let $\varphi : n \to 1$ be an n-ary operation in $\mathfrak{A}$, then we get $\mathscr{X}(\varphi) : A^n \to A$, hence $\mathscr{A}(C, \varphi) = \mathrm{Mor}_\mathscr{C}(C, \mathscr{X}(\varphi)) : \mathrm{Mor}_\mathscr{C}(C, A^n) \to \mathrm{Mor}_\mathscr{C}(C, A)$.

Given $\chi : \mathscr{X} \to \mathscr{X}'$ in $\mathrm{Funct}_\pi(\mathfrak{A}, \mathscr{C})$ we obtain

$$\mathrm{Mor}_\mathscr{C}(-, \chi(-)) : \mathrm{Mor}_\mathscr{C}(-, X(-)) \to \mathrm{Mor}_\mathscr{C}(-, X'(-))$$

and hence a morphism $\mathscr{A} \to \mathscr{A}'$ where $\mathscr{A}'$ is determined by $\mathscr{X}'$. This defines a functor $\mathrm{Funct}_\pi(\mathfrak{A}, \mathscr{C}) \to \mathscr{C}^{(\mathfrak{A})}$. These two functors are, by construction, inverse to each other.

With this construction it is easy to verify that $\mathscr{G} : \mathfrak{B} \to \mathfrak{A}$ defines the commutative diagram in Theorem 1.

A forgetful functor $\mathscr{U}$ from $\mathscr{C}^{(\mathfrak{A})}$ to $\mathscr{C}$ is defined by $(A, \mathscr{A}) \mapsto A$ and $f \mapsto f^*$; then this forgetful functor, composed with the equivalence constructed in the proof, is the evaluation on the object 1, hence $\mathscr{V} : \text{Funct}_\pi(\mathfrak{A}, \mathscr{C}) \to \mathscr{C}$.

Now we show that product-preserving functors preserve $\mathfrak{A}$-objects and $\mathfrak{A}$-morphisms. This is stated more precisely in the following corollary.

COROLLARY 1. *Let $\mathscr{C}$ and $\mathscr{D}$ be categories with finite products. Let $\mathscr{F} : \mathscr{C} \to \mathscr{D}$ be a product-preserving functor. Then there is a functor $\mathscr{G} : \mathscr{C}^{(\mathfrak{A})} \to \mathscr{D}^{(\mathfrak{A})}$ such that the diagram*

$$
\begin{array}{ccc}
\mathscr{C}^{(\mathfrak{A})} & \xrightarrow{\ \mathscr{G}\ } & \mathscr{D}^{(\mathfrak{A})} \\
{\scriptstyle \mathscr{U}}\big\downarrow & & \big\downarrow{\scriptstyle \mathscr{U}} \\
\mathscr{C} & \xrightarrow[\ \mathscr{F}\ ]{} & \mathscr{D}
\end{array}
$$

is commutative.

Proof. Let $\mathscr{G}' = \text{Funct}_\pi(\mathfrak{A}, \mathscr{F})$. Then the diagram

$$
\mathscr{C}^{(\mathfrak{A})} \simeq \text{Funkt}_\pi(\mathfrak{A}, \mathscr{C}) \xrightarrow{\ \mathscr{G}'\ } \text{Funkt}_\pi(\mathfrak{A}, \mathscr{D}) \simeq \mathscr{D}^{(\mathfrak{A})}
$$

is commutative for $\mathscr{F}\mathscr{V}(\mathscr{X}) = \mathscr{G}\mathscr{X}(1) = \mathscr{V}\mathscr{G}'(\mathscr{X})$ and $\mathscr{F}\mathscr{V}(\chi) = \mathscr{F}\chi(1) = \mathscr{V}\mathscr{G}'(\chi)$.

In particular each representable functor $\text{Mor}_{\mathscr{C}}(C, -) : \mathscr{C} \to \mathbf{S}$ preserves products, hence $\mathfrak{A}$-objects and $\mathfrak{A}$-morphisms. But this was the way $\mathfrak{A}$-objects and $\mathfrak{A}$-morphisms were defined.

A *co-$\mathfrak{A}$-object* in $\mathscr{C}$ is an $\mathfrak{A}$-object in $\mathscr{C}^0$. A *co-$\mathfrak{A}$-morphism* in $\mathscr{C}$ is an $\mathfrak{A}$-morphism in $\mathscr{C}^0$.

THEOREM 2. *Let $\mathfrak{A}$ be an algebraic theory. Then the free $\mathfrak{A}$-algebras in $\text{Funct}_\pi(\mathfrak{A}, \mathbf{S})$ are co-$\mathfrak{A}$-objects and the free $\mathfrak{A}$-homomorphisms are co-$\mathfrak{A}$-morphisms.*

Proof. Let $X \in \mathbf{S}$ and $A \in \text{Funct}_\pi(\mathfrak{A}, \mathbf{S})$. Then $\text{Mor}_f(\mathscr{F}X, A) \simeq \text{Mor}_{\mathbf{S}}(X, \mathscr{V}A)$ natural in X and A. But since A is an $\mathfrak{A}$-algebra,

$\mathrm{Mor}_S(X, \mathscr{V}A)$ carries the structure of an $\mathfrak{A}$-algebra (namely the structure of A^X). This again is natural in X and A. Thus

$$\mathrm{Mor}_f(\mathscr{F}X, -) : \mathrm{Funct}_\pi(\mathfrak{A}, \mathbf{S}) \to \mathrm{Funct}_\pi(\mathfrak{A}, \mathbf{S})$$

that is, $\mathscr{F}X$ is a co-$\mathfrak{A}$-object in $\mathrm{Funct}_\pi(\mathfrak{A}, \mathbf{S})$. Similarly, one proves the assertion for the co-$\mathfrak{A}$-morphisms.

By a result of Kan, the free $\mathfrak{A}$-algebras and $\mathfrak{A}$-homomorphisms coincide with the co-$\mathfrak{A}$-objects and co-$\mathfrak{A}$-morphisms in $\mathrm{Funct}_\pi(\mathfrak{A}, \mathbf{S})$ in the case of the algebraic theory of groups $\mathfrak{A}$. This assertion, however, does not hold for arbitrary algebraic theories.

Let $\mathsf{A} : \mathbf{N}^0 \to \mathfrak{A}$ and $\mathsf{B} : \mathbf{N}^0 \to \mathfrak{B}$ be algebraic theories. We define a *tensor product* $\mathfrak{A} \otimes \mathfrak{B}$ of algebraic theories:

$$H(n) = \mathrm{Mor}_\mathfrak{A}(n, 1) \cup \mathrm{Mor}_\mathfrak{B}(n, 1)$$

$$L(n) = L_\mathfrak{A}(n) \cup L_\mathfrak{B}(n) \cup \{(\mathsf{A}(p_n{}^j), \mathsf{B}(p_n{}^j))\}$$

$$\cup \{(\psi_B(\varphi_A \times \cdots \times \varphi_A), \varphi_A(\psi_B \times \cdots \times \psi_B))\}$$

where $L_\mathfrak{A}(n)$ and $L_\mathfrak{B}(n)$ are the identities occurring in the representation of $\mathfrak{A}$ and $\mathfrak{B}$ by $\mathfrak{F}\mathfrak{B}(\mathfrak{A})$ and $\mathfrak{F}\mathfrak{B}(\mathfrak{B})$ respectively, and where $\varphi_A \in \mathrm{Mor}_\mathfrak{A}(m, 1)$, $\psi_B \in \mathrm{Mor}_\mathfrak{B}(r, 1)$, $\psi_B \times \cdots \times \psi_B \in \mathrm{Mor}_\mathfrak{B}(n, m)$, and $\varphi_A \times \cdots \times \varphi_A \in \mathrm{Mor}_\mathfrak{A}(n, r)$. All unions are disjoint unions. Then, in particular, morphisms $\mathfrak{A} \to \mathfrak{A} \otimes \mathfrak{B}$ and $\mathfrak{B} \to \mathfrak{A} \otimes \mathfrak{B}$ of algebraic theories are given.

THEOREM 3. *Let $\mathscr{C}$ be a category with finite products. Then there is an isomorphism*

$$\mathrm{Funct}_\pi(\mathfrak{A} \otimes \mathfrak{B}, \mathscr{C}) \cong \mathrm{Funct}_\pi(\mathfrak{A}, \mathrm{Funct}_\pi(\mathfrak{B}, \mathscr{C}))$$

Proof. By Section 1.14, Lemma 3 we have

$$\mathrm{Funct}(\mathfrak{A} \times \mathfrak{B}, \mathscr{C}) \cong \mathrm{Funct}(\mathfrak{A}, \mathrm{Funct}(\mathfrak{B}, \mathscr{C}))$$

Thereby, $\mathrm{Funct}_\pi(\mathfrak{A}, \mathrm{Funct}_\pi(\mathfrak{B}, \mathscr{C}))$ is carried over into $\mathrm{Funct}_{\pi,\pi}(\mathfrak{A} \times \mathfrak{B}, \mathscr{C})$, the category of those bifunctors that preserve products in each argument separately. We define an isomorphism

$$\mathrm{Funct}_\pi(\mathfrak{A} \otimes \mathfrak{B}, \mathscr{C}) \cong \mathrm{Funct}_{\pi,\pi}(\mathfrak{A} \times \mathfrak{B}, \mathscr{C})$$

Given $F \in \text{Funct}_{\pi,\pi}(\mathfrak{A} \times \mathfrak{B}, \mathscr{C})$ and $G \in \text{Funct}_{\pi}(\mathfrak{A} \otimes \mathfrak{B}, \mathscr{C})$. Then $\mathscr{F}$ and $\mathscr{G}$ are determined by the following properties:

$$\mathscr{F}(i,j) = \mathscr{F}(1,1)^{ij}$$

$$\mathscr{F}(\mu, \rho) = \mathscr{F}(\mu^m, 1_1) \, \mathscr{F}(1_1, \rho^i) = \mathscr{F}(1_1, \rho^k) \, \mathscr{F}(\mu^j, 1_1)$$

$$\mathscr{G}(n) = \mathscr{G}(1)^n$$

$$\mathscr{G}(\tau) = \mathscr{G}(1)^{\tau}$$

We define

$$\Phi(\mathscr{F})(n) = \mathscr{F}(1,1)^n$$

$$\Phi(\mathscr{F})(\varphi_A) = \mathscr{F}(\varphi_A, 1_1), \qquad \Phi(\mathscr{F})(\varphi_B) = \mathscr{F}(1_1, \varphi_B)$$

$$\Psi(\mathscr{G})(i,j) = \mathscr{G}(ij)$$

$$\Psi(\mathscr{G})(\mu, \rho) = \mathscr{G}(\mu^m \rho^i) = \mathscr{G}(\rho^k \mu^j)$$

with $(\mu, \rho) : (i,j) \to (k, m)$. Here φ_A means $\varphi \in \text{Im}(\mathfrak{A} \to \mathfrak{A} \otimes \mathfrak{B})$ and similarly for φ_B. The projections are assumed in $\text{Im}(\mathfrak{A} \to \mathfrak{A} \otimes \mathfrak{B})$.

We define, for natural transformation $\alpha : \mathscr{F}_1 \to \mathscr{F}_2$ and $\beta : \mathscr{G}_1 \to \mathscr{G}_2$,

$$\Phi(\alpha)(n) = \alpha(1,1)^n : \mathscr{F}_1(1,1)^n \to \mathscr{F}_2(1,1)^n$$

$$\Psi(\beta)(i,j) = \beta(ij) : \mathscr{G}_1(ij) \to \mathscr{G}_2(ij)$$

Thus, Φ and Ψ are functors.

Furthermore, we have

$$\Psi\Phi(\mathscr{F})(i,j) = \Phi(\mathscr{F})(ij) = \mathscr{F}(i,j)$$

$$\Psi\Phi(\mathscr{F})(\mu, \rho) = \Phi(\mathscr{F})(\mu^m \rho^i) = \mathscr{F}(\mu, \rho)$$

$$\Psi\Phi(\alpha)(i,j) = \Phi(\alpha)(ij) = \alpha(i,j)$$

$$\Phi\Psi(\mathscr{G})(n) = \Psi(\mathscr{G})(1,1)^n = \mathscr{G}(n)$$

$$\Phi\Psi(\mathscr{G})(\varphi_A) = \Psi(\mathscr{G})(\varphi_A, 1_1) = \mathscr{G}(\varphi_A)$$

$$\Phi\Psi(\mathscr{G})(\varphi_B) = \Psi(\mathscr{G})(1_1, \varphi_B) = \mathscr{G}(\varphi_B)$$

$$\Phi\Psi(\beta)(n) = \Psi(\beta)(1,1)^n = \beta(n)$$

Hence Φ and Ψ are isomorphisms.

COROLLARY 2. *The tensor product of algebraic theories is commutative and associative up to isomorphisms.*

Proof. The algebraic theory is uniquely determined, up to isomorphisms, by the corresponding algebraic category and its forgetful functor. Since

$$\text{Funct}_{\pi,\pi}(\mathfrak{A} \times \mathfrak{B}, \mathbf{S}) \cong \text{Funct}_{\pi,\pi}(\mathfrak{B} \times \mathfrak{A}, \mathbf{S})$$

we also have $\text{Funct}_{\pi}(\mathfrak{A} \otimes \mathfrak{B}, \mathbf{S}) \cong \text{Funct}_{\pi}(\mathfrak{B} \otimes \mathfrak{A}, \mathbf{S})$ and this isomorphism is compatible with the forgetful functors. Hence, $\mathfrak{A} \otimes \mathfrak{B} \cong \mathfrak{B} \otimes \mathfrak{A}$. The assertion about the associativity may be proved analogously.

LEMMA.   *Let $\alpha_i : 0 \to 1$ $(i \in I)$ in $\mathfrak{A}$ and $\beta_j : 0 \to 1$ $(j \in J)$ in $\mathfrak{B}$ be given, and let I and J be nonempty sets. Then the images of the α_i's and β_j's in $\mathfrak{A} \otimes \mathfrak{B}$ are all equal.*

Proof.   This is a consequence of $\psi_B \varphi_A{}^r = \varphi_A \psi_B{}^m$ for $r = m = 0$.

THEOREM 4.   *Given algebraic theories $\mathfrak{A}$ with $\alpha : 0 \to 1$, $\mu : 2 \to 1$ and $\mu(\alpha 0_1, 1_1) = 1_1 = \mu(1_1, \alpha 0_1)$ and $\mathfrak{B}$ with $\beta : 0 \to 1$, $\nu : 2 \to 1$ and $\nu(\beta 0_1, 1_1) = 1_1 = \nu(1_1, \beta 0_1)$. Then we get for the induced multiplications μ^* and ν^* in $\mathfrak{A} \otimes \mathfrak{B}$:*

(1) $\mu^* = \nu^*$
(2) $\mu^*(p_2{}^2, p_2{}^1) = \mu^*$,   *that is μ^* is commutative*
(3) $\mu^*(1_1 \times \mu^*) = \mu^*(\mu^* \times 1_1)$,   *that is μ^* is associative*

Proof.   Consider the commutative square

$$
\begin{array}{ccc}
\begin{array}{c} 1 \times 1 \\ \times \\ 1 \times 1 \end{array} & \xrightarrow[\nu^*]{\nu^*} & \begin{array}{c} 1 \\ \times \\ 1 \end{array} \\
{\scriptstyle \mu^* \times \mu^*} \Big\downarrow & & \Big\downarrow \\
1 \times 1 & \xrightarrow{\nu^*} & 1
\end{array}
$$

Here the object in the left upper corner of the square is the object $4 = 1 \times 1 \times 1 \times 1$ in $\mathfrak{A} \otimes \mathfrak{B}$. Then the square

$$
\begin{array}{ccc}
\begin{array}{c} \text{Mor}(n, 1) \times \text{Mor}(n, 1) \\ \times \\ \text{Mor}(n, 1) \times \text{Mor}(n, 1) \end{array} & \xrightarrow[\nu']{\nu'} & \begin{array}{c} \text{Mor}(n, 1) \\ \times \\ \text{Mor}(n, 1) \end{array} \\
{\scriptstyle \mu' \times \mu'} \Big\downarrow & & \Big\downarrow {\scriptstyle \mu'} \\
\text{Mor}(n, 1) \times \text{Mor}(n, 1) & \xrightarrow{\nu'} & \text{Mor}(n, 1)
\end{array}
$$

is also commutative, where $\mu' = \text{Mor}(n, \mu^*)$ and $\nu' = \text{Mor}(n, \nu^*)$. Let

$$\begin{pmatrix} w & x \\ y & z \end{pmatrix}$$

be an element in $\text{Mor}(n, 4)$ and let $\mu'(w, y) = w \cdot y$ and $\nu'(w, x) = w * x$. Then for all w, x, y, and z we have $(w \cdot y) * (x \cdot z) = (w * x) \cdot (y * z)$. Since $\alpha^* = \beta^*$, let $(n \longrightarrow 0 \overset{\alpha^*}{\longrightarrow} 1) = 0$ be the neutral element with respect to μ' and also ν'. Then we get

$$w * z = (w \cdot 0) * (0 \cdot z) = (w * 0) \cdot (0 * z) = w \cdot z \tag{1}$$

$$y \cdot x = (0 \cdot y) \cdot (x \cdot 0) = (0 \cdot x) \cdot (y \cdot 0) = x \cdot y \tag{2}$$

$$w \cdot (x \cdot z) = (w \cdot 0) \cdot (x \cdot z) = (w \cdot x) \cdot (0 \cdot z) = (w \cdot x) \cdot z \tag{3}$$

COROLLARY 3. *Let $\mathfrak{A}$ be the algebraic theory of groups and $\mathfrak{B}$ the algebraic theory of commutative groups. Then $\mathfrak{B} \cong \mathfrak{A} \otimes \cdots \otimes \mathfrak{A}$ (n times) for $n \geqslant 2$.*

Proof. $\mathfrak{A} \otimes \mathfrak{A}$ has exactly one neutral element and exactly one multiplication which is commutative. Thus at most the commutative groups may be group objects in $\text{Funct}_\pi(\mathfrak{A}, \mathbf{S})$. But all commutative groups are group objects in $\text{Funct}_\pi(\mathfrak{A}, \mathbf{S})$, because $\text{Mor}_{\text{Gr}}(A, B)$ is a group, in case B is a commutative group. Hence,

$$\text{Funct}_\pi(\mathfrak{B}, \mathbf{S}) \cong \text{Funct}_\pi(\mathfrak{A}, \text{Funct}_\pi(\mathfrak{A}, \mathbf{S}))$$

The assertion for $n > 2$ may be shown analogously.

COROLLARY 4. *The only group object in $\mathbf{Ri}$ is the zero ring $\{\varnothing\}$.*

Proof. All multiplications and neutral elements coincide. Thus for a group object in $\mathbf{Ri}$ we get $0 = 1$ and $0 = 0 \cdot a = 1 \cdot a = a$ for all a of the group object.

Let $\mathfrak{A}$ be the algebraic theory of groups. If $\mathscr{C}$ is the category $\mathbf{Top}$, then $\text{Funct}_\pi(\mathfrak{A}, \mathscr{C})$ is called the category of *topological groups*. If $\mathscr{C}$ is the category of analytic varieties, then $\text{Funct}_\pi(\mathfrak{A}, \mathscr{C})$ is called the category of *analytic groups*. If $\mathscr{C}^0$ is the category of finitely generated, unitary, associative, commutative k-algebras and k a field, then $\text{Funct}_\pi(\mathfrak{A}, \mathscr{C})$ is called the category of *affine algebraic groups*. Let S^n be the n-sphere in $\mathbf{Htp}^* = \mathscr{C}$. The homotopy groups of a pointed topological space T are defined by $\pi_n(T) := \text{Mor}_\mathscr{C}(S^n, T)$. These sets have a group structure which is natural in T. Thus the n-spheres are co-group-objects in $\mathbf{Htp}^*$.

Problems

3.1. Show that the following categories are not algebraic categories:

(a)   the torsionfree abelian groups (an abelian group G is called torsionfree, if $ng = 0$ implies $n = 0$ or $g = 0$ for all $n \in w$ and $g \in G$);

(b)   the finite abelian groups.

3.2. Let $\mathfrak{A}$ be an algebraic theory. Let $X \in \mathbf{S}$ and $A \in \text{Funct}_\pi(\mathfrak{A}, \mathbf{S})$. Let A be generated by X and let $f : X \to A(1)$ be an arbitrary map. If f can be extended to an $\mathfrak{A}$-homomorphism $g : A \to A$, then g is uniquely determined by f.

3.3. Let $\mathfrak{A}$ be an algebraic theory. Then there is an $\mathfrak{A}$-algebra A for which $A(1)$ consists of exactly one element. All $\mathfrak{A}$-algebras with one element are isomorphic.

3.4. Under with conditions on the algebraic theory $\mathfrak{A}$ does there exist an empty $\mathfrak{A}$-algebra?

3.5. Let $\mathfrak{A} \to \mathfrak{B}$ be a morphism of algebraic theories, $\mathscr{T} : \text{Funct}_\pi(\mathfrak{B}, \mathbf{S}) \to \text{Funct}_\pi(\mathfrak{A}, \mathbf{S})$ the corresponding algebraic functor, and $\mathscr{S} : \text{Funct}_\pi(\mathfrak{A}, \mathbf{S}) \to \text{Funct}_\pi(\mathfrak{B}, \mathbf{S})$ the left adjoint functor of $\mathscr{T}$. Let $X \in \mathbf{S}$, $\mathscr{F}X$ the $\mathfrak{A}$-algebras freely generated by X, and $B \in \text{Funct}_\pi(\mathfrak{B}, \mathbf{S})$. The coproduct $B_\mathfrak{A}(X)$ of $\mathscr{T}B$ and $\mathscr{F}X$ is called a *generalized polynomial algebra* of B with the variables X. We have $X \subseteq B_\mathfrak{A}(X)(1)$. Each map $f : X \to B(1)$ may uniquely be extended to an $\mathfrak{A}$-homomorphism $B_\mathfrak{A}(X) \to \mathscr{T}(B)$ such that the restriction to $\mathscr{T}B$ is the identity and to X is the map f. This morphism is called the *insertion homomorphism*. Let $\mathfrak{A}$ be the algebraic theory of unitary, associative rings, $\mathfrak{B}$ the algebraic theory of unitary, associative, commutative rings. Describe the insertion homomorphism.

3.6. Let R and S be in **Ri**. Let $f : R \to S$ be a unitary ring homomorphism. Show that f induces a morphism from the algebraic theory of unitary R-modules to the algebraic theory of unitary S-modules. Describe the corresponding algebraic functor $\mathscr{T}$ and its left adjoint functor. What is the meaning of the assertion that the corresponding algebraic functor $\mathscr{T}$ is monadic [Section 2.3, Theorem 2]? Has $\mathscr{T}$ a right adjoint functor?

3.7. Show that polynomial algebras, tensor algebras, and symmetric algebras are co-monoid-objects in the category of associative, unitary (commutative) k-algebras (see Section 3.5).

3.8. Let k be a field. The polynomial algebra $k[X]$ in one variable (generated by one element) and the monoid algebra $k[\mathbb{Z}]$ generated by the additive group of integers $\mathbb{Z}$ (Section 3.5, Example 34 for algebraic functors) are cocommutative co-group-objects (co-$\mathfrak{A}$-objects with the algebraic theory $\mathfrak{A}$ of commutative groups) in the category of unitary, associative, commutative k-algebras. The coproduct in this category is the tensor product. Describe the comultiplications $k[X] \to k[X] \otimes k[X]$ and $k[\mathbb{Z}] \to k[\mathbb{Z}] \otimes k[\mathbb{Z}]$. (Determine the value of $\varnothing \in X = \{\varnothing\}$ and of $1 \in \mathbb{Z}$ under these maps.)

3.9. Let $\mathscr{C}$ be a category with finite products, $\mathfrak{A}$ an algebraic theory, and $\mathscr{B}$ a small category. Characterize the $\mathfrak{A}$-objects in $\text{Funct}(\mathscr{B}, \mathscr{C})$ as "pointwise" $\mathfrak{A}$-objects in $\mathscr{C}$ such that morphisms in $\mathscr{B}$ induce $\mathfrak{A}$-homomorphisms.

3.10. Use Section 2.11, Theorem 4, Section 2.4, Theorem 2, Section 2.3, Theorem 2, the proposition of Section 3.3, and the following remarks to prove the following theorem of Birkhoff:

Let $\mathscr{C}$ be a full subcategory of $\mathrm{Funct}_\pi(\mathfrak{A}, \mathbf{S})$ with

(1) $\mathscr{C}$ contains a nonempty $\mathfrak{A}$-algebra;
(2) $\mathscr{C}$ is closed with respect to subalgebras;
(3) $\mathscr{C}$ is closed with respect to products;
(4) $\mathscr{C}$ is closed with respect to images of $\mathfrak{A}$-homomorphisms with domain in $\mathscr{C}$.

Then $\mathscr{C}$ is an algebraic category.

4

Abelian Categories

Up to now the theory of abelian categories is by far the best developed. The notion stems from a paper of Grothendieck in 1957. Many important theorems, which may be found for module categories in many textbooks, will be proved here more generally for abelian categories. A great deal may be represented in a much nicer and simpler way by these means—for example, the theorems on simple and semisimple rings, where we shall use the Morita theorems. The desire to preserve also the computations with elements (similar to the computations for modules) leads to the embedding theorems. The proof of these theorems uses mainly methods developed by Gabriel. For example, the construction of the 0th right-derived functor originates from the paper of Gabriel listed in the bibliography.

4.1 Additive Categories

Let $\mathscr{C}$ be a category with a zero object, finite coproducts, and finite products. We saw in Chapter 1 that $\mathscr{C}$ is a category with zero morphisms which are uniquely determined.

Let finite index sets I and J and objects A_i with $i \in I$ and B_j with $j \in J$ in $\mathscr{C}$ be given. Furthermore, let a family $f_{ij} : A_i \to B_j$ of morphisms in $\mathscr{C}$ for all $i \in I$ and $j \in J$ be given. The coproduct of the A_i will be denoted by $\coprod A_i$ and the injections by $q_i : A_i \to \coprod A_i$. Similarly, we denote the product of the B_j by $\prod B_j$ and the projections by $p_j : \prod B_j \to B_j$. Then there are uniquely determined morphisms $f_i : A_i \to \prod B_j$ with $p_j f_i = f_{ij}$ and a uniquely determined morphism $f : \coprod A_i \to \prod B_j$ with $p_j f q_i = f_{ij}$.

If, in particular, the morphisms $\delta_{ij} : A_i \to A_j$ are given for all $i, j \in I$ with $\delta_{ii} = 1_{A_i}$ and $\delta_{ij} = 0$ for $i \neq j$, then the morphisms uniquely determined hereby will be denoted by $\delta_A : \coprod A_i \to \prod A_i$. Correspondingly, we define $\delta_B : \coprod B_j \to \prod B_j$.

For a family of morphisms $g_i : A_i \to B_i$ for all $i \in I$ there exists exactly one morphism $\coprod g_i : \coprod A_i \to \coprod B_i$ with $\coprod g_i q_k = q_k g_k$ for all $k \in I$. Furthermore, there is exactly one morphism $\prod g_i : \prod A_i \to \prod B_i$ with $p_k \prod g_i = g_k p_k$ for all $k \in I$. But then the square

$$
\begin{array}{ccc}
\coprod A_i & \xrightarrow{\coprod g_i} & \coprod B_i \\
{\scriptstyle \delta_A}\downarrow & & \downarrow{\scriptstyle \delta_B} \\
\prod A_i & \xrightarrow{\prod g_i} & \prod B_i
\end{array}
$$

is commutative because the morphism from $\coprod A_i$ to $\prod B_i$ is induced by the morphisms

$$
f_{jk} = \begin{array}{cc} g_j & \text{if } j = k \\ 0 & \text{if } j \neq k \end{array}
$$

In fact, $f_{jk} = p_k \delta_B \coprod g_i q_j = p_k \prod g_i \delta_A q_j$.

Let $\Delta_A : A \to \prod A_i$ with $A_i = A$ and $p_i \Delta_A = 1_A$ be the diagonal and let $\nabla_A : \coprod A_i \to A$ with $\nabla_A q_i = 1_A$ be the codiagonal (see Section 1.11). Now assume that δ is an isomorphism for all finite products or coproducts respectively. Then we take for the products—for example, of the $(A_i)_{i \in I}$—the coproducts, that is, $\coprod A_i$; the projections arise from the composition of the original projections with δ, that is, $p_i \delta_A : \coprod A_i \to A_i$. Thus we get $\delta = 1$, that is, we may identify finite products and finite coproducts. The coproduct of finitely many A_i will then also be denoted by $\oplus A_i$ or by $A_1 \oplus A_2 \oplus \cdots \oplus A_n$ and will be called a *direct sum*. We shall treat the morphisms similarly. In fact, by the above considerations finite products and finite coproducts of morphisms also coincide.

A category $\mathscr{C}$ is called *additive category* if

(1) there exists a zero object in $\mathscr{C}$,
(2) there exist finite products and finite coproducts in $\mathscr{C}$,
(3) the morphism δ from finite coproducts to finite products is an isomorphism, and
(4) to each object A in $\mathscr{C}$ there exists a morphism $s_A : A \to A$ such that the diagram

$$
\begin{array}{ccc}
A \oplus A & \xrightarrow{1_A \oplus s_A} & A \oplus A \\
{\scriptstyle \Delta_A}\uparrow & & \downarrow{\scriptstyle \nabla_A} \\
A & \xrightarrow{\;\;0\;\;} & A
\end{array}
$$

is commutative.

Let $\mathscr{C}$ be an additive category. On the morphism sets $\mathrm{Mor}_\mathscr{C}(A, B)$ we define a composition written as addition by

$$f + g := \nabla_B(f \oplus g)\Delta_A$$

for all $f, g \in \mathrm{Mor}_\mathscr{C}(A, B)$. Furthermore, we define a morphism $t_A : A \oplus A \to A \oplus A$ by $p_1 t_A q_1 = p_2 t_A q_2 = 0$ and $p_1 t_A q_2 = p_2 t_A q_1 = 1_A$. Then $t_A \Delta_A = \Delta_A$ by definition of the diagonal and dually $\nabla_B t_B = \nabla_B$. Thus we get

$$f + g = \nabla_B(f \oplus g)\Delta_A = \nabla_B t_B(f \oplus g) t_A \Delta_A = \nabla_B(g \oplus f)\Delta_A = g + f$$

that is, the addition is commutative. The associativity of the addition follows from the commutativity of the diagram

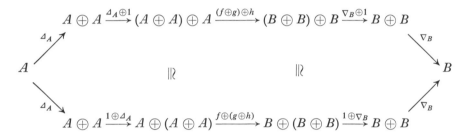

in fact $(\Delta_A \oplus 1)\Delta_A$ as well as $(1 \oplus \Delta_A)\Delta_A$ is the diagonal. One verifies componentwise $(f \oplus 0)q_1 = (f \oplus 0)\Delta_A$ and dually $p_1(f \oplus 0) = \nabla_B(f \oplus 0)$, hence $f + 0 = p_1(f \oplus 0)q_1 = f$. Because of $(f \oplus g)(h \oplus h) = (fh \oplus gh)$ and $\Delta_A h = (h \oplus h)\Delta_A$ we get

$$(f + g)h = \nabla_B(f \oplus g)\Delta_A h = \nabla_B(fh \oplus gh)\Delta_A = fh + gh$$

Dually we get $h(f + g) = hf + hg$. These equations together with the forth condition for additive categories show that the sets $\mathrm{Mor}_\mathscr{C}(A, B)$ with the given addition form abelian groups and that the composition of morphisms is bilinear with respect to this addition.

THEOREM. *$\mathscr{C}$ is an additive category if and only if there exists a zero object in $\mathscr{C}$, if there exist finite coproducts in $\mathscr{C}$ and if each of the morphisms sets $\mathrm{Mor}_\mathscr{C}(A, B)$ carries the structure of an abelian group such that the composition of morphisms is bilinear with respect to the addition of these groups.*

Proof. We saw already in the preceeding considerations that an additive category $\mathscr{C}$ has the properties given in the theorem.

Now assume that these properties hold for $\mathscr{C}$. First we show that the finite coproducts are also finite products. Let $A_1,\ldots, A_n$ be objects in $\mathscr{C}$ and let $\coprod A_i$ be their coproduct. The morphisms $\delta_{ij} : A_i \to A_j$ with $\delta_{ii} = 1_{A_i}$ and $\delta_{ij} = 0$ for $i \neq j$ define for each j exactly one morphism $p_j : \coprod A_i \to A_j$ with

$$p_j q_i = \delta_{ij} \tag{1}$$

Furthermore, we get from

$$\left(\sum_i q_i p_i\right) q_j = \sum_i q_i \delta_{ji} = q_j = 1_{\coprod A_i} q_j$$

for all $j = 1,\ldots, n$ the relation

$$\sum_i q_i p_i = 1_{\coprod A_i} \tag{2}$$

Here we used that the zero morphism is the neutral element for the group structure of $\mathrm{Mor}_{\mathscr{C}}(A, B)$. In fact $0 = 0(1_A + 1_A) = 01_A + 01_A = 0 + 0$. Now let morphisms $f_i : C \to A_i$ be given. Then $\sum q_i f_i : C \to \coprod A_i$ is the desired morphism into the product for $p_j \sum q_i f_i = f_j$. If $g : C \to \coprod A_i$ is another morphism with $p_j g = f_j$, then

$$p_j \left(g - \sum q_i f_i\right) = 0$$

Then by (2) we have

$$\sum_i q_i p_i \left(g - \sum q_i f_i\right) = 0 = g - \sum q_i f_i$$

that is, $\coprod A_i$ together with the projections p_i is a product of the A_i.

The morphism $\delta : \coprod A_i \to \prod A_i$ is defined by $p_j \delta q_i = \delta_{ij}$. But since $p_j 1_{\coprod A_i} q_i = \delta_{ij}$ by (2), we get $\delta = 1_{\coprod A_i}$. Thus also point (3) of the definition of additive categories holds.

As in the beginning of this section, a finite family of morphisms $f_{ij} : A_i \to B_j$ defines exactly one morphism $f : \oplus A_i \to \oplus B_j$ with $p_j f q_i = f_{ij}$. We also write the morphism f as a matrix $f = (f_{ij})$. Let another family of morphisms $g_{jk} : B_j \to C_k$ be given. Let $h = (g_{jk})(f_{ij})$. Then

$$p_k h q_i = p_k (g_{jk}) \sum_j q_j p_j (f_{ij}) q_i = \sum_j g_{jk} f_{ij}$$

Hence the composition of morphisms between direct sums is similar to the multiplication of matrices:

$$(g_{jk})(f_{ij}) = \left(\sum_j g_{jk}f_{ij}\right) \tag{3}$$

Using this matrix notation we get

$$\varDelta_A = \begin{pmatrix} 1_A \\ 1_A \end{pmatrix}; \quad \nabla_B = (1_B , 1_B); \quad f \oplus g = \begin{pmatrix} f & 0 \\ 0 & g \end{pmatrix}$$

Hence $f + g = \nabla_B(f \oplus g) \varDelta_A$. In particular we get $\varDelta_A(1_A \oplus s_A) \varDelta_A = 0$ for $s_A = -1_A$. This completes the proof.

COROLLARY 1.   *Let $\mathscr{C}$ be an additive category. Then there is exactly one way to define an abelian group structure on the morphism sets such that the composition of morphisms in $\mathscr{C}$ is bilinear.*

Proof.   We saw that $f + g = \nabla_B(f \oplus g) \varDelta_A$ must hold. Thus the addition can only depend on the choice of the representatives of the direct sums. The universality of the definition of ∇_B, $f \oplus g$, and $\varDelta_A$ shows that the addition is unique.

The assertion made in Corollary 1 is the main reason for the fact that we did not use the properties that are characteristic for an additive category by the theorem for the definition of an additive category. If we consider $\mathrm{Mor}_{\mathscr{C}}(A, B)$ as an abelian group in the following, then we shall also write $\mathrm{Hom}_{\mathscr{C}}(A, B)$.

COROLLARY 2.   *Let $\mathscr{C}$ be an additive category. Let $A_1 ,..., A_n$ and S be objects in $\mathscr{C}$ and let $q_i : A_i \to S$ and $p_i : S \to A_i$ for $i = 1,..., n$ be morphisms in $\mathscr{C}$. The following are equivalent:*

(a)   *S is a direct sum of the A_i with the injections q_i and the projections p_i.*
(b)   *$p_i q_j = \delta_{ij}$ for all i and j and $\sum q_i p_i = 1_S$.*

Proof.   If S is a direct sum of the A_i, then (b) holds because of (1) and (2).

Assume that (b) holds. As in the proof of the theorem we then see that S together with the projections p_i is a product of the A_i. Dually, we get that S is a coproduct of the A_i with the injections q_i.

Observe that the dual of an additive category is again an additive category because all four properties used in the definition are self-dual.

In an additive category $\mathscr{C}$ the endomorphisms of an object A, that is, the elements of $\text{Hom}_{\mathscr{C}}(A, A)$, form an associative ring with unit, the so-called *endomorphism ring*.

Example 1

The category **Ab** of abelian groups is an additive category. In Chapter 1 we saw that **Ab** has a zero object and products. Let $f, g \in \text{Mor}_{\text{Ab}}(A, B)$. Then $(f + g)(a) := f(a) + g(a)$ defines a group structure on $\text{Mor}_{\text{Ab}}(A, B)$ which satisfies the conditions of the theorem.

Example 2

The category of divisible abelian groups with all group homomorphisms as the morphisms is an additive category. Here we define the addition of morphisms as in Example 1. The only thing to show is that there are finite coproducts. It is sufficient to show that finite coproducts in **Ab** of divisible abelian groups are again divisible. Let A and B be divisible, that is, $nA = A$ and $nB = B$ for all $n \in \mathbb{N}$, then $n(A \oplus B) = nA \oplus nB = A \oplus B$.

4.2 Abelian Categories

In this section let $\mathscr{C}$ be an additive category. Furthermore, assume that each morphism in $\mathscr{C}$ has a kernel and a cokernel. Let two morphisms $f, g \in \text{Hom}_{\mathscr{C}}(A, B)$ be given, and let $h = f - g$. We want to show that the kernel of h coincides with the difference kernel of f and g. Given $c : C \to A$ with $fc = gc$, then $hc = fc - gc = 0$; thus there exists exactly one $d : C \to \text{Ker}(h)$ with $c = (C \to \text{Ker}(h) \to A)$. Furthermore,

$$(\text{Ker}(h) \to A \xrightarrow{f} B) = (\text{Ker}(h) \to A \xrightarrow{g} B)$$

Dually, the cokernel of h also coincides with the difference cokernel of f and g. Thus there are difference kernels and difference cokernels in $\mathscr{C}$.

LEMMA 1. *Let $\mathscr{C}$ be an additive category with kernels. Then $\mathscr{C}$ is a category with finite limits.*

Proof. Since $\mathscr{C}$ is a category with difference kernels and finite products, we can apply Section 2.6, Proposition 2.

Let $f : A \to B$ be a morphism in $\mathscr{C}$. In the diagram

$$
\begin{array}{c}
A \\
{}^{g}\swarrow \quad \downarrow {}^{f} \\
\mathrm{Ker}(p') \xrightarrow{\ q'\ } B \xrightarrow{\ p'\ } \mathrm{Cok}(f)
\end{array}
$$

there is exactly one morphism g with $q'g = f$ because $p'f = 0$. We denote $\mathrm{Ker}(p')$ also by $\mathrm{KerCok}(f)$. Dually, f may be uniquely factored through $\mathrm{CokKer}(f)$.

Both assertions may be combined in the commutative diagram

$$
\begin{array}{ccc}
\mathrm{Ker}(f) \xrightarrow{\ q\ } A \xrightarrow{\ p\ } \mathrm{CokKer}(f) \\
\downarrow {}^{f} \qquad\qquad \downarrow {}^{h} \\
\mathrm{Cok}(f) \xleftarrow{\ p'\ } B \xleftarrow{\ q'\ } \mathrm{KerCok}(f)
\end{array}
$$

where h is uniquely determined by f. In fact the morphism g may uniquely be factored through $\mathrm{CokKer}(f)$ because of $0 = fq = q'gq$, hence $gq = 0$. By Section 1.9, Lemma 1 both q and q' are monomorphisms and p and p' are epimorphisms. If h' instead of h also makes the diagram commutative, then $q'hp = q'h'p$, hence $h = h'$.

An additive category with kernels and cokernels, where for each morphism f the uniquely determined morphism $h : \mathrm{CokKer}(f) \to \mathrm{KerCok}(f)$ is an isomorphism, is called an *abelian category*.

Example

An important and well-known example for an abelian category is the category $_R\mathbf{Mod}$ of unitary R-modules. As in Section 4.1, Example 1, one shows that $_R\mathbf{Mod}$ is an additive category. In the theorem of Section 3.2 and in Section 3.4, Corollary 3 we saw that there are kernels and cokernels in $_R\mathbf{Mod}$. The assertion that $h : \mathrm{CokKer}(f) \to \mathrm{KerCok}(f)$ is an isomorphism is nothing else than the homomorphism theorem for R-modules.

One of the aims of the theory of abelian categories is to generalize theorems known for $_R\mathbf{Mod}$ to abelian categories. This will be done in the following sections. Since there are no elements in the objects of a category, the proof will often be more difficult and different from the proofs for $_R\mathbf{Mod}$. To prevent these difficulties we shall prove meta-theorems at the end of this chapter which transfer certain theorems known for $_R\mathbf{Mod}$ without any further proof to arbitrary abelian categories.

Now let $\mathscr{C}$ be an abelian category for the rest of this chapter unless we ask explicitly for other properties for $\mathscr{C}$.

LEMMA 2.

   (a) *Each monomorphism in $\mathscr{C}$ is a kernel of its cokernel.*
   (b) *Each epimorphism in $\mathscr{C}$ is a cokernel of its kernel.*
   (c) *A morphism f in $\mathscr{C}$ is an isomorphism if and only if f is a monomorphism and an epimorphism.*

Proof. (a) Let f be a monomorphism and let $fg = 0$. Then $g = 0$. Thus g may uniquely be factored through $0 \to D(f)$ ($=$ domain(f)), i.e., $\mathrm{Ker}(f) = 0$. The cokernel of this zero morphism is $1 : D(f) \to D(f)$. The commutative diagram

$$0 \longrightarrow D(f) \overset{1}{\longrightarrow} D(f)$$
$$\downarrow f \qquad\qquad \downarrow h$$
$$\mathrm{Cok}(f) \longleftarrow R(f) \longleftarrow \mathrm{KerCok}(f)$$

implies that $D(f)$ and $\mathrm{KerCok}(f)$ are equivalent subobjects of $R(f)$ ($=$ range(f)).

   (b) follows from (a) because the definition of an abelian category is self-dual.

   (c) In (a) we saw that the kernel of a monomorphism is zero. Similarly, the cokernel of an epimorphism is zero. Then (c) follows from the commutative diagram

$$0 \longrightarrow D(f) \overset{1}{\longrightarrow} D(f)$$
$$\downarrow f \qquad\qquad \downarrow h$$
$$0 \longleftarrow R(f) \overset{1}{\longleftarrow} R(f)$$

LEMMA 3. *For each morphism f in $\mathscr{C}$ the image of f is $\mathrm{KerCok}(f)$ and the coimage of f is $\mathrm{CokKer}(f)$.*

Proof. A morphism f may be factored through $\mathrm{KerCok}(f)$. Since there are fiber products in $\mathscr{C}$, $\mathscr{C}$ is a category with finite intersections. Let A be a subobject of $R(f)$ through which f may be factored, then f may be factored through $A \cap \mathrm{KerCok}(f)$. Since $D(f) \to \mathrm{KerCok}(f)$ is an epimorphism, $A \cap \mathrm{KerCok}(f) \to \mathrm{KerCok}(f)$ is an epimorphism and a monomorphism, hence an isomorphism by Lemma 2. Thus $D(f) \to A$

may also be factored through $\mathrm{KerCok}(f)$. Dually, one gets the proof for the coimage.

Because of Lemma 3, we shall always write $\mathrm{Im}(f)$ instead of $\mathrm{KerCok}(f)$ and $\mathrm{Coim}(f)$ instead of $\mathrm{CokKer}(f)$.

COROLLARY.   *A morphism $f : A \to B$ is an epimorphism if and only if $\mathrm{Im}(f) = B$.*

Proof.   By Lemma 2, f is an epimorphism if and only if $B = \mathrm{CokKer}(f)$. By $\mathrm{CokKer}(f) \cong \mathrm{KerCok}(f) = \mathrm{Im}(f)$, the morphism f is an epimorphism if and only if the subobject $\mathrm{Im}(f)$ of B coincides with B.

4.3   Exact Sequences

A sequence (f_1 , f_2) of two morphisms in an abelian category $\mathscr{C}$

$$A_1 \xrightarrow{f_1} A_2 \xrightarrow{f_2} A_3$$

is called *exact* or *exact in A_2* if $\mathrm{Ker}(f_2) = \mathrm{Im}(f_1)$ as subobjects of A_2. A sequence

$$\cdots A_i \xrightarrow{f_i} A_{i+1} \xrightarrow{f_{i+1}} A_{i+2} \cdots$$

of morphisms in $\mathscr{C}$ is called *exact* if it is exact in each of the A_{i+1}, that is, if $\mathrm{Ker}(f_{i+1}) = \mathrm{Im}(f_i)$ as subobjects of A_{i+1}. If the sequence is finite to the left side or to the right side, then this condition is empty for the last object.

An exact sequence of the form

$$0 \to A \to B \to C \to 0$$

is called a *short exact sequence*.

Let $f : A \to B$ be a morphism in $\mathscr{C}$. Then $B \to \mathrm{Cok}(f)$ is an epimorphism. By Section 4.2, Lemma 2 we then get

$$(B \to \mathrm{Cok}(f)) = (B \to \mathrm{CokKerCok}(f))$$

If $\mathrm{Ker}(f_{i+1}) = \mathrm{Im}(f)$, then $\mathrm{Cok}(f_i) = \mathrm{CokKerCok}(f_i) = \mathrm{CokIm}(f_i) = \mathrm{CokKer}(f_{i+1}) = \mathrm{Coim}(f_{i+1})$. Hence the definition of exactness is self-dual.

LEMMA 1.   *The sequence $A \xrightarrow{f} B \xrightarrow{g} C$ is exact if and only if we have for the morphisms $(A \to B \to C) = 0$ and $(\mathrm{Ker}(g) \to B \to \mathrm{Cok}(f)) = 0$.*

Proof.   Let $A \to B \to C$ be exact. Then we have trivially

$$(A \to B \to C) = 0$$

that is, $\text{Im}(f) \subseteq \text{Ker}(g)$. Furthermore, we obtain an epimorphism $\text{Coim}(g) \to \text{Cok}(f)$ through which $B \to \text{Cok}(f)$ may be factored. But $(\text{Ker}(g) \to B \to \text{Coim}(g)) = 0$.

If $(A \to B \to C) = 0$, then $\text{Im}(f) \subseteq \text{Ker}(g)$. If, furthermore, $(\text{Ker}(g) \to B \to \text{Cok}(f)) = 0$, then $\text{Ker}(g) \to B$ may be factored through $\text{KerCok}(f) = \text{Im}(f)$, hence $\text{Ker}(g) \subseteq \text{Im}(f)$.

A sequence

$$\cdots A_i \xrightarrow{\ f\ } A_{i+1} \xrightarrow{\ f_{i+1}\ } A_{i+2} \cdots$$

with $f_{i+1} f_i = 0$ for all i is called a *complex*. Obviously this notion is self-dual.

LEMMA 2.

(a) $0 \to A \to B$ *is exact if and only if* $A \to B$ *is a monomorphism.*

(b) $0 \to A \to B \to C$ *is exact if and only if* $A \to B$ *is the kernel of* $B \to C$.

(c) $0 \to A \to B \to C \to 0$ *is exact if and only if* $A \to B$ *is the kernel of* $B \to C$ *and if* $B \to C$ *is an epimorphism.*

Proof.   (a) By the corollary of Section 4.2, $A \to B$ is a monomorphism if and only if $\text{Coim}(A \to B) = A = \text{Cok}(0 \to A)$.

(b) If $A \to B$ is the kernel of $B \to C$, then $\text{Im}(A \to B) = \text{ImKer}(B \to C) = \text{Ker}(B \to C)$. Furthermore, $A \to B$ is a monomorphism. The converse is trivial.

(c) arises from (b) and the assertion dual to (a).

LEMMA 3.   *Let $\mathscr{C}$ be an abelian category. Let A_1, A_2, and S be objects in $\mathscr{C}$ and let $q_i : A_i \to S$ and $p_i : S \to A_i$ $(i = 1, 2)$ be morphisms in $\mathscr{C}$. The following are equivalent:*

(1) S *is a direct sum of the A_i with the injections q_i and the projections p_i.*

(2) $p_i q_i = 1_{A_i}$ *for $i = 1, 2$ and the sequences*

$$0 \longrightarrow A_1 \xrightarrow{q_1} S \xrightarrow{p_2} A_2 \longrightarrow 0$$

and

$$0 \longrightarrow A_2 \xrightarrow{q_2} S \xrightarrow{p_1} A_1 \longrightarrow 0$$

are exact.

(3) q_1 and q_2 are monomorphisms, p_1 and p_2 are epimorphisms, and
     we have $q_1 p_1 + q_2 p_2 = 1_S$ and $(q_1 p_1)^2 = q_1 p_1$.

Proof. (1) $\Rightarrow$ (2): By Section 4.1, Corollary 2 it is sufficient to show the
exactness of

$$0 \to A_1 \to S \to A_2 \to 0$$

p_2 is an epimorphism because of $p_2 q_2 = 1$. Given $f : B \to S$ with
$p_2 f = 0$, then $f = (q_1 p_1 + q_2 p_2) f = q_1 p_1 f$, i.e., f may be factored
through q_1. This factorization is unique since q_1 is a monomorphism.
   (2) $\Rightarrow$ (1): Let $f_i : B \to A_i$ be given. Let $f = q_1 f_1 + q_2 f_2$. Then
$p_i f = f_i$. If a morphism $g : B \to S$ satisfies the condition $p_i g = f_i$,
then $p_i(g - f) = 0$. Hence $g - f$ may be factored through A_1, that
is, $g - f = q_1 h$. Then $g - f = q_1 p_1 q_1 h = q_1 p_1(g - f) = 0$.
   (1) $\Rightarrow$ (3): By Section 4.1, Corollary 2, assertion (3) is trivially
implied by (1). If (3) holds, then $q_1 p_1 q_1 p_1 = q_1 p_1 = q_1 1_{A_1} p_1$. By
cancellation of the monomorphism q_1 and the epimorphism p_1 we
obtain $p_1 q_1 = 1_{A_1}$. $(1 - q_1 p_1)^2 = 1 - q_1 p_1$ implies $(q_2 p_2)^2 = q_2 p_2$,
hence $p_2 q_2 = 1_{A_2}$. Furthermore, we have

$$p_1 q_2 = p_1 q_1 p_1 q_2 p_2 q_2 = p_1(q_1 p_1)(1 - q_1 p_1) q_2 = p_1(q_1 p_1 - (q_1 p_1)^2) q_2 = 0$$

and analogously $p_2 q_1 = 0$. Then (1) holds by Section 4.1, Corollary 2.
   Let f be an endomorphism of S with $f^2 = f$. f may be factored through
the image of f. Let $p_1 : S \to \mathrm{Im}(f)$ and $q_1 : \mathrm{Im}(f) \to S$. If we factor
$1 - f = q_2 p_2$, then $S = \mathrm{Im}(f) \oplus \mathrm{Im}(1 - f)$. But by (2) we get
$\mathrm{Im}(1 - f) = \mathrm{Ker}(f)$ and hence, $S = \mathrm{Im}(f) \oplus \mathrm{Ker}(f)$.

LEMMA 4.

(a)   *The commutative diagram*

$$
\begin{array}{ccc}
P & \xrightarrow{a} & A \\
\downarrow{b} & & \downarrow{c} \\
B & \xrightarrow{d} & C
\end{array}
$$

is a fiber product if and only if the sequence

$$0 \to P \xrightarrow{f} A \oplus B \xrightarrow{g} C$$

with

$$f = \binom{a}{b} \quad \text{and} \quad g = (c, -d)$$

is exact.

(b) *Let the commutative diagram in (a) be a fiber product. The morphism* $c : A \to C$ *is a monomorphism if and only if* $b : P \to B$ *is a monomorphism.*

(c) *Let the commutative diagram in (a) be a fiber product. If* $c : A \to C$ *is an epimorphism, then the diagram is also a cofiber product and* $b : P \to B$ *is an epimorphism.*

Proof. (a) We define

$$f = \begin{pmatrix} a \\ b \end{pmatrix} \quad \text{and} \quad g = (c, -d)$$

The minus sign, of course, could stand before any of the other morphisms a, b, or c because the only reason for it is to achieve $gf = 0$. If the diagram in (a) is a fiber product and $h : D \to A \oplus B$ is given with $gh = 0$, then

$$h = \begin{pmatrix} h_A \\ h_B \end{pmatrix} \quad \text{and} \quad ch_A = dh_B$$

Thus there exists exactly one morphism $e : D \to P$ with $ae = h_A$ and $be = h_B$, that is, with $fe = h$. Conversely, each pair of morphisms $h_A : D \to A$ and $h_B : D \to B$ with $ch_A = dh_B$ hence with $gh = 0$, defines exactly one morphism $e : D \to P$ with $fe = h$, i.e., with $ae = h_A$ and $be = h_B$.

(b) If $c : A \to C$ is a monomorphism, then by Section 2.7, Corollary 5 $b : P \to B$ is also a monomorphism. Now let $b : P \to B$ be a monomorphism. Let $(D \to A \to C) = 0$. If we set $(D \to B) = 0$ then there exists exactly one morphism $D \to P$ with $(D \to A) = (D \to P \to A)$ and $(D \to P \to B) = 0$. Since $P \to B$ is a monomorphism, we get $(D \to P) = 0$ and hence $(D \to A) = 0$. This means that $A \to C$ is a monomorphism.

(c) If $c : A \to C$ is an epimorphism, then $c = (A \to A \oplus B \to C)$ is an epimorphism, hence also $A \oplus B \to C$. By Lemma 2, the sequence $0 \to P \to A \oplus B \to C \to 0$ is exact. By (a) the diagram in (a) is a cofiber product. The assertion dual to (b) implies (c).

In the following we shall denote the cokernel of a monomorphism by B/A. This corresponds to the usual notation for R-modules. In the dual case we shall not introduce any particular notation for the kernel of an epimorphism. The applications which assign to each subobject of an object B a quotient object and to each quotient object a subobject are inverse to each other. Furthermore, they invert the order if, in the class of subobjects, we set $A \leqslant A'$ if and only if there is a morphism a such that

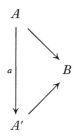

is commutative, and if, in the class of quotient objects, we set $C \leqslant C'$ if and only if there is a morphism c such that

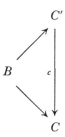

is commutative. This follows from the commutative diagram with exact rows

$$
\begin{array}{ccccccccc}
0 & \longrightarrow & A & \longrightarrow & B & \longrightarrow & C' & \longrightarrow & 0 \\
 & & a\downarrow & & 1_B\downarrow & & c\downarrow & & \\
0 & \longrightarrow & A' & \longrightarrow & B & \longrightarrow & C & \longrightarrow & 0
\end{array}
$$

where a exists if and only if c exists.

LEMMA 5. *In an abelian category $\mathscr{C}$ there exist finite intersections and finite unions of subobjects. The lattice of subobjects is antiisomorphic to the lattice of quotient objects of an object.*

Proof. Since $\mathscr{C}$ has fiber products, there exist finite intersections in $\mathscr{C}$. Let A and B be subobjects of C. Then we define $A \cup B = \mathrm{Im}(A \oplus B \to C)$. In fact, let D be a subobject of C' and let morphisms $C \to C'$, $A \to D$, and $B \to D$ be given such that the diagrams

$$
\begin{array}{ccc}
A & \longrightarrow & C \\
\downarrow & & \downarrow \\
D & \longrightarrow & C'
\end{array}
\qquad
\begin{array}{ccc}
B & \longrightarrow & C \\
\downarrow & & \downarrow \\
D & \longrightarrow & C'
\end{array}
$$

are commutative. Then there exists a morphism $A \oplus B \to D$ such that

$$(A \oplus B \to C \to C') = (A \oplus B \to D \to C')$$

Hence, $\mathrm{Im}(A \oplus B \to C) \to C \to C'$ may be factored through $D \to C'$. Thus the class of subobjects of $\mathscr{C}$ is a lattice. The preceeding considerations imply immediately the second assertion of the Lemma.

COROLLARY. *If there exist infinite products in the abelian category $\mathscr{C}$, then there exist arbitrary intersections of subobjects in the category $\mathscr{C}$. If there exist infinite coproducts in $\mathscr{C}$, then there exist arbitrary unions of subobjects in the category $\mathscr{C}$.*

Proof. If $\mathscr{C}$ has infinite products, then $\mathscr{C}$ is complete and thus there exist arbitrary intersections of subobjects. If $\mathscr{C}$ has infinite coproducts, then the proof of Lemma 5 may be repeated verbally for infinitely many subobjects.

LEMMA 6.

(a) *Let $f : A \to B$ and $g : B \to C$ be morphisms in an abelian category $\mathscr{C}$. Then $\mathrm{Im}(gf) \subseteq \mathrm{Im}(g)$.*

(b) *Let $f, g : A \to B$ be morphisms in $\mathscr{C}$. Then*

$$\mathrm{Im}(f + g) \subseteq \mathrm{Im}(f) \cup \mathrm{Im}(g).$$

Proof. (a) The diagram

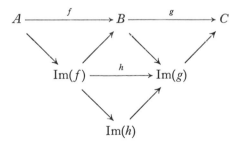

is commutative, $A \to \mathrm{Im}(f) \to \mathrm{Im}(h)$ is an epimorphism, and $\mathrm{Im}(h) \to \mathrm{Im}(g) \to B$ is a monomorphism. Hence $\mathrm{Im}(h) = \mathrm{Im}(gf) \subseteq \mathrm{Im}(g)$.

(b) We have

$$f + g = (A \xrightarrow{\Delta} A \oplus A \xrightarrow{a} \mathrm{Im}(f) \oplus \mathrm{Im}(g) \xrightarrow{b} B \oplus B \xrightarrow{\nabla} B)$$

By definition, $\mathrm{Im}(f) \cup \mathrm{Im}(g) = \mathrm{Im}(\nabla b)$. Hence, by (a), we get $\mathrm{Im}(f + g) \subseteq \mathrm{Im}(f) \cup \mathrm{Im}(g)$.

4.4 Isomorphism Theorems

THEOREM (3×3 lemma). *Let the diagram*

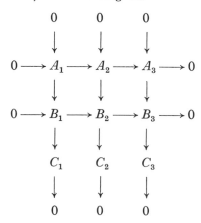

be commutative with exact rows and columns. Then there are uniquely defined morphisms $C_1 \to C_2$ and $C_2 \to C_3$ making the above diagram commutative. Furthermore, the sequence $0 \to C_1 \to C_2 \to C_3 \to 0$ is exact.

Proof. The existence and uniqueness of $C_1 \to C_2$ and $C_2 \to C_3$ is implied by the facts that $C_1 = \mathrm{Cok}(A_1 \to B_1)$ and $(A_1 \to C_2) = 0$ and, respectively, $C_2 = \mathrm{Cok}(A_2 \to B_2)$ and $(A_2 \to C_3) = 0$.

Furthermore, $C_2 \to C_3$ is an epimorphism because

$$(B_2 \to C_2 \to C_3) = (B_2 \to B_3 \to C_3)$$

is an epimorphism. If we omit in the diagram the object C_1 and the morphisms $B_1 \to C_1$ and $C_1 \to C_2$, then the remaining diagram is self-dual. Furthermore, the sequence

$$0 \to A_1 \to B_1 \to C_2 \to C_3 \to 0 \tag{1}$$

is exact. For reasons of duality, it is sufficient to prove the exactness of $0 \to A_1 \to B_1 \to C_2$, that is, $A_1 = \mathrm{Ker}(B_1 \to C_2)$. Let $D \to B_1$ with $(D \to B_1 \to C_2) = 0$ be given. Then there exists $D \to A_2$ with

$$(D \to B_1 \to B_2) = (D \to A_2 \to B_2)$$

Since $(D \to B_3) = 0$ and $A_3 \to B_3$ is a monomorphism, we have $(D \to A_2 \to A_3) = 0$, hence there is a morphism $D \to A_1$ with $(D \to A_2) = (D \to A_1 \to A_2)$. Since $B_1 \to B_2$ is a monomorphism and

$$(D \to B_1 \to B_2) = (D \to A_1 \to B_1 \to B_2)$$

we have $(D \to B_1) = (D \to A_1 \to B_1)$. The uniqueness of this factorization follows from the fact that $A_1 \to B_1$ is a monomorphism.

We have $\text{Ker}(B_1 \to C_2) = A_1$ and $\text{Cok}(B_1 \to C_2) = C_3$. Thus $C_1 = \text{Coim}(B_1 \to C_2) = \text{Im}(B_1 \to C_2) = \text{Ker}(C_2 \to C_3)$ as subobjects of C_2 and $C_2 \to C_3$ is an epimorphism.

COROLLARY 1 (first isomorphism theorem). *Given subobjects $A \subseteq B \subseteq C$. Then we have $B/A \subseteq C/A$ and $(C/A)/(B/A) \cong C/B$.*

Proof. Apply the 3×3 lemma to the diagram

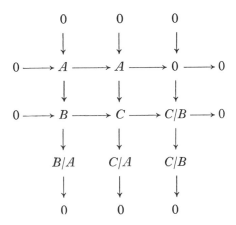

COROLLARY 2 (second isomorphism theorem). *Given subobjects $A \subseteq C$ and $B \subseteq C$. Then we have $(A \cup B)/B \simeq A/(A \cap B)$, that is, the diagram*

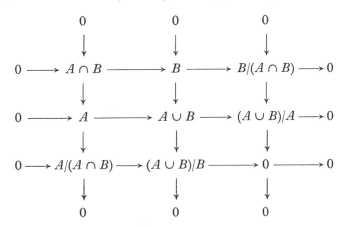

is commutative with exact rows and columns.

Proof. To apply the 3×3 lemma we have to show that $B/(A \cap B) \to$ $(A \cup B)/B$ is a monomorphism. Let $D \to B$ with

$$(D \to B \to A \cup B \to (A \cup B)/A) = 0$$

be given. Then there is exactly one morphism $D \to A$ with

$$(D \to A \to A \cup B) = (D \to B \to A \cup B)$$

Thus there is exactly one $D \to A \cap B$ with

$$(D \to B) = (D \to A \cap B \to B) \quad \text{and} \quad (D \to A) = (D \to A \cap B \to A)$$

that is, $A \cap B$ is the kernel of $B \to (A \cup B)/A$. But the morphism

$$\mathrm{CokKer}(B \to (A \cup B)/A) \to (A \cup B)/A$$

is always a monomorphism.

Now let us apply the 3×3 lemma to show that

$$C_3 = ((A \cup B)/A)/(B/(A \cap B))$$

vanishes. We have $(A \to A \cup B \to C_3) = 0$ and $(B \to A \cup B \to C_3) = 0$. Thus by the definition of a union $(A \cup B \to C_3) = 0$. The diagram implies that $A \cup B \to C_3$ is an epimorphism. Hence, $C_3 = 0$.

COROLLARY 3. *Let $C = A \cup B$ and $A \cap B = 0$. Then C is the direct sum of A and B with injections the embeddings of A and B into C.*

Proof. Insert $A \cap B = 0$ into the diagram of Corollary 2. Then $A \to A/(A \cap B) \to (A \cup B)/B$ and $B \to B/(A \cap B) \to (A \cup B)/A$ are isomorphisms. If we take as projections for the direct sum the inverses of these isomorphisms composed with $A \cup B \to (A \cup B)/B$ and $A \cup B \to (A \cup B)/A$, then we can easily apply Section 4.3, Lemma 3.

4.5   The Jordan–Hölder Theorem

An object $A \neq 0$ in an abelian category $\mathscr{C}$ is called *simple* if for each subobject B of A either $B = 0$ or $B = A$ holds.

Let $0 = B_0 \subset B_1 \subset \cdots \subset B_n = A$ be a sequence of subobjects of A which are all different. Such a sequence is called a *composition series* if the objects B_i/B_{i-1} are simple for all $i = 1, \ldots, n$. The objects B_i/B_{i-1} are called *factors* of the composition series and n is called *length* of the composition series.

LEMMA 1. *Let $A \subseteq C$ and $B \subseteq C$ be nonequivalent subobjects of C. Let C/A and C/B be simple. Then $C = A \cup B$.*

Proof. $A \subseteq A \cup B$ and $B \subseteq A \cup B$ imply that at least one of the subobjects, for example B, is different from $A \cup B$. By the 3×3 lemma there is a commutative diagram with exact rows and columns

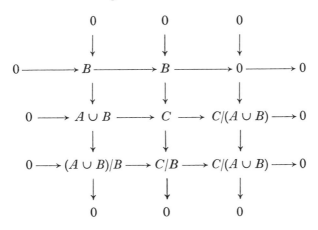

By hypothesis, we have $(A \cup B)/B \neq 0$ and $(A \cup B)/B \subseteq C/B$. Since C/B is simple, we get $C/(A \cup B) = 0$ hence $C = A \cup B$.

LEMMA 2. *Let $0 = B_0 \subset \cdots \subset B_n = A$ be a composition series. Let $C \subseteq A$ and let A/C be simple. Then there exists a composition series of A through C of length n:*

$$0 = C_0 \subset \cdots \subset C_{n-2} \subset C \subset A$$

Proof. The proof is by complete induction with respect to n. For $n = 1$, the only composition series of A (up to equivalence of subobjects) is $0 \subset A$. Assume that the lemma holds for composition series of length $n - 1$. Consider the diagram

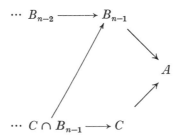

where we may assume that C and B_{n-1} are nonequivalent subobjects of A, since otherwise there exists already a composition series through C. Thus by Lemma 1 we have $A = C \cup B_{n-1}$. By the second isomorphism theorem $B_{n-1}/(C \cap B_{n-1}) = A/C$ is simple. Since B_{n-1} has a composition series of length $n - 1$, there exists a composition series of B_{n-1} through $C \cap B_{n-1}$ of length $n - 1$. Hence, $C \cap B_{n-1}$ has a composition series of length $n - 2$. This may be extended through C and A, for $C/(C \cap B_{n-1}) = A/B_{n-1}$ and A/C are simple.

THEOREM 1 (Jordan–Hölder). *Assume that the object A in $\mathscr{C}$ has a composition series. Then all composition series of A have the same length and isomorphic factors up to the order.*

Proof. By complete induction with respect to the length of a composition series of minimal length of A. For $n = 1$, there exists only one composition series of A, as above. Assume that the theorem is already proved for all A with composition series of length $\leqslant n - 1$. Let two composition series $0 = B_0 \subset \cdots \subset B_n = A$ and $0 = C_0 \subset \cdots \subset C_m = A$ be given. We form

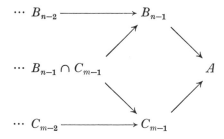

Since, by the second isomorphism theorem, all factors of the diagram are simple

$$A/B_{n-1} \cong C_{m-1}/(B_{n-1} \cap C_{m-1}) \qquad \text{and} \qquad A/C_{m-1} \cong B_{n-1}/(B_{n-1} \cap C_{m-1})$$

all sequences in the above diagram are composition series because the theorem holds already for B_{n-1}. Here we used that B_{n-1} and C_{m-1} are nonequivalent subobjects, for otherwise the assertion may be reduced to B_{n-1}. Since B_{n-1} and C_{m-1} have composition series of equal length, namely through $B_{n-1} \cap C_{m-1}$, we get $m = n$. The factors of the composition series of B_{n-1} and C_{m-1} differ only in $B_{n-1}/(B_{n-1} \cap C_{m-1})$ and $C_{m-1}/(B_{n-1} \cap C_{m-1})$. But both factors appear in the composition series of A through $B_{n-1} \cap C_{m-1}$. Hence both given composition series of A have the same length and isomorphic factors up to the order.

If A has a composition series of length n, then we also say that the object A *has length* n. If A has a composition series, which by definition is finite, then we also say that A is an *object of finite length*.

PROPOSITION 1. *Let A be an object of finite length and let C be a subobject of A. Then there exists a composition series of A in which C appears as an element.*

Proof. Let $0 = B_0 \subset \cdots \subset B_n = A$ be a composition series of A. We form the sequences

$$0 = C \cap B_0 \subseteq \cdots \subseteq C \cap B_n = C$$

and

$$C = C \cup B_0 \subseteq \cdots \subseteq C \cup B_n = A$$

As in the proof of the second isomorphism theorem, one shows with the 3×3 lemma that the diagram

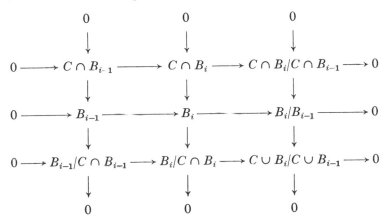

is commutative with exact rows and columns. In fact, we have $C \cap B_{i-1} = (C \cap B_i) \cap B_{i-1}$. Furthermore, using both isomorphism theorems we obtain

$$C \cup B_i / C \cup B_{i-1} \cong (C \cup B_i / C) / (C \cup B_{i-1} / C) \cong (B_i / C \cap B_i) / (B_{i-1} / C \cap B_{i-1})$$

Since B_i / B_{i-1} is simple, each factor object of B_i / B_{i-1} is either simple or 0, since the kernel of the morphism into the factor object is either 0 or simple. Hence just one of the objects $C \cap B_i / C \cap B_{i-1}$ or $C \cup B_i / C \cup B_{i-1}$ is simple and the other one is 0. If one connects the sequences given above, and if one drops all of the members which appear several times, except one, then this new sequence is a composition series through C.

An object of finite length may well have infinitely many nonequivalent subobjects (see Problem 8). But by Proposition 1 each proper subobject has a length smaller than the length of the object. Hence in each set of proper subobjects of an object of finite length, the subobjects of maximal length are maximal, and the subobjects of minimal length are minimal, and such subobjects always exist if the given set is nonempty.

COROLLARY 1. *An object has finite length if and only if it is artinian and noetherian.*

Proof. The only thing we have to prove is that each artinian and noetherian object A has finite length. In the class of subobjects of A, which are not equivalent to A, there is a maximal subobject B_1. Since B_1 is again artinian and noetherian, we may construct B_2, B_3,..., in the same way. This defines a descending sequence of subobjects of A. Since A is artinian, this sequence stops after finitely many steps. Furthermore, the factors of this sequence are simple by construction, hence this is a composition series of A.

COROLLARY 2. *Let B be an object of finite length, and let the sequence $0 \to A \to B \to C \to 0$ be exact. Then A and C are objects of finite length, and we have*

$$\text{length}(B) = \text{length}(A) + \text{length}(C)$$

In particular, an epimorphism between objects of equal length is an isomorphism.

Proof. Let $0 = B_0 \subset \cdots \subset B_i = A \subset \cdots \subset B_n = B$ be a composition series of B through A. Then $(B_k/A)/(B_{k-1}/A) \cong B_k/B_{k-1}$ is simple for all $i < k \leqslant n$. Hence, $0 = B_i/A \subset \cdots \subset B_n/A = C$ is a composition series of length $n - i$. Furthermore, A has length i. The second assertion follows from the fact that the kernel of the epimorphism has length 0, and that each object of length 0 is a zero object.

4.6 Additive Functors

The facts that the morphism sets of an additive category $\mathscr{C}$ are additive groups and that the composition of morphisms is bilinear correspond to the condition for the functors $\mathscr{F} : \mathscr{C} \to \mathscr{D}$ between additive categories that for all $A, B \in \mathscr{C}$ the maps

$$\mathscr{F}(A, B) : \text{Hom}_{\mathscr{C}}(A, B) \to \text{Hom}_{\mathscr{D}}(\mathscr{F}A, \mathscr{F}B) \tag{1}$$

are group homomorphisms. A functor $\mathscr{F}$ which satisfies condition (1) is called an *additive functor*. Of course, there are also other functors between additive categories which are not necessarily additive.

Because of the bilinearity of the composition of morphisms in an additive category $\mathscr{C}$, the representable functor represented by any object A in $\mathscr{C}$ is additive where we mean the functor $\mathrm{Hom}_{\mathscr{C}}(A, -)$ with values in **Ab**.

THEOREM 1. *A functor $\mathscr{F} : \mathscr{C} \to \mathscr{D}$ between additive categories is additive if and only if $\mathscr{F}$ preserves finite direct sums with the corresponding injections and projections.*

Proof. If $\mathscr{F}$ is additive, then $\mathscr{F}$ preserves condition (2) of Section 4.2, Corollary 2 for direct sums. If $\mathscr{F}$ preserves finite direct sums with their injections and projections then $\mathscr{F}(f + g) = \mathscr{F}(f) + \mathscr{F}(g)$. In fact, let objects A, B, C, D in $\mathscr{C}$ and morphisms $f : A \to B$ and $g : B \to D$ be given, then $f \oplus g$ is uniquely determined by $(f \oplus g)\, q_A = q_C f$ and $(f \oplus g)\, q_B = q_D g$. These conditions are preserved by $\mathscr{F}$. Furthermore, $\mathscr{F}$ preserves diagonals and codiagonals of finite direct sums. Hence by Section 4.1, Corollary 1 we have

$$\mathscr{F}(f + g) = \mathscr{F}(\nabla_B)\, \mathscr{F}(f \oplus g)\, \mathscr{F}(\Delta_A) = \nabla_{\mathscr{F}B}(\mathscr{F}f \oplus \mathscr{F}g)\, \Delta_{\mathscr{F}A} = \mathscr{F}f + \mathscr{F}g$$

For an abelian category we can also ask for the preservation of certain exact sequences by the functor $\mathscr{F}$. In the diagram

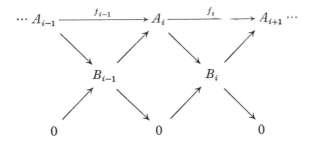

the sequence of the f_i is exact if and only if the sequences $0 \to B_{i-1} \to A_i \to B_i \to 0$ are exact where $B_i = \mathrm{Im}(f_i)$. Then this is equivalent to $B_{i-1} = \mathrm{Ker}(f_i)$. If $\mathscr{F}$ preserves short exact sequences, then $\mathscr{F}$ also preserves arbitrary exact sequences. Thus we call $\mathscr{F}$ an *exact functor* if $\mathscr{F}$ preserves short exact sequences. If $\mathscr{F}$ preserves exact sequence of the form

$$0 \to A \to B \to C \quad \text{or} \quad A \to B \to C \to 0$$

then $\mathscr{F}$ is called *left* or *right exact* respectively. If for each exact sequence $0 \to A \to B \to C \to 0$ the sequence $\mathscr{F}A \to \mathscr{F}B \to \mathscr{F}C$ is exact, then $\mathscr{F}$ is called a *half-exact* functor.

Be careful not to confuse the condition for a half-exact functor with the condition that for each exact sequence $A \to B \to C$, the sequence $\mathscr{F}A \to \mathscr{F}B \to \mathscr{F}C$ is also exact, since in this case $\mathscr{F}$ is exact. A functor $\mathscr{F}$ is left or right exact if and only if $\mathscr{F}$ preserves kernels or cokernels respectively. Obviously, each exact functor is left exact and right exact, and each left or right exact functor is half exact. Furthermore, a functor which is left and right exact is exact, as one can easily see by Section 4.3, Lemma 2.

PROPOSITION 1. *A half-exact functor $\mathscr{F} : \mathscr{C} \to \mathscr{D}$ between abelian categories is additive.*

Proof. By Theorem 1 we only have to show that $\mathscr{F}$ preserves direct sums of two objects with the corresponding injections and projections. If we characterize these by Sections 4.3, Lemma 3, then we obtain by the half exactness of $\mathscr{F}$ that $\mathscr{F}p_i\mathscr{F}q_i = 1_{\mathscr{F}A_i}$, and we obtain the exactness of the sequences

$$\mathscr{F}A_1 \xrightarrow{\mathscr{F}q_1} \mathscr{F}S \xrightarrow{\mathscr{F}p_2} \mathscr{F}A_2$$

$$\mathscr{F}A_2 \xrightarrow{\mathscr{F}q_2} \mathscr{F}S \xrightarrow{\mathscr{F}p_1} \mathscr{F}A_1$$

From the first condition, we may already conclude that the $\mathscr{F}p_i$ are epimorphisms and the $\mathscr{F}q_i$ are monomorphisms. Thus the sequences

$$0 \to \mathscr{F}A_1 \xrightarrow{\mathscr{F}q_1} \mathscr{F}S \xrightarrow{\mathscr{F}p_2} \mathscr{F}A_2 \to 0$$

$$0 \to \mathscr{F}A_2 \xrightarrow{\mathscr{F}q_2} \mathscr{F}S \xrightarrow{\mathscr{F}p_1} \mathscr{F}A_1 \to 0$$

are exact by Section 4.3, Lemma 2. This proves the proposition by Section 4.3, Lemma 3.

An example of a left-exact functor from an abelian category $\mathscr{C}$ into the category **Ab** is again the functor $\mathrm{Hom}_{\mathscr{C}}(A, -) : \mathscr{C} \to \mathbf{Ab}$ represented by an object $A \in \mathscr{C}$. In fact, if $0 \to B \xrightarrow{f} C \xrightarrow{g} D$ is exact and $h : A \to B$ is a morphism with $\mathrm{Hom}_{\mathscr{C}}(A,f)(h) = 0$, then $fh = 0$. Since f is a monomorphism, we have $h = 0$; hence $\mathrm{Hom}_{\mathscr{C}}(A,f)$ is a monomorphism. If $h' : A \to C$ is a morphism with $\mathrm{Hom}_{\mathscr{C}}(A, g)(h') = gh' = 0$, then there exists a morphism $h : A \to B$ with $fh = h'$ because $f : B \to C$ is the kernel of g. Consequently, $\mathrm{Hom}_{\mathscr{C}}(A, f)(h) = h'$. Together with $\mathrm{Hom}_{\mathscr{C}}(A, g)\,\mathrm{Hom}_{\mathscr{C}}(A, f) = 0$, this implies the exactness of the sequence

$$0 \to \mathrm{Hom}_{\mathscr{C}}(A, B) \xrightarrow{\ \mathrm{Hom}_{\mathscr{C}}(A, f)\ } \mathrm{Hom}_{\mathscr{C}}(A, C) \xrightarrow{\ \mathrm{Hom}_{\mathscr{C}}(A, g)\ } \mathrm{Hom}_{\mathscr{C}}(A, D)$$

4.7   Grothendieck Categories

Let $\mathscr{E}$ be a small category. Then the functors from $\mathscr{E}$ into the abelian category $\mathscr{C}$ together with the natural transformations form a category $\mathrm{Funct}(\mathscr{E}, \mathscr{C})$.

PROPOSITION 1.   *$\mathrm{Funct}(\mathscr{E}, \mathscr{C})$ is an abelian category.*

Proof.   By Section 2.7, Theorem 1, $\mathrm{Funct}(\mathscr{E}, \mathscr{C})$ is finitely complete and cocomplete. Furthermore, the functor $\mathcal{O} : \mathscr{E} \to \mathscr{C}$ with $\mathcal{O}(E) = 0$ for all $E \in \mathscr{E}$ is a zero object for $\mathrm{Funct}(\mathscr{E}, \mathscr{C})$. As in Section 4.1, we can define a morphism δ from the coproducts into the products. Then for the functors $\mathscr{F}_i \in \mathrm{Funct}(\mathscr{E}, \mathscr{C})$ the morphism $\delta_{\mathscr{F}}(E) : \coprod \mathscr{F}_i(E) \to \prod \mathscr{F}_i(E)$ coincides with $\delta_{\mathscr{F}(E)}$, that is, δ is formed argumentwise. Hence by Section 1.5, δ is an isomorphism in $\mathrm{Funct}(\mathscr{E}, \mathscr{C})$. Correspondingly, $\varDelta$ and ∇ have to be formed argumentwise. Furthermore, the morphisms $s_{\mathscr{F}_i(E)}$ are natural transformations satisfying condition (4) for additive categories. The natural transformation h of Section 4.2 from the coimage into the image of a morphism in $\mathrm{Funct}(\mathscr{E}, \mathscr{C})$ is also formed argumentwise. Thus h is always an isomorphism and $\mathrm{Funct}(\mathscr{E}, \mathscr{C})$ is an abelian category.

Since by Section 2.7, Corollary 2 the colimits commute with coproducts and cokernels, we obtain the following corollary.

COROLLARY 1.   *The functor $\varinjlim : \mathrm{Funct}(\mathscr{E}, \mathscr{C}) \to \mathscr{C}$ is right exact if it exists.*

In the following let $\mathscr{C}$ be an abelian cocomplete category. Furthermore, we require that a certain condition holds in $\mathscr{C}$ which holds in all module categories. For each subobject $B \subseteq A$ and each chain of subobjects $\{A_i\}$ of A,

$$\left(\bigcup A_i \right) \cap B = \bigcup (A_i \cap B) \tag{1}$$

holds. This condition is called the *Grothendieck condition*. Observe that

Equation (1) does not hold for arbitrary sets $\{A_i\}$ of subobjects of A in module categories. An abelian, cocomplete, locally small category with the Grothendieck condition will be called a *Grothendieck category*.

In the following we shall need condition (1) not only for chains of subobjects of A, but also for directed families of subobjects. Here we mean by a *directed family of subobjects* of A a functor $\mathscr{F}$ from a directed small category $\mathscr{E}$ into the category $\mathscr{C}$ such that $\mathscr{F}(E)$ is a subobject of A for all $E \in \mathscr{E}$ and such that for all $E \to E'$ in $\mathscr{E}$ the morphisms $\mathscr{F}(E) \to \mathscr{F}(E')$ together with the monomorphisms into A form a commutative diagram

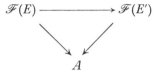

This means that there is a natural transformation $\mu : \mathscr{F} \to \mathscr{K}_A$ from the functor $\mathscr{F}$ into the constant functor $\mathscr{K}_A : \mathscr{E} \to \mathscr{C}$ such that $\mu(E) : \mathscr{F}(E) \to \mathscr{K}_A(E)$ is a monomorphism for all $E \in \mathscr{E}$.

LEMMA 1. *Let $\mathfrak{B}$ be an ordered set in which for each subset $\{v_i\}$ there exists a supremum $\bigcup v_i$. Let $\mathfrak{W}$ be a subset of $\mathfrak{B}$ which is closed with respect to forming suprema in $\mathfrak{B}$ of chains in $\mathfrak{W}$. Let $\varnothing \neq \mathfrak{B}' \subseteq \mathfrak{B}$. If then $\bigcup_{v \in \mathfrak{B}'} v \notin \mathfrak{W}$, then there are already finitely many $v_1 ,..., v_n \in \mathfrak{B}'$ with $v_1 \cup \cdots \cup v_n \notin \mathfrak{W}$.*

Proof. Let $\mathfrak{P}(\mathfrak{B}')$ be the power set of $\mathfrak{B}'$. Each subset of $\mathfrak{B}$ may be well-ordered in different ways (independent of the given order in $\mathfrak{B}$). Let $\mathfrak{Q}(\mathfrak{B}')$ be the set of all well-orderings of all subsets of $\mathfrak{B}'$. Thus each element of $\mathfrak{Q}(\mathfrak{B}')$ has an ordinal number. Let $\mathfrak{Q}'(\mathfrak{B}')$ be the subset of those elements of $\mathfrak{Q}(\mathfrak{B}')$ for whose corresponding set $P \in \mathfrak{P}(\mathfrak{B}')$ we have $\bigcup_{v \in P} v \notin \mathfrak{W}$. By hypothesis, $\mathfrak{Q}'(\mathfrak{B}')$ is not empty; thus there exists a $Q \in \mathfrak{Q}'(\mathfrak{B}')$ with smallest ordinal number γ. Let $P \in \mathfrak{P}(\mathfrak{B}')$ be the corresponding subset of $\mathfrak{B}$ and assume that the elements of P have as subscripts ordinal numbers smaller than γ in the order of the given well-ordering. Then for all $\beta < \gamma$ we get $\bigcup_{\alpha < \beta} v_\alpha \in \mathfrak{W}$. Hence, $\bigcup_{\beta < \gamma} \bigcup_{\alpha < \beta} v_\alpha \neq \bigcup_{\alpha < \gamma} v_\alpha$, because $\mathfrak{W}$ is closed with respect to suprema of chains. The set of the $\bigcup_{\alpha < \beta} v_\alpha$ is, in fact, a chain. Hence, γ cannot be a limit. If γ is infinite, then there is a bijection between the ordinal numbers smaller than γ and the ordinal numbers smaller than $\gamma - 1$. This bijection maps $\gamma - 1$ to 0 and n to $n + 1$. This reordering does not change the value of $\bigcup_{v \in P} v$. This is a contradiction to the minimality of γ. Consequently, γ is finite.

LEMMA 2. *Let $\mathscr{C}$ be a Grothendieck category. Let $B \subseteq A$ be a subobject of $A \in \mathscr{C}$ and let $\{A_i\}$ be a directed family of subobjects of A.*

Then

$$\left(\bigcup A_i\right) \cap B = \bigcup (A_i \cap B)$$

Proof. Since $A_i \cap B \subseteq (\bigcup A_i) \cap B$, we get in general $\bigcup (A_i \cap B) \subseteq (\bigcup A_i) \cap B$. Let $C = \bigcup (A_i \cap B)$. The set of the subobjects of A forms an ordered set with suprema. We define a subset of the subobjects of A by $D \in \mathfrak{W}$ if and only if $D \cap B \subseteq C$. By the Grothendieck condition, $\mathfrak{W}$ is closed with respect to suprema of chains. Assume that $(\bigcup A_i) \cap B \not\subseteq C$. Then, by Lemma 1, there exist $A_1, ..., A_n$ with $(A_1 \cup \cdots \cup A_n) \cap B \not\subseteq C$. Since the $\{A_i\}$ form a directed family of subobjects, there exists an A_k with $A_j \subseteq A_k$ for $j = 1, ..., n$. Hence, $A_k \cap B \not\subseteq C$. Obviously, this is a contradiction. Consequently, $(\bigcup A_i) \cap B = \bigcup (A_i \cap B)$.

After having extended the Grothendieck condition to directed families of subobjects we now want to discuss the importance for direct limits. For this purpose, let $\mathscr{C}$ be a Grothendieck category, $\mathscr{E}$ be a small directed category, and $\mathscr{F} : \mathscr{E} \to \mathscr{C}$ be a functor. We denote the objects in $\mathscr{E}$ by $i, j, k, ...,$ and set $\mathscr{F}(i) = F_i$. For $i \leqslant j$ we denote the morphism from F_i into F_j induced by $\mathscr{F}$ by $f_{ij} : F_i \to F_j$. The injection will be denoted by $q_i : F_i \to \varinjlim \mathscr{F}$.

LEMMA 3.   *Let $\mathscr{C}$ be a Grothendieck category and $\mathscr{E}$ be a directed small category. Let $\mathscr{F} \in \mathrm{Funct}(\mathscr{E}, \mathscr{C})$. Then we have*

$$\mathrm{Ker}(q_i : F_i \to \varinjlim \mathscr{F}) = \bigcup_{i \leqslant j} \mathrm{Ker}(f_{ij} : F_i \to F_j)$$

Proof. We denote $\mathrm{Ker}(q_i)$ by K_i and $\mathrm{Ker}(f_{ij})$ by K_{ij}. Because of the commutativity of

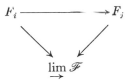

for all $i \leqslant j$ we get $K_{ij} \subseteq K_i$, hence $\bigcup_{i \leqslant j} K_{ij} \subseteq K_i$.

By Section 2.6, Proposition 2 $\varinjlim \mathscr{F}$ is the cokernel of $g : \coprod_{i \leqslant j} F_{ij} \to \coprod F_i$ where $F_{ij} = F_i$ for all $i \leqslant j$ and where g is defined componentwise for the F_{ij} by $g_{ij} = q_i - q_j f_{ij}$. Let $A_{ij} = \mathrm{Im}(g_{ij})$. Then the sequence

$$0 \to \bigcup A_{ij} \to \coprod F_i \to \varinjlim \mathscr{F} \to 0$$

is exact. Let E be a finite subset of the set of pairs (i, j) with $i \leqslant j$ and $i, j \in \mathscr{E}$ and let

$$A_E = \bigcup_{(i,j) \in E} A_{ij}$$

The set of finite sets E defined in this way together with the relation of containment forms again a directed small category $\mathscr{E}'$. We get $\bigcup_{i \leqslant j} A_{ij} = \bigcup_{E \in \mathscr{E}'} A_E$.

The diagram

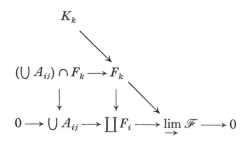

is commutative with exact lower row. Since $(K_k \to \coprod F_i \to \varinjlim \mathscr{F}) = 0$, there exists exactly one morphism $K_k \to \bigcup A_{ij}$ with

$$\left(K_k \to \bigcup A_{ij} \to \coprod F_i\right) = (K_k \to F_k \to \coprod F_i)$$

Hence there exists a unique morphism $K_k \to (\bigcup A_{ij}) \cap F_k$ with $(K_k \to (\bigcup A_{ij}) \cap F_k \to F_k) = (K_k \to F_k)$. Conversely, let

$$\left(\left(\bigcup A_{ij}\right) \cap F_k \to F_k \to \varinjlim \mathscr{F}\right) = 0,$$

then there exists a unique morphism $(\bigcup A_{ij}) \cap F_k \to K_k$ with

$$\left(\left(\bigcup A_{ij}\right) \cap F_k \to K_k \to F_k\right) = \left(\left(\bigcup A_{ij}\right) \cap F_k \to F_k\right)$$

This implies that $(\bigcup A_{ij}) \cap F_k = K_k$ as subobjects of $\coprod F_i$.

For $E \in \mathscr{E}'$ let $l \geqslant j$ for all j with $(i, j) \in E$ and $l \geqslant k$. Furthermore, define morphisms $h_{il} : F_i \to F_l$ by $h_{il} = f_{il}$ for $i \leqslant l$, and $h_{il} = 0$ otherwise. This defines a morphism $h : \coprod F_i \to F_l$. The diagram

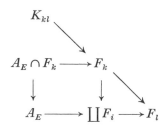

is commutative and we get $(A_E \to \coprod F_i \to F_l) = 0$ because $(F_{ij} \to \coprod F_i \to F_l) = 0$ for $j \leqslant l$ by definition of h. Hence, $(A_E \cap F_k \to F_l) = 0$. Since $K_{kl} = \mathrm{Ker}(F_k \to F_l)$ and $A_E \cap F_k$ is a subobject of F_k, we have $A_E \cap F_k \subseteq K_{kl}$. This proves

$$K_k = \left(\bigcup A_{ij}\right) \cap F_k = \left(\bigcup_{E \in \mathscr{E}'} A_E\right) \cap F_k = \bigcup_{E \in \mathscr{E}'} (A_E \cap F_k) \subseteq \bigcup_{k \leqslant l} K_{kl}$$

where we used Lemma 2.

THEOREM 1. *Let $\mathscr{C}$ be an abelian, cocomplete, locally small category. The following assertions are equivalent*:

(1) *Direct limits in $\mathscr{C}$ are exact.*

(2) *For each directed family $(A_i)_{i \in I}$ of subobjects of $A \in \mathscr{C}$, the morphism $\varinjlim(A_i) \to A$ is a monomorphism.*

(3) *$\mathscr{C}$ is a Grothendieck category.*

Proof. (1) $\Rightarrow$ (2): We consider I as a directed small category and form the functors $\mathscr{F} : I \to \mathscr{C}$ with $\mathscr{F}(i) = A_i$ and $\mathscr{G} : I \to \mathscr{C}$ with $\mathscr{G}(i) = A$ for all i. The morphisms of I are mapped into the monomorphisms of the A_i and A into A respectively. Since $\varinjlim \mathscr{G} = A$, (1) implies that $\varinjlim \mathscr{F} \to A$ is a monomorphism.

(2) $\Rightarrow$ (3): Let $\{A_i\}$ be a chain of subobjects of A and $B \subseteq A$. By the second isomorphism theorem, we get a commutative diagram with exact rows and columns

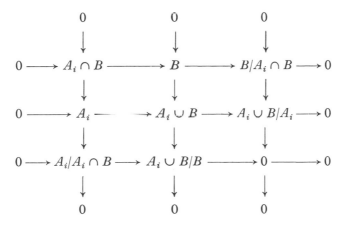

for all $i \in I$. Morphisms $A_i \to A_j$ induce morphisms between the corresponding 3×3 diagrams such that all occuring squares are commutative.

If we apply the functor $\varinjlim$ to this chain of 3×3 diagrams, then we get that $\varinjlim(A_i \cap B) \to A$, $\overline{B} \to A$, $\varinjlim A_i \to A$, and $\varinjlim(A_i \cup B) \to A$ are monomorphisms by (2). Since $\coprod A_i \to A$ may be factored through $\varinjlim A_i$ and $\coprod A_i \to \varinjlim A_i$ is an epimorphism we may identify $\varinjlim A_i$ with $\bigcup A_i$ as subobjects of A. Since $\varinjlim$ is right exact and preserves isomorphisms, the diagram

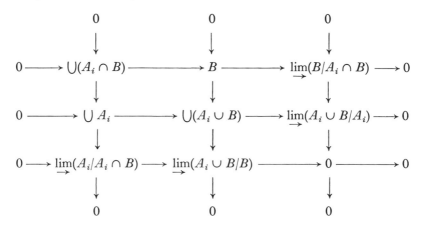

is commutative with exact rows and columns. Now let morphisms $D \twoheadrightarrow B$ and $D \to \bigcup A_i$ with

$$\left(D \to B \to \bigcup (A_i \cup B)\right) = \left(D \to \bigcup A_i \to \bigcup (A_i \cup B)\right)$$

be given. Then $(D \to \varinjlim(B/A_i \cap B)) = 0$ and $(D \to \varinjlim(A_i/A_i \cap B)) = 0$. Hence, there exist $f : D \to \bigcup (A_i \cap B)$ with

$$(D \to B) = \left(D \xrightarrow{f} \bigcup (A_i \cap B) \to B\right)$$

and

$$g : D \to \bigcup (A_i \cap B)$$

with $(D \to \bigcup A_i) = (D \xrightarrow{g} \bigcup (A_i \cap B) \to \bigcup A_i)$. However, since $(D \xrightarrow{f} \bigcup (A_i \cap B) \to \bigcup (A_i \cup B)) = (D \xrightarrow{g} \bigcup (A_i \cap B) \to \bigcup (A_i \cup B))$ and since $\bigcup (A_i \cap B) \to \bigcup (A_i \cup B)$ is a monomorphism, we get $f = g$. Consequently, $\bigcup (A_i \cap B)$ is the fiber product of $\bigcup A_i$ and B over $\bigcup (A_i \cup B)$, hence $\bigcup (A_i \cap B) = (\bigcup A_i) \cap B$.

(3) $\Rightarrow$ (1): By Corollary 1 and Section 4.3, Lemma 2 it is sufficient to show that for a directed category $\mathscr{E}$ and a natural monomorphism

$\mu : \mathscr{F} \to \mathscr{G}$ also $\lim_{\to} \mu : \lim_{\to} \mathscr{F} \to \lim_{\to} \mathscr{G}$ is a monomorphism. Since Funct$(\mathscr{E}, \mathscr{C})$ is abelian and kernels are formed argumentwise in Funct$(\mathscr{E}, \mathscr{C})$, the morphisms $\mu(i) : \mathscr{F}(i) \to \mathscr{G}(i)$ are monomorphisms for all $i \in \mathscr{E}$. We denote $\mathscr{F}(i) = F_i$ and $\mathscr{G}(i) = G_i$. Let $K_i = \mathrm{Ker}(F_i \to \lim_{\to} \mathscr{F})$, $L_i = \mathrm{Ker}(G_i \to \lim_{\to} \mathscr{G})$, $A_i = \mathrm{Im}(F_i \to \lim_{\to} \mathscr{F})$, $B_i = \mathrm{Im}(G_i \to \lim_{\to} \mathscr{G})$, $K = \mathrm{Ker}(\lim_{\to} \mu)$, and C be the fiber product of $A_i \cap K$ with F_i over A_i. Then we get a commutative diagram

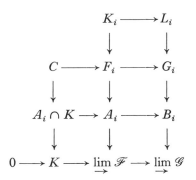

where the last row is exact. Because of $\bigcup A_i = \lim_{\to} \mathscr{F}$ and the Grothendieck condition, we get $K = (\bigcup A_i) \cap K = \bigcup (A_i \cap K)$, for the A_i form a directed family of subobjects of $\lim_{\to} \mathscr{F}$. If all $A_i \cap K = 0$, then also $K = 0$ and $\lim_{\to} \mu$ is a monomorphism, which we had to show. Since $F_i \to A_i$ is an epimorphism, $C \to A_i \cap K$ is an epimorphism by Section 4.3, Lemma 4. It is sufficient to show that this epimorphism is a zero morphism. We have $(C \to \lim_{\to} \mathscr{G}) = 0$. Since $C \to G_i$ is a monomorphism, we get $C \subseteq L_i$ as subobject of G_i. By Lemma 3 $L_i = \bigcup_{i \leqslant j} L_{ij}$ where $L_{ij} = \mathrm{Ker}(G_i \to G_j)$, hence $C = C \cap L_i = (\bigcup L_{ij}) \cap C = \bigcup (L_{ij} \cap C)$. The diagram

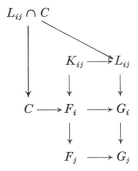

is commutative. Since $(L_{ij} \cap C \to G_j) = 0$ and $F_j \to G_j$ is a monomorphism, we get $(L_{ij} \cap C \to F_j) = 0$, hence $L_{ij} \cap C \subseteq K_{ij}$. Consequently, $C = \bigcup (L_{ij} \cap C) \subseteq \bigcup K_{ij} = K_i$. Then the preceeding diagram implies $(C \to F_i \to A_i) = 0$. Since $A_i \cap K \to A_i$ is a monomorphism, we get $(C \to A_i \cap K) = 0$.

COROLLARY 2. *Let $\mathscr{C}$ be a Grothendieck category; then the morphism $\delta : \coprod A_i \to \prod A_i$ (in Section 4.1) is a monomorphism.*

Proof. Let $\{A_i\}_{i \in I}$ be a set of objects in $\mathscr{C}$. Let E be a finite subset of I. We define $A_E = \bigoplus_{i \in E} A_i$. Since

$$\left(A_E \to \coprod_{i \in I} A_i \to \prod_{i \in I} A_i \to A_E \right) = 1_{A_E}$$

we get that A_E is a subobject of $\coprod A_i$. The set of these subobjects forms a directed family of subobjects and we have $\bigcup A_E = \coprod A_i$. Hence, $\coprod A_i = \varinjlim A_E$. On the other hand, the A_E are also subobjects of $\prod A_i$. Thus, $\varinjlim A_E \to \prod A_i$ is a monomorphism.

As in the preceeding cases, we used here also a method which is typical for proofs in Grothendieck categories. We replace an infinite arbitrary union $\bigcup A_i = \coprod A_i$ by a union of a directed family of subobjects which all are finite unions. The corresponding conclusion in module categories, where the unions are sums (not necessarily direct sums) and where one can compute with elements, is that for

$$x \in \sum A_i \left(= \bigcup A_i \right)$$

there is a finite index set $i_1, ..., i_n$ with $x \in A_{i_1} + \cdots + A_{i_n}$.

COROLLARY 3. *Let monomorphisms $\mu_i : A_i \to B_i$ be given and assume that $\coprod A_i$, $\prod A_i$ and $\coprod B_i$, $\prod B_i$ exist in the Grothendieck category $\mathscr{C}$. Then the morphism $\mu : \coprod A_i \to \coprod B_i$ induced by the μ_i is a monomorphism.*

Proof. There is a commutative diagram

$$\begin{array}{ccc} \coprod A_i & \longrightarrow & \coprod B_i \\ {\scriptstyle \delta} \downarrow & & {\scriptstyle \delta} \downarrow \\ \prod A_i & \longrightarrow & \prod B_i \end{array}$$

as in Section 4.1. By Section 2.6, Corollary 5, products preserve monomorphisms.   Since $\coprod A_i \to \prod A_i \to \prod B_i$ is   a   monomorphism, $\coprod A_i \to \coprod B_i$ is also a monomorphism.

COROLLARY 4.   *Let $\mathscr{C}$ be a Grothendieck category. Let $\{A_i\}$ be a directed family of subobjects of A and $f : B \to A$ be a morphism in $\mathscr{C}$. Then*

$$\bigcup f^{-1}(A_i) = f^{-1}\left(\bigcup A_i\right)$$

Proof.   Let $\mathrm{Im}(f) = A'$. The commutative diagram

$$f^{-1}(A_i) \longrightarrow A_i \cap A' \longrightarrow A_i$$

$$B \longrightarrow A' \longrightarrow A$$

and Section 2.6, Lemma 3 imply that the left square is a fiber product. By Section 4.3, Lemma 4(c) we get that $f^{-1}(A_i) \to A_i \cap A'$ is an epimorphism. Furthermore, $f^{-1}(A_i)$ contains the kernel K of f. With the 3×3 lemma we get a commutative diagram with exact rows and columns

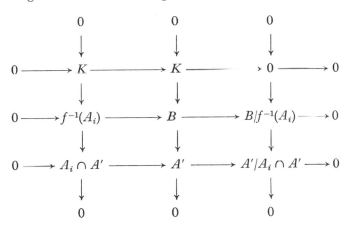

In particular, the morphism $B/f^{-1}(A_i) \to A'/A_i \cap A'$ induced by the epimorphism $B \to A'$ is an isomorphism. Hence, we also have $B/f^{-1}(\bigcup A_i) \cong A'/(\bigcup A_i) \cap A'$. Since direct limits are exact, we get by the application of a direct limit to the above diagram again a corresponding commutative diagram with exact rows and columns. This implies an isomorphism $B/\bigcup f^{-1}(A_i) \cong A'/\bigcup (A_i \cap A')$. By the Grothendieck condition, we have $A'/\bigcup (A_i \cap A') = A'/(\bigcup A_i) \cap A'$. Consequently, $B/\bigcup f^{-1}(A_i) = B/f^{-1}(\bigcup A_i)$ and $\bigcup f^{-1}(A_i) = f^{-1}(\bigcup A_i)$.

4.8   The Krull–Remak–Schmidt–Azumaya Theorem

In Section 4.5 we investigated the uniqueness of sufficiently fine chains of subobjects of an object. Each decomposition of an object into a coproduct induces chains of subobjects in different ways. These, however, are not fine enough in the general case to allow the application of the Jordan–Hölder theorem, even if we make the decomposition as fine as possible. Thus we shall use different methods to investigate the uniqueness of sufficiently fine decompositions into coproducts. Here we shall also admit infinite decompositions.

In this section let $\mathscr{C}$ be a Grothendieck category. An object $A \in \mathscr{C}$ is *indecomposable* if $A \neq 0$ and if, for each decomposition of A into a direct sum $A = A_1 \oplus A_2$, either $A = A_1$ or $A = A_2$. If A is not indecomposable, then A is said to be *decomposable*.

An element r of a unitary associative ring R is called a *nonunit*, if $Rr \neq R$ and $rR \neq R$. This is equivalent to saying that there is neither an $x \in R$ with $xr = 1$ nor a $y \in R$ with $ry = 1$. $R \neq 0$ is called a *local ring* if each sum of two nonunits in R is again a nonunit. An element $r \in R$ is called *idempotent* if $r^2 = r$.

LEMMA 1.   *Let r be an idempotent in a local ring R. Then either $r = 0$ or $r = 1$.*

Proof.   We have $(1 - r)^2 = 1 - r$. Since $1 = (1 - r) + r$ is not a nonunit, either r or $1 - r$ is not a nonunit. If r is not a nonunit, then $xr = 1$, hence $r = xr^2 = xr = 1$. Symmetrically $rx = 1$ implies $r = 1$. If $x(1 - r) = 1$ and $(1 - r)x = 1$, then $1 - r = 1$, hence $r = 0$.

An element $r \in R$ is called a *unit* if there is an $x \in R$ with $xr = rx = 1$.

LEMMA 2.   *Let R be a local ring. Then the nonunits form an ideal N. All elements in R which are not in N are units.*

Proof.   Let r be a nonunit and $x \in R$. We have to show that xr is a nonunit. By definition, there cannot exist a $y \in R$ with $yxr = 1$. However, if $xry = 1$, then $(yxr)(yxr) = y(xry)xr = yxr$. Since yxr is an idempotent, we have $yxr = 1$. In fact if $yxr = 0$, then $1 = (xry)(xry) = xr(yxr)y = 0$, hence $R = 0$, a case which we want to exclude. Consequently, N is closed with respect to addition and multiplication with ring elements from both sides. If $r \in R$ and $r \notin N$, then there is an $x \in R$ with $xr = 1$ or $rx = 1$. Assume $xr = 1$. As above, we get $(rx)^2 = rx$, hence $rx = 1$. r is a unit.

LEMMA 3.   *Let $A \in \mathscr{C}$ with local endomorphism ring. Then A is indecomposable. If A is indecomposable and of finite length, then the endomorphism ring of A is local.*

Proof.   Let $A = B \oplus C$ and $f = (A \to B \to A)$, where $p : A \to B$ is the projection and $q : B \to A$ the injection with respect to the decomposition into the direct sum. Then $f^2 = qpqp = f = 0$ or $f = 1$. Hence, either $B = 0$ or $B = A$. Since the endomorphism ring of A is not the zero ring, we get $A = 0$, hence A is indecomposable.

Let A be indecomposable and of finite length. Let $f : A \to A$ be given. Then $\mathrm{Ker}(f) \subseteq \mathrm{Ker}(f^2) \subseteq \cdots$ is an ascending chain of subobjects of A. The commutative diagram

$$
\begin{array}{ccccccccc}
0 & \longrightarrow & \mathrm{Ker}(f^2) & \longrightarrow & A & \xrightarrow{p''} & \mathrm{Im}(f^2) & \longrightarrow & 0 \\
& & & & \downarrow{\scriptstyle f} & & \downarrow{\scriptstyle q''} & & \\
0 & \longrightarrow & \mathrm{Ker}(f) & \longrightarrow & A & \xrightarrow{p*} & \mathrm{Im}(f) & \longrightarrow & 0 \\
& & & & \downarrow{\scriptstyle f} & \swarrow{\scriptstyle q*} & & & \\
& & & & A & & & &
\end{array}
$$

with exact rows implies that $\mathrm{Im}(f) \supseteq \mathrm{Im}(f^2) \supseteq \cdots$, for $q*q''p''$ is the unique factorization of f^2 through $\mathrm{Im}(f^2)$. Both chains become stable after n steps, that is, we get $\mathrm{Ker}(f^n) = \mathrm{Ker}(f^{n+r})$ and $\mathrm{Im}(f^n) = \mathrm{Im}(f^{n+r})$ for all $r \in \mathbb{N}$, because A is of finite length. Let $g = f^n$. Let $qp = g$ be the factorization of g through $\mathrm{Im}(g)$ and $q'p' = g^2$ be the factorization of g^2 through $\mathrm{Im}(g^2)$. Since $\mathrm{Im}(g) = \mathrm{Im}(g^2)$, we get $q = q'$. We get a commutative diagram

$$
\begin{array}{ccccc}
A & \xrightarrow{p} & \mathrm{Im}(g) & \xrightarrow{q} & A \\
\downarrow{\scriptstyle g} & \searrow{\scriptstyle p'} & \downarrow{\scriptstyle g'} & & \downarrow{\scriptstyle g} \\
A & \xrightarrow{p} & \mathrm{Im}(g^2) & \xrightarrow{q} & A
\end{array}
$$

In fact, we have $gqp = qpg$. Since

$$(\mathrm{Ker}(g) \to A \xrightarrow{g} A \to \mathrm{Im}(g^2)) = 0$$

there exists a unique g' with $g'p = pg = p'$. $qg'p = gqp$ implies $qg' = gq$, since p is an epimorphism. The fact that p' is an epimorphism implies that also g' is an epimorphism. Since $\mathrm{Im}(g)$ and $\mathrm{Im}(g^2)$ have equal length, g' is an isomorphism with the inverse morphism h.

Then

$$(qhp)(qhp) = qh^2g'pqhp = qh^2pgqhp = qh^2pqg'hp$$
$$= qh^2pg = qh^2g\,p = qhp$$

Hence, qhp is an idempotent with image $\mathrm{Im}(g)$. By Section 4.3, Lemma 3, we get $A = \mathrm{Im}(g) \oplus \mathrm{Ker}(qhp)$. Since A is indecomposable, either $\mathrm{Im}(g) = A$ or $\mathrm{Im}(g) = 0$. In the first case, g and also f are isomorphisms because A is of finite length. In the second case $f^n = 0$.

Consequently, in the endomorphism ring $\mathrm{Hom}_{\mathscr{C}}(A, A)$ each element f which is not a unit, that is, which is not an isomorphism, is nilpotent, that is, there is an $n \in \mathbb{N}$ with $f^n = 0$. Let f and f' be nonunits. We assume that $f + f'$ is not a nonunit. Then there exists an $x \in \mathrm{Hom}_{\mathscr{C}}(A, A)$ with $xf + xf' = 1$. Since xf and xf' are not units, they are nilpotent. Let i be minimal with $(xf)^i = 0$ and let j be minimal with $(xf')^j (xf)^{i-1} = 0$. i and j are necessarily different from zero. Then

$$(xf')^{j-1}(xf)^{i-1} = (xf')^{j-1}(xf' + xf)(xf)^{i-1}$$
$$= (xf')^j(xf)^{i-1} + (xf')^{j-1}(xf)^i = 0$$

contradicting the minimality of i and j. Hence $f + f'$ is a nonunit and $\mathrm{Hom}_{\mathscr{C}}(A, A)$ is a local ring.

If, in the following, we talk about coproducts of subobjects of an object in $\mathscr{C}$, then the monomorphisms which belong to the subobjects are assumed to be the injections of the coproduct. Nonequivalent subobjects, even if they are isomorphic as objects, will be denoted differently. The projections into the direct summands, however, may change without us changing the notation for the object which could be considered as a quotient object with respect to the projection.

LEMMA 4.   Let $A = \coprod A_i$ and let the endomorphism rings $\mathrm{Hom}_{\mathscr{C}}(A_i, A_i)$ be local. Let f and g be endomorphisms of A with $f + g = 1_A$. Let $E = \{i_1, ..., i_n\}$ be a finite subset of I. Then there exist subobjects $B_1, ..., B_n$ of A and isomorphisms $h_j : A_{i_j} \to B_j$ for $j = 1, ..., n$ such that for each j the diagram

$$
\begin{array}{ccc}
A_{ij} & \xrightarrow{\ h_j\ } & B_j \\
\downarrow & & \downarrow \\
A & \xrightarrow{\ h\ } & A
\end{array}
$$

is commutative for $h = f$ *or for* $h = g$. *Furthermore, there exists a decomposition*

$$A = B_1 \oplus \cdots \oplus B_n \oplus \coprod_{i \notin E} A_i$$

Proof. The injections and projections of the A_i will be denoted by q_i and p_i respectively. We have $p_i f q_i + p_i g q_i = 1_{A_i}$ for $i \in I$. Since $\mathrm{Hom}_{\mathscr{C}}(A_i, A_i)$ is a local ring, one of the two summands, e.g., $p_i f q_i$, is an automorphism with the inverse morphism $a_i : A_i \to A_i$. Let $i = i_1 \in E$. We factor $f q_{i_1} : A_{i_1} \to A$ through $B_1 := \mathrm{Im}(f q_{i_1})$ as $f q_{i_1} = q_1' h_1$ with $q_1' : B_1 \to A$ and $h_1 : A_{i_1} \to B_1$. Since $p_{i_1} q_1' h_1 = p_{i_1} f q_{i_1}$ is a monomorphism, h_1 is the isomorphism we were looking for. Furthermore, $(q_1' h_1 a_{i_1} p_{i_1})^2 = q_1' h_1 a_{i_1} p_{i_1}$ and $\mathrm{Im}(q_1' h_1 a_{i_1} p_{i_1}) = B_1$,

$$\mathrm{Ker}(q_1' h_1 a_{i_1} p_{i_1}) = \mathrm{Ker}(p_{i_1}) = \coprod_{i \neq i_1} A_i$$

By Section 4.3, Lemma 3 we have $A = B_1 \oplus \coprod_{i \neq i_1} A_i$. Starting with this coproduct we now may replace A_{i_2} by B_2. Then after n steps the lemma is proved.

THEOREM (Krull–Remak–Schmidt–Azumaya). *Let* $\mathscr{C}$ *be a Grothendieck category and* $A \in \mathscr{C}$. *Let*

$$A = \coprod_{i \in I} A_i \qquad \text{with local rings} \quad \mathrm{Hom}_{\mathscr{C}}(A_i, A_i)$$

and

$$A = \coprod_{j \in J} B_j \qquad \text{with indecomposable} \quad B_j$$

be given. Then there exists a bijection $\varphi : I \to J$ *such that for all* $i \in I$ *we have* $A_i \cong B_{\varphi(i)}$.

Proof. The injections and projections of the A_i will be denoted by q_i and p_i respectively, those of the B_j by q_j' and p_j' respectively. First, we show that to each B_j there exists an isomorphic A_i and that this isomorphism is induced by $q_j' p_j' : A \to A$. Then also the endomorphism rings of the B_j are local, the A_i are indecomposable, and the hypotheses of the theorem are symmetric.

Let $f = q_j' p_j'$ and $f' = 1 - f$. Then $f + f' = 1$, $f^2 = f$, and $f'^2 = f'$. Furthermore, $\mathrm{Im}(f) = \mathrm{Ker}(f') = B_j$ by Section 4.3, Lemma 3. Let $E \subseteq I$ be a finite subset and $A_E = \oplus_{i \in E} A_i$. The A_E form a directed family of subobjects of A. There exists an E with $A_E \cap B_j \neq 0$, since $B_j = (\bigcup A_E) \cap B_j = \bigcup (A_E \cap B_j)$. Let

$E = \{i_1, ..., i_n\}$. By Lemma 4, there exist $C_k \subseteq A$ and isomorphisms $h_k : A_{i_k} \to C_k$, $k = 1, ..., n$, which are induced by f or by f'. We assume that all h_k are induced by f'. Let $C_E = \oplus_{k=1}^n C_k$. Then we get a commutative diagram

$$
\begin{array}{ccc}
A_E \cap B_j & \longrightarrow & A_E \cong C_E \\
\downarrow & & \downarrow \qquad \downarrow \\
B_j & \xrightarrow{q_j'} & A \xrightarrow{f'} A
\end{array}
$$

Since $f'q_j' = 0$ and $A_E \cap B_j \to A_E \cong C_E \to A$ is a monomorphism we get a contradiction to $A_E \cap B_j \neq 0$. Hence there exists at least one $i_0 \in E$ such that the square

$$
\begin{array}{ccc}
A_{i_0} & \xrightarrow{h_{k_0}} & C_{k_0} \\
\downarrow & & \downarrow \\
A & \xrightarrow{f} & A
\end{array}
$$

is commutative. By definition of f, we get $C_{k_0} \subseteq B_j$. But since C_{k_0} is a direct summand of A, C_{k_0} is also a direct summand of B_j. B_j is indecomposable, hence $C_{k_0} = B_j$. $fq_{i_0} = q_j' p_j' q_{i_0}$ implies $h_{k_0} = p_j' q_{i_0}$.

Now let $A_{i_0} \cong B_{j_0}$. We have to compare the number $|\alpha|$ of the A_i isomorphic to A_{i_0} with the number $|\beta|$ of the B_j isomorphic to B_{j_0}. By symmetry, it is sufficient to show that $|\alpha| \geqslant |\beta|$. First, assume that $|\alpha|$ is finite. By the preceeding construction there exists corresponding to $j_1 \in \beta$ an $i_1 \in \alpha$ such that $f_1 = q_{j_1}' p_{j_1}'$ induces an isomorphism $A_{i_1} \cong B_{j_1}$. Furthermore,

$$
A = B_{j_1} \oplus \coprod_{j \neq j_1} B_j = A_{i_1} \oplus \coprod_{j \neq j_1} B_j
$$

Now, if we compare the second direct sum with $A = \coprod_{i \in I} A_i$ and apply the same procedure, then we get after n steps

$$
A = B_{j_1} \oplus \cdots \oplus B_{j_n} \oplus \coprod_{j \neq j_1, ..., j_n} B_j = A_{i_1} \oplus \cdots \oplus A_{i_n} \oplus \coprod_{j \neq j_1, ..., j_n} B_j
$$

Here we have to observe again that the injections of the A_i and B_j remain unchanged but that the projections change. The fact that the injections of the A_i remain unchanged also guarantees that the $i_1, ..., i_n$ are all pairwise distinct because for a decomposition into a direct sum, no two injections can be equal. $i_1, ..., i_n \in \alpha$ implies now $|\alpha| \geqslant |\beta|$.

Now let $\mid \alpha \mid$ be infinite. Let $E \subseteq J$ be a finite subset, let $j \in \beta$ and $j \notin E$. Further, assume that $A_i \cong B_j$ by the isomorphism induced by $f = q_j' p_j'$. Then the diagram

$$
\begin{array}{ccc}
A_i \cap B_E & \longrightarrow & A_i \cong B_j \\
\downarrow & \downarrow \quad \downarrow & \\
B_E & \longrightarrow & A \xrightarrow{f} A
\end{array}
$$

is commutative where $B_E = \oplus_{j \in E} B_j$. We get $A_i \cap B_E = 0$ because $(B_E \to A \to A) = 0$ and $A_i \cap B_E \to A_i \cong B_j \to A$ is a monomorphism. On the other hand

$$
A_i = \left(\bigcup_{E \subseteq J} B_E \right) \cap A_i = \bigcup_{E \subseteq J} (A_i \cap B_E) \neq 0
$$

Hence there exists a finite subset $E \subseteq J$ with $A_i \cap B_E \neq 0$. Each $j \in J$ which induces an isomorphism $A_i \cong B_j$ by $q_j' p_j'$ for the above determined i must lie in this E. Hence there are only finitely many such j. We call this number $E(i)$. To each $j \in \beta$ we may construct such an i. Hence,

$$
\bigcup_{i \in \alpha} E(i) = \beta
$$

This proves $\mid \alpha \mid \geqslant \mid \beta \mid$.

4.9   Injective and Projective Objects and Hulls

Let $\mathscr{C}$ be an abelian category. An object $P \in \mathscr{C}$ is called *projective* if the functor $\mathrm{Hom}_{\mathscr{C}}(P, -)$ is exact. Dually, an object $Q \in \mathscr{C}$ is called *injective* if the functor $\mathrm{Hom}_{\mathscr{C}}(-, Q)$ is exact. Since the functor $\mathrm{Hom}_{\mathscr{C}}(A, -)$ is left exact for each $A \in \mathscr{C}$, P is projective if and only if $\mathrm{Hom}_{\mathscr{C}}(P, -)$ preserves epimorphisms, that is, if for each exact sequence $A \to B \to 0$ and for each morphism $f : P \to B$ there is a morphism $g : P \to A$ such that the diagram

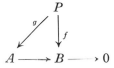

is commutative. Dually, Q is injective if and only if for each exact

sequence $0 \to A \to B$ and each morphism $f : A \to Q$ there is a morphism
$g : B \to Q$ such that the diagram

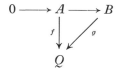

is commutative.

Since in a module category all epimorphisms are surjective morphisms,
the projective modules in a module category coincide with the relatively
projective modules introduced in Section 3.4 with respect to the forgetful
functor into the category of sets.

LEMMA 1.   *Let $P_i \in \mathscr{C}$ and $P = \coprod P_i$ be given. P is projective if and only
if all P_i are projective.*

Proof.   Let $A \to B \to 0$ be exact. Let morphisms $f_i : P_i \to B$ and
$f : P \to B$ with $q_i f = f_i$ be given. We use the diagram

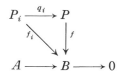

If P is projective, then there exists $P \to A$ with $(P \to B) = (P \to A \to B)$.
Hence, for each i, we obtain $(P_i \to P \to A \to B) = f_i$. Since f is uniquely
determined by the f_i, all P_i are projective.

Let the P_i be projective, then there exist $P_i \to A$, making the above
diagram commutative. In a unique way, these determine a morphism
$P \to A$ with $(P \to A \to B) = f$. Hence, P is projective.

LEMMA 2.   *P is projective if and only if each epimorphism $A \to P$ is
a retraction.*

Proof.   Let P be projective and $A \to P$ be an epimorphism. Then the
morphism g in

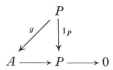

is a section for $A \to P$.

Let $A \to B \to 0$ be exact and $P \to B$ be given. We form the fiber product

$$
\begin{array}{ccc}
C & \longrightarrow & P \\
\downarrow & & \downarrow \\
A & \longrightarrow & B
\end{array}
$$

Since $A \to B$ is an epimorphism, $C \to P$ is an epimorphism, hence a retraction with section $P \to C$. Consequently,

$$(P \to B) = (P \to C \to A \to B)$$

A monomorphism $A \to B$ is called an *essential extension* of A if each morphism $B \to C$, for which $A \to B \to C$ is a monomorphism, is a monomorphism itself. A subobject A of B is called *large* if for each nonzero subobject C of B also $A \cap C$ is nonzero.

LEMMA 3. $A \to B$ is an essential extension if and only if A is a large subobject of B.

Proof.   We use the commutative diagram with exact rows

$$
\begin{array}{ccccccccc}
0 & \longrightarrow & A \cap C & \longrightarrow & A & \longrightarrow & A/A \cap C & \longrightarrow & 0 \\
& & \downarrow & & \downarrow & & \downarrow & & \\
0 & \longrightarrow & C & \longrightarrow & B & \longrightarrow & D & \longrightarrow & 0
\end{array}
$$

where, as in the proof of the second isomorphism theorem, the vertical morphisms are monomorphisms. If $A \to B$ is an essential extension, and $C \neq 0$, then $B \to D$ is not a monomorphism, nor is $A \to D$ a monomorphism. Hence, $A \cap C = \mathrm{Ker}(A \to D) \neq 0$ (see Section 4.4(1)). If A is large in B, and $B \to D'$ is not a monomorphism, and D is the image of $B \to D'$, then $C \neq 0$, hence also $A \cap C = \mathrm{Ker}(A \to D) \neq 0$.

COROLLARY 1.

(a)   *An essential extension of an essential extension is essential.*

(b)   *Let $A \to B$ be a monomorphism in a Grothendieck category and $\{C_i\}$ be a chain of subobjects of B, all containing A. If all C_i are essential extensions of A, then also $\bigcup C_i$ is an essential extension of A.*

Proof.   (a) If $A \subseteq B$ is large, and $B \subseteq C$ is large, and $0 \neq D \subseteq C$, then $A \cap D = A \cap (B \cap D) \neq 0$.

(b)   Let $0 \neq D \subseteq \bigcup C_i$. Then $D = (\bigcup C_i) \cap D = \bigcup (C_i \cap D)$. For some i, we have $C_i \cap D \neq 0$. Hence, $A \cap D = A \cap C_i \cap D \neq 0$.

Since in a Grothendieck category $\varinjlim C_i = \bigcup C_i$ for a chain $\{C_i\}$, and since by Section 4.7, Lemma 3, the morphisms $C_i \twoheadrightarrow \varinjlim C_i$ are monomorphisms, in the preceding corollary the assumption that B exists is superfluous because B can always be replaced by $\varinjlim C_i$.

A monomorphism $A \to Q$ with an injective object Q is called an *injective extension* of A. An injective, essential extension is called an *injective hull* (injective envelope). An essential extension $A \to B$ will be called *maximal* if for each essential extension $A \to C$, which may be factored through B

$$(A \to C) = (A \to B \to C)$$

the morphism $B \to C$ is an isomorphism. An essential extension $A \to B$ is called a *largest* essential extension if $A \to B$ may be factored through each essential extension $A \to C$

$$(A \to B) = (A \to C \to B)$$

An injective extension $A \to B$ is called *minimal* if for each factorization $A \to C \to B$ of $A \to B$ with an injective object C and a monomorphism $C \to B$ the morphism $C \to B$ is an isomorphism. An injective extension $A \to B$ is called a *smallest* injective extension if for each injective extension $A \to C$, there exists a monomorphism $B \to C$ with $(A \to C) = (A \to B \to C)$.

PROPOSITION 1. *Let $A \in \mathscr{C}$ and assume that A has an injective hull. The following are equivalent for a monomorphism $A \to B$:*

(1) $A \to B$ *is an injective hull of* A.
(2) $A \to B$ *is a maximal essential extension of* A.
(3) $A \to B$ *is a largest essential extension of* A.
(4) $A \to B$ *is a minimal injective extension of* A.
(5) $A \to B$ *is a smallest injective extension of* A.

Proof. We shall use the diagrams

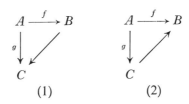

$$(1) \qquad\qquad (2)$$

$(1) \Leftrightarrow (2)$: Let f be an injective hull and g an essential extension in (1). Since f is essential and g is a monomorphism, h is a monomorphism.

Since B is injective, h is a section: $C = B \oplus D$. Since g is essential, $D = 0$, hence h is an isomorphism. Conversely, let f be a maximal essential extension and g be an injective hull of A in (1). h exists because C is injective, and is a monomorphism because g is a monomorphism and f is essential. Since f is maximal, h is an isomorphism and B is injective.

(1) $\Leftrightarrow$ (3):   If in (2), f is an injective hull and g an essential extension, then there exists h because B is injective. Conversely, let f be a largest essential extension of A and g be an injective hull of A in (2), then h is a monomorphism because g is essential and f is a monomorphism. C being injective implies that h is a section, hence an isomorphism.

(1) $\Leftrightarrow$ (4):   If in (2), f is an injective hull, g an injective extension, and h a monomorphism, then h is a section, hence an isomorphism. Conversely, if in (2), f is a minimal injective extension and g an injective hull, then there exists a monomorphism h, which must be an isomorphism.

(1) $\Leftrightarrow$ (5):   If in (1), f is an injective hull and g an injective extension, then there exists a monomorphism h. Conversely, if in (1), f is a smallest injective extension of A and g an injective hull, then there exists a monomorphism h, which is a section, hence an isomorphism.

LEMMA 4.   *Let $\mathscr{C}$ be a Grothendieck category and $Q \in \mathscr{C}$. Assume that Q has no proper essential extension. Then Q is injective.*

Proof.   Let $f : Q \to A$ be a monomorphism. Let $\mathfrak{B}$ be the set of subobjects B of A with $Q \cap B = 0$. If $\{B_i\}$ is a chain in $\mathfrak{B}$, then $(\bigcup B_i) \cap Q = \bigcup (B_i \cap Q) = 0$ implies $\bigcup B_i \in \mathfrak{B}$. By Zorn's lemma there exists a maximal object B' in $\mathfrak{B}$. We shall show that $Q \to A \to A/B'$ is an isomorphism. Then f is a section and Q is injective by the assertion dual to Lemma 2. Because of $\operatorname{Ker}(gf) = B' \cap Q = 0$, we get that gf is a monomorphism. Consider Q as a subobject of A and $Q' = g(Q)$ as a subobject of A/B'. Let $C \subseteq A/B'$ and $Q' \cap C = 0$. Then $Q \cap g^{-1}(C) \subseteq g^{-1}(Q' \cap C) = B'$ and $Q \cap g^{-1}(C) \subseteq Q$, hence $Q \cap g^{-1}(C) \subseteq B' \cap Q = 0$. On the other hand, $g^{-1}(C) \supseteq B'$, hence we get $g^{-1}(C) = B'$ because of the maximality of B'. $C = gg^{-1}(C) = 0$ because g is an epimorphism, that is, gf is an essential monomorphism. By hypothesis we get that gf is an isomorphism.

THEOREM 1.   *If $\mathscr{C}$ is a Grothendieck category with a generator then each object in $\mathscr{C}$ has an injective hull.*

Proof.   To each object $A \in \mathscr{C}$ we shall construct a maximal essential extension. By Corollary 1, this will not have a proper essential extension any more, hence by Lemma 4 it will be injective. Into the class of all proper essential monomorphisms in $\mathscr{C}$ we introduce an equivalence relation $f \sim g$ if and only if $D(f) = D(g)$. Then by the strong axiom of choice we assign to each noninjective object $B \in \mathscr{C}$ a proper essential extension. To the injective objects, we assign the identical morphisms, since they do not possess a proper essential extension by Proposition 1. Now we construct a sequence of essential extensions

$$A \to B_1 \to \cdots \to B_\alpha \to B_{\alpha+1} \cdots$$

for all ordinals α. If the sequence has been constructed up to B_α, let $B_\alpha \to B_{\alpha+1}$ be the essential extension determined above by the strong axiom of choice. If β is a limit, then we define $B_\beta = \varinjlim B_\alpha$ for all $\alpha < \beta$ as in Corollary 1. Then for all α, the monomorphism $A \to B_\alpha$ is an essential monomorphism.

Now we want to show that this sequence will become constant after a certain ordinal. Since for noninjective objects B_α, the extensions must be proper by construction, the object B_α, from where on the sequence will be constant, will be injective.

Let G be a generator in $\mathscr{C}$ and G' be an arbitrary subobject of G. Let $\alpha < \beta$ be ordinal numbers. We form the set (G', α, β) of morphisms $f : G' \to B_\alpha$ for which there is a morphism $g : G \to B_\beta$ such that the diagram

$$\begin{array}{ccc} G' & \longrightarrow & G \\ \scriptstyle f \downarrow & & \downarrow \scriptstyle g \\ B_\alpha & \longrightarrow & B_\beta \end{array}$$

is commutative. Hence, $(G', \alpha, \beta) \subseteq \operatorname{Hom}_{\mathscr{C}}(G', B_\alpha)$. For $\beta < \beta'$, we have $(G', \alpha, \beta) \subseteq (G', \alpha, \beta')$; this sequence must become constant because $\operatorname{Hom}_{\mathscr{C}}(G', B_\alpha)$ has only a set of subsets. Since G has also only a set of subobjects G', there exists even an ordinal $\alpha^* > \alpha$ with $(G', \alpha, \alpha^*) \supseteq (G', \alpha, \beta)$ for all $G' \subseteq G$ and all $\beta > \alpha$. Since it is sufficient to show that a cofinal subsequence becomes constant, we may assume that $\alpha^* = \alpha + 1$.

Let γ be the first ordinal which has larger cardinality than the set of subobjects of G. γ is a limit and we have $B_\gamma = \varinjlim B_\alpha$ for all $\alpha < \gamma$. If we consider the B_α as subobjects of $B_{\gamma+1}$, then $B_\gamma = \bigcup_{\alpha < \gamma} B_\alpha$. Now $f : G \to B_{\gamma+1}$ is a morphism which cannot be factored through B_γ. Such a morphisms exists as long as $B_\gamma \neq B_{\gamma+1}$, which we want to assume now. We get a chain of subobjects $f^{-1}(B_\alpha)$ of G and by Section 4.7, Corollary 4 we have $f^{-1}(B_\gamma) = \bigcup_{\alpha < \gamma} f^{-1}(B_\alpha)$. Let

$$K = \{\alpha \mid f^{-1}(B_\alpha) \subsetneqq f^{-1}(B_{\alpha+1})\}$$

and let $|K|$ be the cardinal number of K. Then $|K| < |\gamma|$ by the assumption on γ. Furthermore, $|\alpha| < |\gamma|$. By Lemma 2 of the appendix, there exists a $\beta < \gamma$ with $\alpha < \beta$ for all $\alpha \in K$, that is, for all $\beta' > \beta$ we have $f^{-1}(B_{\beta'}) = f^{-1}(B_\beta)$, hence $f^{-1}(B_\gamma) = f^{-1}(B_\beta)$.

Since by our construction $\beta^* = \beta + 1$ we get $(f^{-1}(B_\beta), \beta, \gamma) = (f^{-1}(B_\beta), \beta, \gamma + 1)$. The morphism $f' : f^{-1}(B_\beta) \to B_\beta$ induced by f can already be extended to a morphism $g' : G \to B_\gamma$ such that the diagram

$$
\begin{array}{ccc}
f^{-1}(B_\beta) & \longrightarrow & G \\
{\scriptstyle f'}\downarrow & & \downarrow{\scriptstyle g'} \\
B_\beta & \longrightarrow & B_\gamma
\end{array}
$$

is commutative. Let $g : G \to B_{\gamma+1}$ be the morphism induced by g'. Then $g \neq f$, but $(g - f)(f^{-1}(B_\gamma)) = (g - f)(f^{-1}(B_\beta)) = 0$.

Since B_γ is large in $B_{\gamma+1}$, we have $\mathrm{Im}(g - f) \cap B_\gamma \neq 0$; hence there exists a morphism $h' : G \to (g - f)^{-1}(\mathrm{Im}(g - f) \cap B_\gamma)$ such that

$$(G \to (g - f)^{-1}(\mathrm{Im}(g - f) \cap B_\gamma) \to \mathrm{Im}(g - f) \cap B_\gamma \neq 0$$

Let $h : G \to G$ be the morphism induced by h'. Then $(g - f)h \neq 0$ and $\mathrm{Im}((g - f)h) \subseteq B_\gamma$. Since $\mathrm{Im}(gh) \subseteq \mathrm{Im}(g) \subseteq B_\gamma$, we have $\mathrm{Im}(fh) \subseteq B_\gamma$, that is, $\mathrm{Im}(h) \subseteq f^{-1}(B_\gamma)$. Then, however, $(g - f)h = 0$ must hold. This is a contradiction to our assumption that $B_\gamma \neq B_{\gamma+1}$.

In this proof we did not use all objects of the category $\mathscr{C}$ to test the maximal essential extension, but only the generator G and the subobjects of G. Consequently, it is also sufficient to test the injectivity of objects only for the subobjects of G.

COROLLARY 2. *Let $\mathscr{C}$ be a Grothendieck category with a generator G. Let $Q \in \mathscr{C}$ be an object such that for all subobjects $G' \subseteq G$ the map $\mathrm{Hom}_\mathscr{C}(G, Q) \to \mathrm{Hom}_\mathscr{C}(G', Q)$ is surjective, then Q is injective.*

Proof. If Q has no proper essential extension, then Q is injective by Lemma 4. Let $Q \to A$ be a proper monomorphism. Then there exists a morphism $f : G \to A$ which cannot be factored through Q. We form the commutative diagram

$$
\begin{array}{ccc}
f^{-1}(Q) & \longrightarrow & G \\
{\scriptstyle f'}\downarrow & & \downarrow{\scriptstyle f} \\
Q & \longrightarrow & A
\end{array}
$$

By hypothesis there exists $G \twoheadrightarrow Q$ with

$$(f^{-1}(Q) \to Q) = (f^{-1}(Q) \to G \to Q)$$

Let $g = (G \to Q \to A)$. Then $g \neq f$. As in the last paragraph of the preceeding proof, we then get $\mathrm{Im}(g - f) \cap Q = 0$. Hence, $Q \to A$ cannot be an essential monomorphism.

With the present means we can now show that the Krull–Remak–Schmidt–Azumaya theorem can also be applied to injective objects, similar to the case of objects of finite length that we proved in Section 4.8, Lemma 3. In fact, the difficulty is always to show that the endomorphism ring of certain indecomposable objects is local.

THEOREM 2. *Let $\mathscr{C}$ be a Grothendieck category with a generator. An injective object $Q \in \mathscr{C}$ is indecomposable if and only if $\mathrm{Hom}_{\mathscr{C}}(Q, Q)$ is local.*

Proof. By Section 4.8, Lemma 3 we need only show one direction. Let Q be indecomposable and injective. Each monomorphism $f : Q \to Q$ is an isomorphism because f is a section and Q is indecomposable. Furthermore, each nonzero subobject of Q is large. In fact, let $0 \neq A \subseteq Q$ be given and let Q' be the injective hull of A. By Theorem 1(5) we get $Q' \subseteq Q$. Hence we get $Q' = Q$ because Q is indecomposable, that is, Q is an injective hull of A. The nonunits of $\mathrm{Hom}_{\mathscr{C}}(Q, Q)$ are the morphisms with kernel different from zero. If f, $g \in \mathrm{Hom}_{\mathscr{C}}(Q, Q)$ with nonzero kernels are given, then $\mathrm{Ker}(f + g) \supseteq \mathrm{Ker}(f) \cap \mathrm{Ker}(g) \neq 0$ by Section 2.8, Lemma 1 and because all nonzero subobjects of Q are large. Hence $f + g$ is a nonunit.

If an injective object is given as a coproduct of indecomposable objects which then are necessarily also injective because they are all direct factors, then this representation is unique in the sense of the Krull–Remak–Schmidt–Azumaya theorem. Conversely, however, not each coproduct of injective objects is injective. Thus it will be of interest to know under which conditions we can decompose each injective object into a coproduct of indecomposable objects and when each coproduct of indecomposable injective objects is injective.

We observe that each module category is a Grothendieck category and possesses a generator, namely the ring R. Thus all theorems proved in this section are also valid in module categories.

Another important application of Theorem 1 will be used later on, namely the existence of injective cogenerators in a Grothendieck category with a generator. So we prove now the following more general theorem.

THEOREM 3.   *Let $\mathscr{C}$ be an abelian category with a generator G in which to each object there exists an injective extension. If $\mathscr{C}$ is complete or cocomplete, then there exists an injective cogenerator in $\mathscr{C}$.*

Proof.   We prove the theorem for the case that $\mathscr{C}$ has coproducts. In case of the existence of products one may replace the coproducts by products everywhere in the proof.

Since G has only a set of (normal) subobjects (Section 2.10, Lemma 1), G has only a set of quotient objects G'. Let H be the coproduct of all these quotient objects and let K be an injective extension of H. We want to show that K is a cogenerator. Let $f : A \rightarrow B$ in C be given with $f \neq 0$. Then there exists a morphism $G \rightarrow A$ such that $(G \rightarrow A \rightarrow B) \neq 0$. Let $G \rightarrow G' \rightarrow B$ be the factorization of this morphism through the image. Then $G' \neq 0$ is a quotient object of G. Since the injection $G' \rightarrow H$ is a monomorphism, there exists a monomorphism

$$(G' \rightarrow H \rightarrow K) \neq 0,$$

hence also $(G \rightarrow G' \rightarrow H \rightarrow K) \neq 0$. Since K is injective and $G' \rightarrow B$ is a monomorphism, there exists a morphism $B \rightarrow K$ such that the diagram

$$
\begin{array}{ccc}
G & \longrightarrow G' & \longrightarrow H \\
\downarrow & \downarrow \quad \searrow & \downarrow \\
A & \xrightarrow{\ f\ } B & \longrightarrow K
\end{array}
$$

is commutative. $(G \rightarrow K) \neq 0$ implies also $(A \rightarrow K) \neq 0$. This proves that K is a cogenerator.

COROLLARY 3.   *Let $\mathscr{C}$ be a Grothendieck category with a generator. Then $\mathscr{C}$ has an injective cogenerator.*

Proof.   The corollary is implied by Theorems 1 and 3.

COROLLARY 4.   *Let $_R\mathbf{Mod}$ be a module category and $\mathfrak{M}$ be the set of maximal ideals M of R. Then each injective extension of $\coprod_{M \in \mathfrak{M}} R/M$ and $\prod_{M \in \mathfrak{M}} R/M$ respectively is an injective cogenerator.*

Proof.   If we observe that R is a generator in $_R\mathbf{Mod}$, then in comparison with the construction of the injective cogenerator in the proof of Theorem 3, we see that in the coproduct and product there are fewer factors. But since in a ring R each ideal I is contained in a maximal ideal M (see Appendix, Zorn's lemma), each nonzero quotient module of R

may be epimorphically mapped onto a module of the form R/M. Hence, we extend the diagram in the proof of Theorem 3 to a commutative diagram

$$\begin{array}{ccccccc} R & \longrightarrow & R' & \longrightarrow & R/M & \longrightarrow & H \\ \downarrow & & \downarrow & & & & \downarrow \\ A & \longrightarrow & B & & \longrightarrow & & K \end{array}$$

where H is the coproduct or the product of the R/M and K is an injective extension of H. The morphism $R \to K$ is different from zero, thus the proof of Theorem 3 can be transferred to this case.

COROLLARY 5 (Watts). *Let $_R$**Mod** and $_S$**Mod** be module categories. Let $\mathscr{T} : {}_R$**Mod** $\to {}_S$**Mod** be a functor. $\mathscr{T}$ preserves limits if and only if there exists an R-S-bimodule $_R A_S$ such that $\mathscr{T} \simeq {}_S\mathrm{Hom}_R({}_R A_S , -)$, that is, if $\mathscr{T}$ is representable.*

Proof. If $\mathscr{T}$ is representable, then the assertion is clear. Assume that $\mathscr{T}$ preserves limits. By Corollary 4 and Section 2.11, Theorem 2 $\mathscr{T}$ has a left adjoint functor $*\mathscr{T}$. Then $\mathscr{T}B \simeq \mathrm{Hom}_S(S, \mathscr{T}B) \simeq \mathrm{Hom}_R(*\mathscr{T}S, B)$ natural in B, hence $\mathscr{T}$ is representable. Here $*\mathscr{T}S$ has by definition the structure of an R-left-module. For $s \in S$ the right multiplication of S with s is an S-left-homomorphism $r(s)$. Hence $*\mathscr{T}(r(s))$ defines the structure of an R-S-bimodule on $*\mathscr{T}S$.

4.10   Finitely Generated Objects

Let $\mathscr{C}$ be a category with unions. An object $A \in \mathscr{C}$ is called *finitely generated* if for each chain of proper subobjects $\{A_i\}$ of A also $\bigcup A_i$ is a proper subobject of A. An object $A \in \mathscr{C}$ is called *compact* if for each family of subobjects $\{A_i\}$ of A with $\bigcup A_i = A$, there is a finite number $A_1 ,..., A_n$ of subobjects in this family such that $A_1 \cup \cdots \cup A_n = A$.

THEOREM 1. *An object $A \in \mathscr{C}$ is finitely generated if and only if it is compact.*

Proof. Let A be compact. Let $\{A_i\}$ be a chain of subobjects of A, with $\bigcup A_i = A$. Then there exist $A_1 ,..., A_n$ in this chain with $A_1 \cup \cdots \cup A_n = A$. One of these, e.g., A_1, is the largest. Hence $A = A_1$, and A is finitely generated.

Let A be finitely generated. Let $\mathfrak{B}$ be a set of subobjects of A that is closed with respect to unions, and which contains A. Let $\mathfrak{W}$ be a subset of $\mathfrak{B}$ that contains all elements except A. Since A is finitely generated,

$\mathfrak{B}$ and $\mathfrak{W}$ fulfill the hypotheses of Section 4.7, Lemma 1. If $\bigcup A_i = A$ for objects $A_i \in \mathfrak{B}$, then there exist finitely many $A_1, \ldots, A_n$ with $A_1 \cup \cdots \cup A_n = A$, that is, A is compact.

With this theorem an algebraic notion (finitely generated) and a topological notion (compact) are set in relation with each other. Here we have to remark that the usual definition in algebra of finitely generated objects is given with elements (Section 3.4 and Exercise 14), but that for proofs only the condition of the definition given here is used. This condition also admits easily the application of the Grothendieck condition.

COROLLARY 1. *Let A be a module over a ring R. A is finitely generated in the algebraic sense if and only if A is finitely generated in the categorical sense.*

Proof. If $A = Ra_1 + Ra_2 + \cdots + Ra_n$, that is, if A is finitely generated in the algebraic sense, and if $\{A_i\}$ is a chain of submodules of A with $\bigcup A_i = A$, then, for each a_j, there exists an A_k with $a_j \in A_k$. Let $l = \max(k)$, then $a_j \in A_l$ for all $j = 1, \ldots, n$, hence $A = A_l$.

Now let A be finitely generated in the categorical sense, then A is compact. Let $\{a_i\}$ be a generating system for A, that is, $A = \bigcup Ra_i$, then $A = Ra_1 \cup \cdots \cup Ra_n$ for suitable $a_1, \ldots, a_n$. Hence, A is finitely generated in the algebraic sense.

Let $\mathscr{C}$ be again an abelian cocomplete category.

LEMMA 1. *Let $f : A \to B$ be an epimorphism in $\mathscr{C}$. If A is finitely generated, then B is also finitely generated.*

Proof. Let $\{B_i\}$ be a chain of subobjects of B with $\bigcup B_i = B$. Let $A_i = f^{-1}(B_i)$. Then $f(\bigcup A_i) = f(\bigcup f^{-1}(B_i)) = \bigcup B_i = B$. Since f is an epimorphism and the kernel of f is contained in $\bigcup A_i$, we get $\bigcup A_i = A$, which may easily be seen by the 3×3 lemma. Furthermore, $B_i \subseteq B_j$ implies $A_i \subseteq A_j$, that is, $\{A_i\}$ is a chain of subobjects of A. Since A is finitely generated, we get $A_i = A$ for some i. But $B_i = f(A_i) = f(A) = B$, hence B is finitely generated.

An object $A \in \mathscr{C}$ is said to be *transfinitely generated* if there is a set of finitely generated subobjects A_i in A such that $\bigcup A_i = A$.

LEMMA 2. *If $\mathscr{C}$ has a finitely-generated generator, then each object is transfinitely generated.*

Proof. Let $A \in \mathscr{C}$. Since by Section 2.10, Lemma 2 for each proper subobject $A' \subseteq A$ there is a morphism $G \to A$, which cannot be factored through A', the morphism $\coprod G \to A$ which is induced by all morphisms of $\operatorname{Hom}_{\mathscr{C}}(G, A)$ is an epimorphism, where we use in the coproduct as many objects as $\operatorname{Hom}_{\mathscr{C}}(G, A)$ has elements. In fact, the image must coincide with A. Hence $A = \bigcup A'$ where the A' are the images of the morphisms $G \to A$. Since G is finitely generated, also the A' are finitely generated by Lemma 1. Hence, A is transfinitely generated.

THEOREM 2.   *Let $\mathscr{C}$ be a Grothendieck category. Let $A \in \mathscr{C}$ be transfinitely generated. Then A is a direct limit of finitely generated subobjects.*

Proof.   We shall show that the union of finitely many finitely generated subobjects of A is again finitely generated. If then $A = \bigcup A_i$ and for each finite subset E of the index set $A_E = \bigcup_{i \in E} A_i$, then these (finitely generated) A_E form a directed family of subobjects of A and we have $A = \bigcup A_E$.

Let B and C be finitely generated subobjects of A. Let $\{D_i\}$ be a chain of subobjects of $B \cup C$ with $\bigcup D_i = B \cup C$. Then we have

$$\left(\bigcup D_i\right) \cap C = C \quad \text{and} \quad \left(\bigcup D_i\right) \cap B = B$$

By the Grothendieck condition, we then get $\bigcup (D_i \cap C) = C$ and $\bigcup (D_i \cap B) = B$. Since B and C are finitely generated there is a j with $D_j \cap C = C$ and $D_j \cap B = B$, that is, $D_j \supseteq B$ and $D_j \supseteq C$. Hence, $D_j = B \cup C$ and $B \cup C$ is finitely generated. By induction one shows that all finite unions of finitely generated subobjects are finitely generated.

LEMMA 3.   *Let $\mathscr{C}$ be a Grothendieck category and $A \in \mathscr{C}$ be finitely generated. Let $f : A \to \coprod B_i$ be a morphism in $\mathscr{C}$. Then there exist $B_1, \ldots, B_n$ such that f may be factored through $B_1 \oplus \cdots \oplus B_n \to \coprod B_i$.*

Proof.   Let $B = \coprod B_i$ and let for each finite subset E of the index set $B_E = \bigoplus_{i \in E} B_i$. Then the B_E form a directed family of subobjects of B and we have $B = \bigcup B_E$. Let $A_E = f^{-1}(B_E)$. Then $A = f^{-1}(B) = f^{-1}(\bigcup B_E) = \bigcup f^{-1}(B_E) = \bigcup A_E$. Since A is compact, we get $A = A_{E_1} \cup \cdots \cup A_{E_r}$. Hence,

$$f(A) = f(A_{E_1}) \cup \cdots \cup f(A_{E_r}) \subseteq B_{E_1} \cup \cdots \cup B_{E_r} \subseteq B_E = B_1 \oplus \cdots \oplus B_n$$

If we compare the definition of a noetherian object with the definition of a finitely generated object, then it becomes clear that each noetherian object must be finitely generated. The converse does not necessarily hold. A Grothendieck category with a noetherian generator will be called *locally noetherian*. A module category over a noetherian ring R (that is, R

is noetherian in $_R$**Mod**) is locally noetherian. We want to investigate some of the properties of the locally noetherian categories.

THEOREM 3.

(a) *In a locally noetherian category the coproduct of injective objects is injective.*

(b) *Let $\mathscr{C}$ be a Grothendieck category in which all objects are transfinitely generated and in which each coproduct of injective objects is injective. Then each finitely generated object is noetherian.*

Proof. (a) Let $G \in \mathscr{C}$ be a noetherian generator and let $\{Q_i\}$ be a family of injective objects in $\mathscr{C}$. Let $G' \subseteq G$ be a subobject of G. Since G is noetherian, G' is noetherian, hence finitely generated. Let a morphism $f : G' \to \coprod Q_i$ be given which we want to extend to G. Then f may be factored through $Q_1 \oplus \cdots \oplus Q_n$ by Lemma 3. This direct sum is injective as a product of injective objects. Hence the morphism $G' \to Q_1 \oplus \cdots \oplus Q_n$ may be extended to G. Thus also f may be extended to G. Hence by Section 4.9, Corollary 2, $\coprod Q_i$ is injective.

(b) Let B be a finitely generated object in $\mathscr{C}$. To prove that B is noetherian it is sufficient to show that each ascending chain $A_1 \subseteq A_2 \subseteq \cdots$ of subobjects of B becomes constant. Let $A - \bigcup A_i$ and Q_i be an injective hull of A/A_i . The morphisms $A \to A/A_i \to Q_i$ define a morphism $A \to \prod Q_i$. Since A is transfinitely generated, $A = \bigcup C_j$ with finitely generated subobjects C_j . We have $C_j = (\bigcup A_i) \cap C_j = \bigcup (A_i \cap C_j)$. Since C_j is finitely generated, we get $C_j = A_{i_0} \cap C_j$ for some i_0 . Hence $C_j \subset A_i$ for all $i \geqslant i_0$, that is, $(C_j \to A \to Q_i) = 0$ for all $i \geqslant i_0$. Thus $C_j \to A \to \prod Q_i$ may be factored through $Q_1 \oplus \cdots \oplus Q_{i_0}$. Hence each morphism $C_j \to A \to \prod Q_i$ may be factored through $\coprod Q_i$. Since $A = \bigcup C_j$, the morphism $A \to \prod Q_i$ may be factored through $\coprod Q_i$. By hypothesis $\coprod Q_i$ is injective. Hence, $A \to \prod Q_i$ may be extended to B:

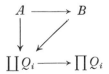

Since B is finitely generated, $B \to \coprod Q_i$ may be factored through a direct sum $Q_1 \oplus \cdots \oplus Q_n$. Then the same also holds for A and we get

$$\left(A \to \prod Q_i \right) = \left(A \to Q_1 \oplus \cdots \oplus Q_n \to \prod Q_i \right)$$

Thus, for almost all i, the morphism $(A \to Q_i) = (A \to \prod Q_i \to Q_i) = 0$. This means that, for almost all i, we have $A = A_i$.

COROLLARY 2. *In a locally noetherian category all finitely generated objects are noetherian.*

Proof. By Lemma 2, all objects in $\mathscr{C}$ are transfinitely generated.

COROLLARY 3. *Let R be a ring. R is noetherian if and only if the coproduct of injective modules in $_R$Mod is injective.*

Proof. If R is noetherian, then $_R$Mod is locally noetherian. If, conversely, each coproduct of injective modules is injective, then R is noetherian as a finitely generated object.

LEMMA 4. *Let $\mathscr{C}$ be a locally noetherian category. Then each injective object contains an indecomposable injective subobject.*

Proof. An object $A \in \mathscr{C}$ is called *coirreducible* if for subobjects B, $C \subseteq A$ with $B \cap C = 0$ we always have $B = 0$ or $C = 0$. If A is coirreducible then the injective hull $Q(A)$ is indecomposable. In fact, let $Q(A) = Q' \oplus Q''$, then $Q' \cap Q'' = 0 = (Q' \cap A) \cap (Q'' \cap A)$. Hence, $Q' \cap A = 0$ or $Q'' \cap A = 0$. Since A is large in $Q(A)$, we get $Q' = 0$ or $Q'' = 0$.

Let $Q \in \mathscr{C}$ be an injective object and let $Q \neq 0$. Since Q is transfinitely generated, Q contains a nonzero finitely generated subobject A. Since $\mathscr{C}$ is locally noetherian, A is noetherian. If A is not coirreducible, then there exist nonzero subobjects A_1 and B_1 of A with $A_1 \cap B_1 = 0$. If A_1 is not coirreducible, then there exist nonzero subobjects A_2 and B_2 of A_1 with $A_2 \cap B_2 = 0$. By continuing this process we get an ascending chain $B_1 \subset B_1 \oplus B_2 \subset \cdots$ of subobjects of A. This sequence must become constant since A is noetherian. Hence, by this construction after finitely many steps, we must get a nonzero coirredicible subobject A' of Q. The injective hull of A' is again a subobject of Q and is indecomposable by the above remarks.

With these means and the Krull–Remak–Schmidt–Azumaya theorem we now can make assertions about the structure of injective objects in locally noetherian categories. Here we refer again to Section 4.9, Theorem 2 and the remarks we made after this theorem.

THEOREM 4 (Matlis). *Let $\mathscr{C}$ be a locally noetherian category. Each injective object Q in $\mathscr{C}$ may be decomposed into a coproduct of indecomposable* *injective objects $Q = \coprod_{i \in I} Q_i$. If $Q = \coprod_{j \in J} Q_j'$ is another decomposition into indecomposable injective objects Q_j', then there exists a bijection $\varphi : I \to J$ such that $Q_i \cong Q_{\varphi(i)}'$ for all $i \in I$.*

Proof. It is sufficient to show the first assertion. The second assertion is implied by the theorem of Section 4.8, and Theorem 2 of Section 4.9. Since there is a generator in $\mathscr{C}$, Q has only a set of subobjects. We consider families $\{Q_i\}$ of indecomposable injective subobjects of Q with the property that $\bigcup Q_i = \coprod Q_i$ as subobjects of Q. By Zorn's lemma, there exists a maximal family $\{Q_i\}$. Let $Q' = \coprod Q_i$. Since Q' is an injective subobject of Q, by Theorem 3 we have $Q = Q' \oplus Q''$. If Q'' is nonzero, then Q'' contains an indecomposable injective subobject Q^* and $\{Q_i\} \cup \{Q^*\}$ fulfills the conditions for the families of subobjects defined above in contradiction to the maximality of $\{Q_i\}$. Hence, $Q = Q' = \coprod Q_i$.

THEOREM 5 (exchange theorem).   *Let $\mathscr{C}$ be a locally noetherian category, $\{Q_i\}_{i \in I}$ a family of indecomposable injective objects in $\mathscr{C}$ and Q' an injective subobject of $Q = \coprod Q_i$. Then there is a subset $K \subseteq I$ such that $\coprod_{i \in K} Q_i \oplus Q' = Q$.*

Proof. Consider the subset $J \subseteq I$ with the property that $Q' \cap \coprod_{i \in J} Q_i = 0$. Among these there is a maximal subset K by Zorn's lemma. Then $Q'' = Q' \oplus \coprod_{i \in K} Q_i$ is an injective subobject of Q. So for all Q_i, we have $Q'' \cap Q_i \neq 0$. Since the Q_i are indecomposable injectives, they are the injective hull of $A_i = Q'' \cap Q_i$. We want to show that Q is the injective hull of Q'' and hence $Q = Q''$.

First $Q_{i_1} \oplus Q_{i_2}$ is an essential extension of $A_{i_1} \cup A_{i_2}$. In fact, if $B \neq 0$ is a subobject, then the image of B under $f : Q_{i_1} \oplus Q_{i_2} \to Q_{i_1}$ or $g : Q_{i_1} \oplus Q_{i_2} \to Q_{i_2}$ is different from zero. Let $B' \neq 0$ be the image of B in Q_{i_1}. Then $B' \cap A_{i_1} \neq 0$. In Section 2.8, Lemma 2 the morphism g and hence also $f^{-1}(D) \cap C \to f(C) \cap D$ are epimorphisms. Thus $B_1 = B \cap f^{-1}(A_{i_1}) \neq 0$. If $g(B_1) \neq 0$, then $B_1 \cap g^{-1}(A_{i_2}) \neq 0$. Then $B \cap (A_{i_1} \cup A_{i_2}) = B \cap f^{-1}(A_{i_1}) \cap g^{-1}(A_{i_2}) \neq 0$. But if $g(B_1) = 0$, then $B_1 \subseteq Q_{i_1}$ and $B_1 \cap A_{i_1} \neq 0$. Hence

$$B \cap (A_{i_1} \cup A_{i_2}) \supseteq B \cap f^{-1}(A_{i_1}) \cap A_{i_1} \neq 0$$

By induction one shows that direct sums Q_E of indecomposable injective objects Q_i are an essential extension of a finite union A_E of the A_i with the same index set. The A_E and the Q_E form directed families of subobjects of Q. We have $Q'' = Q'' \cap (\bigcup Q_i) \supseteq \bigcup (Q'' \cap Q_i) = \bigcup A_i = \bigcup A_E$. Let $C \neq 0$ be a subobject of $Q = \bigcup Q_E$. Then $(\bigcup Q_E) \cap C = \bigcup (Q_E \cap C) = C$, hence $Q_E \cap C \neq 0$ for some E. So we get $A_E \cap C \neq 0$,

But $Q'' \cap C \supseteq (\bigcup A_E) \cap C = \bigcup (A_E \cap C) \neq 0$ means that Q'' is a large subobject of Q.

By Corollary 2 the last two theorems hold in each module category over a noetherian ring.

4.11   Module Categories

In this section we want to characterize the abelian categories equivalent to module categories. Since we shall determine simultaneously the equivalences between module categories, we shall obtain a general view of these equivalences. In this connection we shall prove the Morita theorems, which we shall apply in the next section for the discussion of the Wedderburn theorems for semisimple and simple rings.

A projective object P in an abelian category is called *finite* if the functor $\operatorname{Hom}_{\mathscr{C}}(P, -)$ preserves coproducts.

LEMMA 1.   *Each finite projective object P in $\mathscr{C}$ is finitely generated. If $\mathscr{C}$ is a Grothendieck category, then each finitely generated projective object is finite.*

Proof.   Let $\{P_i\}$ be a chain of subobjects of P with $\bigcup P_i = P$. Then $\coprod P_i \to P$ is an epimorphism, hence there exists a morphism $p : P \to \coprod P_i$ with $(P \to \coprod P_i \to P) = 1_P$. But $p \in \operatorname{Hom}_{\mathscr{C}}(P, \coprod P_i) \cong \coprod \operatorname{Hom}_{\mathscr{C}}(P, P_i)$ has the form $p = p_1 + \cdots + p_n$. Thus we have also $(P \to P_1 \oplus \cdots \oplus P_n \to P) = 1_P$. Thus $\bigcup_{i=1}^{n} P_i = P$. Since the P_i form a chain, we get $P = P_i$ for some i.

Let $\mathscr{C}$ be a Grothendieck category. Then each morphism $f : P \to \coprod A_i$ may be factored through a finite subsum $A_1 \oplus \cdots \oplus A_n$ by Section 4.10, Lemma 3 because P is finitely generated and projective. f induces a morphism $g : P \to \prod A_i$ in $\operatorname{Hom}_{\mathscr{C}}(P, \prod A_i) \cong \prod \operatorname{Hom}_{\mathscr{C}}(P, A_i)$. Since $\mathscr{C}$ is a Grothendieck category, the morphisms $\coprod A_i \to \prod A_i$ and $\operatorname{Hom}_{\mathscr{C}}(P, \coprod A_i) \to \operatorname{Hom}_{\mathscr{C}}(P, \prod A_i)$ are monomorphisms. Because $\operatorname{Hom}_{\mathscr{C}}(P, \prod A_i) \cong \prod \operatorname{Hom}_{\mathscr{C}}(P, A_i)$, we may regard f as an element of $\prod \operatorname{Hom}_{\mathscr{C}}(P, A_i)$. Since f can be factored through $A_1 \oplus \cdots \oplus A_n$, $p_i g : P \to A_i$ is nonzero only for finitely many i, that is, f has in $\prod \operatorname{Hom}_{\mathscr{C}}(P, A_i)$ only finitely many nonzero components. Thus f lies in the subgroup $\coprod \operatorname{Hom}_{\mathscr{C}}(P, A_i)$ of $\prod \operatorname{Hom}_{\mathscr{C}}(P, A_i)$. Conversely, each element of $\coprod \operatorname{Hom}_{\mathscr{C}}(P, A_i)$ considered as a morphism from P into $\prod A_i$ may be factored through a direct sum of (finitely many) A_is, hence lies in $\operatorname{Hom}_{\mathscr{C}}(P, \coprod A_i)$. This proves that the isomorphism

$\prod \text{Hom}_\mathscr{C}(P, A_i) \cong \text{Hom}_\mathscr{C}(P, \prod A_i)$ induces an isomorphism of the subgroups $\coprod \text{Hom}_\mathscr{C}(P, A_i) \cong \text{Hom}_\mathscr{C}(P, \coprod A_i)$.

A finite projective generator is called a *progenerator*. Now we can characterize the module categories among the abelian categories (up to equivalence).

THEOREM 1.   *Let $\mathscr{C}$ be an abelian category. There exists an equivalence $\mathscr{F} : \mathscr{C} \to \textbf{Mod}_R$ between $\mathscr{C}$ and a category of right modules if and only if $\mathscr{C}$ contains a progenerator P and arbitrary coproducts of copies of P. If $\mathscr{F}$ is an equivalence, then P may be chosen such that $\text{Hom}_\mathscr{C}(P, P) \cong R$ and $\mathscr{F} \cong \text{Hom}_\mathscr{C}(P, -)$.*

Proof.   Let P be a progenerator in $\mathscr{C}$. Then $\text{Hom}_\mathscr{C}(P, -) : \mathscr{C} \to \textbf{Mod}_R$ with $R = \text{Hom}_\mathscr{C}(P, P)$ is defined as $\text{Hom}_\mathscr{C}(P, -) : \mathscr{C} \to \textbf{Ab}$, only that the abelian groups $\text{Hom}_\mathscr{C}(P, A)$ have the structure of an R-right-module owing to the composition of morphisms of $\text{Hom}_\mathscr{C}(P, P)$ and of $\text{Hom}_\mathscr{C}(P, A)$. A morphism $f : A \to B$ then defines an R-homomorphism $\text{Hom}_\mathscr{C}(P, A) \to \text{Hom}_\mathscr{C}(P, B)$. The functor $\text{Hom}_\mathscr{C}(P, -)$ defines an isomorphism

$$\text{Hom}_\mathscr{C}(P, P) \cong \text{Hom}_R(\text{Hom}_\mathscr{C}(P, P), \text{Hom}_\mathscr{C}(P, P))$$

First, $\text{Hom}_\mathscr{C}(P, -)$ is faithful because P is a generator. Now let $f : \text{Hom}_\mathscr{C}(P, P) \to \text{Hom}_\mathscr{C}(P, P)$ be an R-homomorphism and let $g = f(1_P)$, then $f(r) = f(1_P \cdot r) = f(1_P)r = gr = \text{Hom}_\mathscr{C}(P, g)(r)$, that is, in this case $\text{Hom}_\mathscr{C}(P, -)$ is surjective. Since P is finite projective, we get for families $\{P_i\}_{i \in I}$ and $\{P_j\}_{j \in J}$ with $P_i \cong P \cong P_j$

$$\text{Hom}_\mathscr{C}\left(\coprod_{i \in I} P_i, \coprod_{j \in J} P_j\right) \cong \prod_{i \in I} \coprod_{j \in J} \text{Hom}_\mathscr{C}(P_i, P_j) \cong \prod_{i \in I} \coprod_{j \in J} \text{Hom}_R(R_i, R_j)$$

$$\cong \text{Hom}_R\left(\coprod_{i \in I} R_i, \coprod_{j \in J} R_j\right)$$

where $R_i = \text{Hom}_\mathscr{C}(P, P_i) \cong R$, $R_j \cong R$ and the isomorphism is induced by $\text{Hom}_\mathscr{C}(P, -)$. Hence, the functor $\text{Hom}_\mathscr{C}(P, -)$ induces an equivalence between the full subcategory of the coproducts of copies of P in $\mathscr{C}$ and the full subcategory of coproducts of copies of R in $\textbf{Mod}_R$ (Section 2.1, Proposition 3).

For each $A \in \mathscr{C}$ there exists an epimorphism $\coprod_{i \in I} P_i \to A$. Thus we can construct for each $A \in \mathscr{C}$ an exact sequence

$$\coprod P_j \xrightarrow{f} \coprod P_i \to A \to 0$$

and correspondingly for each $B \in \mathbf{Mod}_R$ an exact sequence

$$\coprod R_j \xrightarrow{g} \coprod R_i \to B \to 0$$

where the index sets $\{i\} = I$ and $\{j\} = J$ certainly depend on A and B respectively. A and B are uniquely determined up to isomorphisms by f and g respectively as cokernels of these morphisms. If we apply to the first exact sequence the functor $\operatorname{Hom}_\mathscr{C}(P, -)$, then we get an exact sequence of the form of the second exact sequence because P is projective and thus $\operatorname{Hom}_\mathscr{C}(P, -)$ is exact. Then g has the form $\operatorname{Hom}_\mathscr{C}(P, f)$. To each B there exists a $g = \operatorname{Hom}_\mathscr{C}(P, f)$. Thus $B = \operatorname{Hom}_\mathscr{C}(P, \operatorname{Cok}(f))$.

Each morphism $c : A \to A'$ in $\mathscr{C}$ induces a commutative diagram with exact sequences

$$
\begin{array}{ccccccc}
\coprod P_j & \xrightarrow{f} & \coprod P_i & \longrightarrow & A & \longrightarrow & 0 \\
{\scriptstyle a}\downarrow & & {\scriptstyle b}\downarrow & & {\scriptstyle c}\downarrow & & \\
\coprod P_{j'} & \xrightarrow{f'} & \coprod P_{i'} & \longrightarrow & A' & \longrightarrow & 0
\end{array}
$$

since the coproducts of copies of P are projective. Correspondingly, we get for each R-homomorphism $z : B \to B'$ a commutative diagram with exact sequences

$$
\begin{array}{ccccccc}
\coprod R_j & \xrightarrow{g} & \coprod R_i & \longrightarrow & B & \longrightarrow & 0 \\
{\scriptstyle x}\downarrow & & {\scriptstyle y}\downarrow & & {\scriptstyle z}\downarrow & & \\
\coprod R_{j'} & \xrightarrow{g'} & \coprod R_{i'} & \longrightarrow & B' & \longrightarrow & 0
\end{array}
$$

The pair (x, y) has the form $(\operatorname{Hom}_\mathscr{C}(P, a), \operatorname{Hom}_\mathscr{C}(P, b))$. Furthermore, c is uniquely determined by (a, b) and similarly z is uniquely determined by (x, y) as morphisms between cokernels. Thus $z = \operatorname{Hom}_\mathscr{C}(P, c)$, that is, $\operatorname{Hom}_\mathscr{C}(P, -)$ is full. Since P is a generator, $\operatorname{Hom}_\mathscr{C}(P, -)$ is also faithful and thus an isomorphism on all morphism sets.

Thus the hypothesis for Section 2.1, Proposition 3 are satisfied and $\operatorname{Hom}_\mathscr{C}(P, -)$ is an equivalence of categories.

Let $\mathscr{F} : \mathscr{C} \to \mathbf{Mod}_R$ be an equivalence of categories and $\mathscr{G} : \mathbf{Mod}_R \to \mathscr{C}$ be the corresponding inverse equivalence. Then $\mathscr{G}$ is left adjoint to $\mathscr{F}$, so $\operatorname{Hom}_\mathscr{C}(\mathscr{G}R, -) \cong \operatorname{Hom}_R(R, \mathscr{F}-) \cong \mathscr{F}$ as functors. Furthermore, $R \cong \operatorname{Hom}_R(R, R) \cong \operatorname{Hom}_\mathscr{C}(\mathscr{G}R, \mathscr{G}R)$. Since R is a progenerator in $\mathbf{Mod}_R$, also $\mathscr{G}R$ is a progenerator in $\mathscr{C}$. This proves the theorem.

The categorical properties of module categories are also satisfied by cocomplete abelian categories with a progenerator by this theorem. In particular, we have the following corollary.

COROLLARY 1. *A cocomplete abelian category with a progenerator is a Grothendieck category and has an injective cogenerator.*

Let R, S, and T be rings and $_RA_S$, $_SB_T$, and $_RC_T$ be bimodules. If we denote the R-S-bimodule homomorphisms by $\mathrm{Hom}_{R-S}(-, -)$, then it is easy to verify that the isomorphism which defines the adjointness between the tensor product and the Hom functor preserves also the corresponding operator rings such that we get a natural isomorphism for the bimodules A, B, and C

$$\mathrm{Hom}_{R-T}(_RA \otimes {_SB_T}, {_RC_T}) \cong \mathrm{Hom}_{S-T}(_SB_T, {_S}\mathrm{Hom}_R(_RA_S, {_RC_T})_T)$$

where we gave the operator rings in each case explicitly. For $f \in \mathrm{Hom}_R(_RA_S, {_RC_T})$, $a \in A$, $s \in S$, and $t \in T$ we define $(sft)(a) = (f(as))t$ so that $\mathrm{Hom}_R(_RA_S, {_RC_T})$ is an S-T-bimodule.

THEOREM 2 (Morita). *Let rings R and S and an R-S-bimodule $_RP_S$ be given. Then the following assertions are equivalent*:

    (a)   *The functor $P \otimes_S -$: $_R\mathbf{Mod} \to {_S}\mathbf{Mod}$ is an equivalence.*
    (b)   *The functor $- \otimes_R P$: $\mathbf{Mod}_R \to \mathbf{Mod}_S$ is an equivalence.*
    (c)   *The functor $\mathrm{Hom}_R(P, -)$: $_R\mathbf{Mod} \to {_S}\mathbf{Mod}$ is an equivalence.*
    (d)   *The functor $\mathrm{Hom}_S(P, -)$: $\mathbf{Mod}_S \to \mathbf{Mod}_R$ is an equivalence.*
    (e)   *$_RP$ is a progenerator and the multiplication of S on P defines an isomorphism $S \cong \mathrm{Hom}_R(P, P)^0$.*
    (f)   *P_S is a progenerator and the multiplication of R on P defines an isomorphism $R \cong \mathrm{Hom}_S(P, P)$.*

Proof. The equivalence of (d) and (f) was proved in Theorem 1. The equivalence of (c) and (e) follows by symmetry if we observe that by our definition endomorphism rings operate always on the left side whereas S operates on P from the right side.

The equivalence of (a) and (c) and of (b) and (d) can be obtained because the functors $P \otimes_S -$ and $- \otimes_R P$ are left adjoint to the functors $\mathrm{Hom}_R(P, -)$ and $\mathrm{Hom}_S(P, -)$ respectively.

To show the equivalence of (e) and (f) we need some prerequisites. The bimodule $_RP_S$ is a generator in $\mathbf{Mod}_S$ if and only if there is a bimodule $_SQ_R$ and an epimorphism $Q \otimes_R P \to S$ of S-S-bimodules. In fact, let P be a generator and $Q = \mathrm{Hom}_S(P, S)$ and the evaluation as homomorphism. If $Q \otimes_R P \to S$ is an epimorphism, then there exists an epimorphism $\coprod_{q \in Q} P_q \to S$ with $P_q = P$. Since S is a generator, P is also a generator.

Let $_RP_S$, $_SQ_R = \mathrm{Hom}_S(P, S)$, and $R = \mathrm{Hom}_S(P, P)$ be given. Then there exists an R-R-homomorphism $\varphi : P \otimes_S Q \to R$ which is defined by $\varphi(p \otimes q)(p') = pq(p')$ where $q(p') \in S$. P_S is finitely generated and projective if and only if φ is an epimorphism. In fact, if P is finitely generated and projective and if $\{p_1, \ldots, p_n\}$ generates P, then there exists an epimorphism $g : e_1 S \oplus \cdots \oplus e_n S \to P$ with $e_i \mapsto p_i$ and $e_i S \cong S$. Since P is projective there exists a section $f : P \to e_1 S \oplus \cdots \oplus e_n S$. This induces homomorphisms $f_i : P \to S$. Then

$$p = gf(p) = \sum g(e_i f_i(p)) = \sum p_i f_i(p)$$

for all $p \in P$, that is, $\varphi(\sum p_i \otimes q_i) = 1_P$. Since φ is an R-R-homomorphism, φ is an epimorphism. Conversely, if φ is an epimorphism, then there exist finite families $\{p_i\}$ and $\{f_i\}$ with $p = \sum p_i f_i(p)$ for all $p \in P$. Let $\{e_i\}$ be a finite family of elements with the same index set, then we define $P \to e_1 S \oplus \cdots \oplus e_n S$ by $p \mapsto \sum e_i f_i(p)$ and $e_1 S \oplus \cdots \oplus e_n S \to P$ by $e_i \mapsto p_i$. Then

$$(P \to e_1 S \oplus \cdots \oplus e_n S \to P) = 1_P$$

hence P is finitely generated. Since $e_1 S \oplus \cdots \oplus e_n S$ is projective, also P is projective.

Assume that (f) holds. Then we have an epimorphism $P \otimes_S Q \to R$. Hence $_R P$ is a generator. Furthermore, this epimorphism induces a homomorphism $Q \to \mathrm{Hom}_R(P, R)$ of S-R-bimodules. Since $Q \otimes_R P \to S$ is an epimorphism, $1 \in S$ occurs in the image of this homomorphism. So $1_P \in \mathrm{Hom}_R(P,P)$ occurs in the image of $\mathrm{Hom}_R(P,R) \otimes_R P \to \mathrm{Hom}_R(P,P)$. This $\mathrm{Hom}_R(P, P)$-$\mathrm{Hom}_R(P, P)$-homomorphism is an epimorphism. Hence, $_R P$ is finitely generated and projective, so it is a progenerator. We still have to show that $S \cong \mathrm{Hom}_R(P, P)^0$ by the homomorphism induced by the right multiplication. Let $ps = 0$ for all $p \in P$, then $s = 1s = \sum f_i(p_i)s = \sum f_i(p_i s) = 0$. If $f \in \mathrm{Hom}_R(P, P)$, then $f(p) = f(p1_s) = f(\sum p f_i(p_i)) = f(\sum \varphi(p \otimes f_i)(p_i)) = \sum \varphi(p \otimes f_i) f(p_i) = p(\sum f_i(f(p_i)))$. So (e) is satisfied. By symmetry, one shows that (e) implies (f)

We call P an *R-S-progenerator* if P satisfies one of the equivalent conditions of Theorem 2.

LEMMA 2. *Let $\mathscr{F}$ and $\mathscr{G}$ be additive functors from $_R\mathbf{Mod}$ to $_S\mathbf{Mod}$. Let $\eta : \mathscr{F} \to \mathscr{G}$ be a natural transformation. If $\eta(R) : \mathscr{F}(R) \to \mathscr{G}(R)$ is an isomorphism then $\eta(P) : \mathscr{F}(P) \to \mathscr{G}(P)$ is an isomorphism for all finitely generated projective R-modules P.*

Proof. Let $P \oplus P' \cong R \oplus \cdots \oplus R = R^n$. Since $\mathscr{F}$ and $\mathscr{G}$ are additive we have that $\eta(R^n) : \mathscr{F}(R^n) \to \mathscr{G}(R^n)$ is an isomorphism for $\mathscr{F}(R^n) \cong$

$(\mathscr{F}(R))^n$ and $\mathscr{G}(R^n) \cong (\mathscr{G}(R))^n$. The injection $P \to R^n$ and the projection $R^n \to P$ induce a commutative diagram

$$
\begin{array}{ccccc}
\mathscr{F}(P) & \longrightarrow & \mathscr{F}(R^n) & \longrightarrow & \mathscr{F}(P) \\
\downarrow & & \downarrow & & \downarrow \\
\mathscr{G}(P) & \longrightarrow & \mathscr{G}(R^n) & \longrightarrow & \mathscr{G}(P)
\end{array}
$$

where the middle morphism is an isomorphism. The left square implies that $\eta(P)$ is a monomorphism, the right square that $\eta(P)$ is an epimorphism.

This lemma certainly still holds if $\mathscr{F}$ and $\mathscr{G}$ are bifunctors and if we restrict our considerations to one of the arguments. Two applications of this lemma are the natural transformation

$$A \otimes {}_R B \ni a \otimes b \mapsto (f \mapsto f(a)\, b) \in \operatorname{Hom}_R(\operatorname{Hom}_R(A, R), B)$$

which is natural in A and B and the natural transformation

$$\operatorname{Hom}_R(A, R) \otimes {}_R B \ni f \otimes b \mapsto (a \mapsto f(a)\, b) \in \operatorname{Hom}_R(A, B)$$

which is also natural in A and B. For these natural transformations, we have $R \otimes_R B \cong \operatorname{Hom}_R(\operatorname{Hom}_R(R, R), B)$ and $\operatorname{Hom}_R(R, R) \otimes_R B \cong \operatorname{Hom}_R(R, B)$. In particular we get for an R-S-progenerator ${}_R P_S$ isomorphisms between the following functors:

$$P \otimes_S - \cong \operatorname{Hom}_S(\operatorname{Hom}_S(P, S), -)$$
$$- \otimes_R P \cong \operatorname{Hom}_R(\operatorname{Hom}_R(P, R), -)$$
$$\operatorname{Hom}_S(P, -) \cong - \otimes_S \operatorname{Hom}_S(P, S)$$
$$\operatorname{Hom}_R(P, -) \cong \operatorname{Hom}_R(P, R) \otimes_R -$$

COROLLARY 2.   *Let P be an R-S-progenerator and let $Q = \operatorname{Hom}_R(P, R)$. Then*

(a)   *Q is an S-R-progenerator.*
(b)   *$Q \cong \operatorname{Hom}_S(P, S)$ as S-R-bimodules.*
(c)   *$\operatorname{Center}(R) \cong \operatorname{Center}(S)$.*
(d)   *The lattice $\mathfrak{B}({}_R P)$ of R-submodules of P is isomorphic to the lattice $\mathfrak{B}({}_S S)$ of left ideals of S. Correspondingly, we have*

$$\mathfrak{B}(P_S) \cong \mathfrak{B}(R_R),\ \mathfrak{B}(Q_R) \cong \mathfrak{B}(S_S),\ \mathfrak{B}({}_S Q) \cong \mathfrak{B}({}_R R)$$

and

$$\mathfrak{B}({}_R P_S) \cong \mathfrak{B}({}_S S_S) \cong \mathfrak{B}({}_R R_R) \cong \mathfrak{B}({}_S Q_R)$$

Proof. (a) By Lemma 2, $\mathrm{Hom}_R(Q, -) : \mathbf{Mod}_R \to \mathbf{Mod}_S$ is an equivalence of categories.

(b) $P \otimes_S -$ is adjoint to $\mathrm{Hom}_R(P, -)$. Thus by the preceeding remark $\mathrm{Hom}_S(\mathrm{Hom}_S(P, S), -)$ is adjoint to $Q \otimes_R -$. But also $\mathrm{Hom}_S(Q, -)$ is adjoint to $Q \otimes_R -$. Hence, $Q \cong \mathrm{Hom}_S(P, S)$ as S-modules. Since R^0 is the endomorphism ring of $_S Q$ as well as of $_S\mathrm{Hom}_S(P, S)$, the isomorphism is an S-R-isomorphism.

(c) We show that between the elements of the center $\mathfrak{Z}(R)$ and the endomorphisms of the identity functor $\mathscr{I}$ of $_R\mathbf{Mod}$ there is a bijection which preserves the addition of natural transformations and of elements of $\mathfrak{Z}(R)$ as well as the composition of natural transformations and the multiplication in $\mathfrak{Z}(R)$. Since between the endomorphisms of the identity functor of $_R\mathbf{Mod}$ and the endomorphisms of the identity functor of $_S\mathbf{Mod}$ there exists a bijection which preserves all compositions, this proves (c).

Let $\rho : \mathscr{I} \to \mathscr{I}$ be an endomorphism of the identity functor of $_R\mathbf{Mod}$. ρ determines an R-homomorphism $\rho(R) : R \to R$. Let $r_\rho = \rho(R)(1)$, then $\rho(R)(r) = r\rho(R)(1) = rr_\rho$. For each R-module A and each R-homomorphism $f : R \to A$ we get a commutative diagram

$$\begin{array}{ccc} R & \xrightarrow{\rho(R)} & R \\ \downarrow{\scriptstyle f} & & \downarrow{\scriptstyle f} \\ A & \xrightarrow{\rho(A)} & A \end{array}$$

Hence, $f\rho(R)(1) = \rho(A)f(1)$, that is, for all $A \in A$, we have $\rho(A)(a) = r_\rho a$ because f can always be chosen such that $f(1) = a$ (R is a generator). For all $r \in R$, we have $rr_\rho = \rho(R)(r) = r_\rho r$, hence $r_\rho \in \mathfrak{Z}(R)$. Now let $\rho_1, \rho_2 : \mathscr{I} \to \mathscr{I}$ be given. Then $(\rho_1 + \rho_2)(R)(1) = (\rho_1(R) + \rho_2(R))(1) = \rho_1(R)(1) + \rho_2(R)(1)$ and $(\rho_1\rho_2)(R)(1) = \rho_1(R)\rho_2(R)(1) = (\rho_2(R)(1))(\rho_1(R)(1))$. Conversely, the multiplication with an element of the center defines an R-endomorphism for each R-module A. These R-endomorphisms are compatible with all R-homomorphisms, and hence define an endomorphism of $\mathscr{I}$. This application is inverse to the above given application.

(d) The equivalence $\mathrm{Hom}_R(P, -)$ preserves lattices of subobjects. $\mathrm{Hom}_R(P, P)^0 \cong S$ implies the first assertion. Multiplication with elements of S defines R-homomorphisms of P. These are preserved by $\mathrm{Hom}_R(P, -)$ as multiplications because for $s, s' \in S$ considered as elements of S as well as right multiplicators of P we get $\mathrm{Hom}_R(P, s)(s') = s \cdot s' = (s's)$ by $S \cong \mathrm{Hom}_R(P, P)^0$. The given isomorphism of lattices carries R-S-submodules of P over into S-S-submodules of S. Conversely, the inverse equivalence carries S-S-submodules of S over into R-S-submodules of P because we also have $\operatorname{Hom}_S(S, S)^0 \cong S$. The other lattice isomorphisms follow by symmetry.

We also observe that $\operatorname{Hom}_R(Q, R) \cong \operatorname{Hom}_S(Q, S) \cong P$ as R-S-bimodules because of the remarks which follow Lemma 2. By the same reasons, we get $P \otimes_S Q \cong R$ as R-R-bimodules and $Q \otimes_R P \cong S$ as S-S-bimodules.

4.12 Semisimple and Simple Rings

Among many other applications of the Morita theorems (Frobenius extensions, Azumaya algebras), the structure theory of semisimple and simple rings is one of the best-known applications of this theory. We want to present it as far as it is interesting from the point of view of categories.

Let $R \neq 0$ be a ring. R is called *artinian*, if R is artinian as an object in $_R\mathbf{Mod}$. A left ideal (= R-submodule in $_R\mathbf{Mod}$) is called *nilpotent* if $A^n = 0$ for some $n \geqslant 1$. A ring R is called *semisimple* if R is artinian and has no nonzero nilpotent left ideals. A ring R is called *simple* if R is artinian and has no two-sided ideal (= R-R-submodule) different from zero and R.

LEMMA 1. *Each simple ring is semisimple.*

Proof. Let $A \neq 0$ be a nilpotent ideal in a simple ring R. $A^n = 0$ is equivalent to the assertion that for each sequence $a_1, \ldots, a_n$ of elements of A we get $a_1 \cdots a_n = 0$. We show that $C = \sum A$ for all nilpotent ideals A is a two-sided ideal. It is sufficient to show that for each $a \in A$ and $r \in R$ the element ar is in a nilpotent ideal. We have $ar \in Rar$ and

$$(r_1 ar) \cdots (r_n ar) = (r_1 a)(r r_2 a) \cdots (r r_n a)\, r = 0r = 0$$

hence $(Rar)^n = 0$. $A \neq 0$ implies $C \neq 0$. Since R is simple, $R = C$, hence $1 \in C$. Thus $1 \in A_1 + \cdots + A_n$ for certain nilpotent ideals. The sum of two nilpotent ideals A and B is again nilpotent. In fact let $A^n = B^n = 0$, then $(a_1 b_1) \cdots (a_n b_n) = a_1(b_1 a_2) \cdots (b_{n-1} a_n)\, b_n = 0$. Thus $A + B$ is nilpotent. This proves that $1 \in R$ is an element of a nilpotent ideal, hence $1^n = 0$. This contradiction arose from the assumption that R has a nonzero nilpotent ideal. Consequently, R is semisimple.

LEMMA 2. *If R is a semisimple ring, then each ideal of R is a direct summand.*

Proof. Since R is artinian, there exists in the set of ideals which are not direct summands a minimal element A (in case that this set is not empty). If A contains a proper subideal $B \subset A$, then B is a direct summand of R, hence, there is a morphism $R \to B$ such that $(B \to A \to R \to B) = 1_B$. Thus B is also a direct summand in A and we have $A = B \oplus C$. But also C is a direct summand of R. The morphisms $R \to B$ and $R \to C$ induce a morphism $R \to B \oplus C$ such that $(A = B \oplus C \to R \to B \oplus C) = 1_A$. If A is not a direct summand in R, then A must be a simple ideal. For some $a \in A$, we have $Aa \neq 0$ because otherwise $A^2 = 0$. Since A is simple we have $Aa = A$ hence $(A \to R \xrightarrow{a} A) \cong 1_A$. Therefore, the set of ideals which are not direct summands of R is empty.

LEMMA 3.   *Let R be a semisimple ring, then all R-modules are injective and projective.*

Proof.   We apply Section 4.9, Corollary 2 to the generator R. Since each ideal A is a direct summand of R, for each R-module B, the group $\mathrm{Hom}_R(A, B)$ is a direct summand of $\mathrm{Hom}_R(R, B)$; hence the map $\mathrm{Hom}_R(R, B) \to \mathrm{Hom}_R(A, B)$ is surjective. Thus all objects are injective. For all exact sequences $0 \to A \to B \to C \to 0$, the morphism $A \to B$ is a section. Hence each epimorphism $B \to C$ must be a retraction. By Section 4.9, Lemma 2, each R-module is projective.

LEMMA 4.   *Each finite product (in the category of rings) of semisimple rings is semisimple.*

Proof.   It is sufficient to prove the lemma for two semisimple rings R_1 and R_2. Let $R = R_1 \times R_2$. If we recall the construction of the product of rings in Section 1.11 and the theorem of Section 3.2, then it is clear that R_1 and R_2 annihilate each other and that $R = R_1 \oplus R_2$ as R-modules. Let $p : R \to R_2$ be the projection of the direct sum onto R_2. Let A_i be a descending sequence of ideals in R. Then $p(A_i)$ is a descending sequence of ideals in R_2. Let $K_i = \mathrm{Ker}(A_i \to p(A_i))$. The K_i form a descending sequence of ideals in R_1. The last two sequences become constant for $i \geqslant n$. Thus we get a commutative diagram with exact sequences

$$
\begin{array}{ccccccccc}
0 & \longrightarrow & K_{n+j} & \longrightarrow & A_{n+j} & \longrightarrow & p(A_{n+j}) & \longrightarrow & 0 \\
& & \| & & \downarrow & & \| & & \\
0 & \longrightarrow & K_n & \longrightarrow & A_n & \longrightarrow & p(A_n) & \longrightarrow & 0
\end{array}
$$

where $A_{n+j} \subseteq A_n$. This morphism is also an epimorphism. In fact let $a_n \in A_n$, then there exists an $a_{n+j} \in A_{n+j}$ with $p(a_{n+j}) = p(a_n)$. Hence, $a_n - a_{n+j} \in K_n = K_{n+j} \subseteq A_{n+j}$. Thus also, $a_n \in A_{n+j}$. Therefore R is artinian.

Let $A \subseteq R$ be a nilpotent ideal with $A^n = 0$, then for $a \in A$ also $(Ra)^n = 0$. We have $Ra = Ra_1 + Ra_2 = R_1a_1 + R_2a_2$ with $a_i \in R_i$. In fact

$$r_1a_1 + r_2a_2 = (r_1 + r_2)(a_1 + a_2)$$

Hence,

$$(R_1a_1 + R_2a_2)^n = (R_1a_1)^n + (R_2a_2)^n = 0$$

and consequently $a_1 = a_2 = a = 0$, since R_1 and R_2 have no nonzero nilpotent ideals. Therefore R is semisimple.

THEOREM 1. *If R is semisimple, then $R = A_1 \oplus \cdots \oplus A_n$, where the A_i are simple left ideals in R.*

Proof. Since each R-module is injective, each coproduct of injective modules is injective. By Section 4.10, Corollary 3 R is noetherian. Each indecomposable injective object is simple because all objects are injective. By Section 4.10, Theorem 4, R may be decomposed into a coproduct of simple left ideals. Since R is finitely generated, Section 4.10, Lemma 3 holds, that is, R may be decomposed into a finite direct sum of simple left ideals.

THEOREM 2. *The ring R is simple if and only if R is isomorphic to a full matrix ring with coefficients in a skew-field.*

Proof. A skew-field is a not necessarily commutative field. A full matrix ring over a skew-field is the ring of all $n \times n$ matrices with coefficients in the skew-field. It is well known that such a ring is isomorphic to the endomorphism ring of an n-dimensional vector space over the skew-field K. A vector space of finite dimension is a progenerator. If we denote the full matrix ring by $M_n(K)$, then the categories of K-modules (K-vector spaces) and of $M_n(K)$-modules are equivalent. Since the n-dimensional K-vector space K^n is artinian, also $M_n(K)$ is artinian by Section 4.11, Corollary 2. Since K has no ideals, also $M_n(K)$ has no two-sided ideals by the same corollary. Hence $M_n(K)$ is simple.

Let R be simple and P be a simple R-module, then P is finitely generated and projective by Lemma 1 and Lemma 3. Let $K = \text{End}_R(P)$. Then K is a skew-field. In fact, let $f : P \to P$ be a nonzero endomorphism of P, then the image of f is a submodule of P, hence coincides with P

since P is simple. Also the kernel of f is zero, hence f is an isomorphism and has an inverse isomorphism in K. This assertion, which holds for all simple objects in an abelian category, is called Schur's lemma.

The evaluation homomorphism $P \otimes_K \mathrm{Hom}_R(P, R) \to R$ is an R-R-homomorphism. The image of this homomorphism is a two-sided ideal in R. Since P is simple, there exists an epimorphism $R \to P$. Since P is projective, this epimorphism is a retraction and there is a nonzero homomorphism $P \to R$. Therefore, the image of the evaluation homomorphism is nonzero. Since R is simple, the image must coincide with R. The evaluation homomorphism is an epimorphism. In the proof of Section 4.11, Theorem 2 we observed that this condition is sufficient for the fact that P is a generator. Hence P is an R-K-progenerator. By Section 4.11, Theorem 2(f), $R \cong \mathrm{Hom}_K(P, P)$ and P_K is a finitely generated projective K-module, that is, a finite dimensional K-vector space.

THEOREM 3.   *For the ring R the following assertions are equivalent*:

 (a) *R is semisimple.*
 (b) *Each R-module is projective.*
 (c) *R is a finite product (in the category of rings) of simple rings.*

Proof.   Lemma 3 shows that (a) implies (b). Lemma 4 shows that (c) implies (a). Thus we have to show that (b) implies (c).

Since each R-module is projective, each epimorphism is a retraction. Then each monomorphism is a section as a kernel of an epimorphism. This means that, by Section 4.9, Lemma 2, each R-module is an injective R-module. Each R-module may be decomposed into a coproduct of simple R-modules as we saw in the proof of Theorem 1. There are only finitely many nonisomorphic simple R-modules A_i. In fact if A_i is simple, then there is an epimorphism $R \to A_i$ which is a retraction. Hence A_i is a direct summand of R up to an isomorphism. By Section 4.10, Theorem 4, A_i occurs up to an isomorphism in a decomposition of R into a coproduct of simple R-modules. By Section 4.10, Theorem 5, A_i is isomorphic to a direct summand of R in the decomposition given in Theorem 1.

Let $E_1, \dots, E_r$ be all classes of isomorphic simple R-modules. Let $R = A_1 \oplus \cdots \oplus A_n$ with simple R-modules A_i be given. We collect the isomorphic A_i of this decomposition, which are in E_1, to a direct sum $A_{i_1} \oplus \cdots \oplus A_{i_s} = B_1$. Correspondingly we collect the A_i in E_j to a direct sum B_j. So we get $R = B_1 \oplus \cdots \oplus B_r$. Since there are only zero morphisms into nonisomorphic simple R-modules, and since all simple R-modules in B_i are isomorphic because of the uniqueness of the decomposition, there exists only the zero morphism for different i and j between B_i and B_j. For $b_j \in B_j$ the right multiplication $b_j : B_i \to B_j$ is an R-(left)-homomorphism. This proves that $B_i B_j = 0$ for $i \neq j$ and $B_i B_i \subseteq B_i$. Each B_i is a two-sided ideal, and the B_i annihilate each other.

In the decomposition $R = B_1 \oplus \cdots \oplus B_r$ we have $1 = e_1 + \cdots + e_r$. For $b_i \in B_i$ we have $b_i = 1 b_i = e_i b_i$. Hence e_i operates in B_i as a unit, that is, B_i is a ring and R the product of the rings $B_1, \ldots, B_n$. Each B_i-module is an R-module if one has the B_j with $j \neq i$ as zero multipliers for the B_i-modules. The R-homomorphisms and the B_i-homomorphisms between the B_i-modules coincide. Hence all B_i-modules are projective. By construction, B_i is a direct sum of simple isomorphic R-modules, which are simple and isomorphic also as B_i-modules. Let P be such a simple B_i-module, then P is finitely generated and projective and also a generator, since $B_i = P \oplus \cdots \oplus P$. Hence P is a B_i-K-progenerator with a skew-field K, where we used Schur's lemma. As in Theorem 2 we now have $B_i \cong \mathrm{End}_K(K^m)$, that is, a simple ring.

We conclude with a remark about the properties of simple rings which may now be proved easily.

COROLLARY 1. *The center of a full matrix ring over a skew-field K is isomorphic to the center of K.*

Proof. The category of modules over a full matrix ring over K is equivalent to the category of K-vector spaces. By Section 4.11, Theorem 2 and Section 4.11, Corollary 2(c) the assertion is proved.

COROLLARY 2. *Let R be a simple ring. Then each finitely generated R-module P is a progenerator and $\mathrm{Hom}_R(P, P)$ is a simple ring.*

Proof. The category of R-modules is equivalent to the category of K-vector spaces with a skew-field K. In $_K\mathbf{Mod}$ the assertion is trivial.

4.13 Functor Categories

The results of this section shall mainly prepare the proof of the embedding theorems for abelian categories presented Section 4.14. Therefore we shall restrict ourselves to the most important properties of the functor categories under consideration.

Let $\mathscr{A}$ and $\mathscr{C}$ be abelian categories and let the category $\mathscr{A}$ be small. By Section 4.7, Proposition 1, we know that $\mathrm{Funct}(\mathscr{A}, \mathscr{C})$ is an abelian category. We form the full subcategory $\mathfrak{A}(\mathscr{A}, \mathscr{C})$ of Funct($\mathscr{A}, \mathscr{C}$) which consists of the additive functors from $\mathscr{A}$ to $\mathscr{C}$.

PROPOSITION. $\mathfrak{A}(\mathscr{A}, \mathscr{C})$ *is an abelian category.*

Proof. We know that limits preserve difference kernels and that colimits preserve difference cokernels (Section 2.7, Corollary 2). By Section 4.6, Proposition 1, limits and colimits are additive functors. Since by Section 2.7, Theorem 1, limits and colimits of functors are formed argumentwise, a limit as well as a colimit of additive functors in Funct($\mathscr{A}, \mathscr{C}$) is again an additive functor. Thus the full subcategory $\mathfrak{A}(\mathscr{A}, \mathscr{C})$ of Funct($\mathscr{A}, \mathscr{C}$) is closed with respect to forming limits and colimits. In $\mathfrak{A}(\mathscr{A}, \mathscr{C})$ there exist kernels, cokernels, finite direct sums, and a zero object and they coincide with the corresponding limits and colimits in Funct($\mathscr{A}, \mathscr{C}$). Furthermore, each isomorphism in Funct($\mathscr{A}, \mathscr{C}$) which is in $\mathfrak{A}(\mathscr{A}, \mathscr{C})$ is also an isomorphism in $\mathfrak{A}(\mathscr{A}, \mathscr{C})$ because $\mathfrak{A}(\mathscr{A}, \mathscr{C})$ is full. Therefore, $\mathfrak{A}(\mathscr{A}, \mathscr{C})$ is an abelian category.

For our considerations we need still another full subcategory of Funct($\mathscr{A}, \mathscr{C}$), namely $\mathfrak{L}(\mathscr{A}, \mathscr{C})$, the category of left-exact functors from $\mathscr{A}$ to $\mathscr{C}$. Obviously $\mathfrak{L}(\mathscr{A}, \mathscr{C})$ is also a full subcategory of $\mathfrak{A}(\mathscr{A}, \mathscr{C})$ because each left-adjoint functor is additive. We want to investigate $\mathfrak{L}(\mathscr{A}, \mathscr{C})$ further and we want to show in particular that this category is abelian. It will turn out that the cokernels formed in $\mathfrak{L}(\mathscr{A}, \mathscr{C})$ are different from the cokernels formed in $\mathfrak{A}(\mathscr{A}, \mathscr{C})$. This means that the embedding functor is not exact. To construct the cokernel in $\mathfrak{L}(\mathscr{A}, \mathscr{C})$ we shall show that $\mathfrak{L}(\mathscr{A}, \mathscr{C})$ is a reflexive subcategory of $\mathfrak{A}(\mathscr{A}, \mathscr{C})$. For this purpose, we solve the corresponding universal problem with the following construction.

Let $A \in \mathscr{A}$. Denote the set of monomorphisms $a : A \to X$ in $\mathscr{A}$ with domain A and arbitrary range $X \in \mathscr{A}$ by $S(A)$. Observe that $\mathscr{A}$ is small. To $S(A)$ we construct a small directed category $T(A)$ with the elements of $S(A)$ as object. We define $a \leqslant b$, that is, there is a morphism from a to b in $T(A)$ if and only if there is a commutative diagram

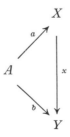

in $\mathscr{A}$, that is, if b may be factored through a. This factorization x need not be uniquely determined. On the other hand, by definition of the directed category, there can exist at most one morphism between a and b in $T(A)$. We call x the representative of this morphism. Trivially $a \leqslant a$ is satisfied by the identity. Also the composition of morphisms in $T(A)$ holds because morphisms may be composed in $\mathscr{A}$. Given objects a and b in $T(A)$, we get a c in $T(A)$ with $a \leqslant c$ and $b \leqslant c$ by the following cofiber product

$$
\begin{array}{ccc}
A & \xrightarrow{\ a\ } & X \\
{\scriptstyle b}\big\downarrow & & \big\downarrow \\
Y & \longrightarrow & Z
\end{array}
$$

as the diagonal $A \to Z$, for by the dual assertion of Section 4.3, Lemma 3(c) with b also $X \to Z$ is a monomorphism. Consequently, c is a monomorphism.

Let $f : A \to B$ be a morphism in $\mathscr{A}$. If a and a' are monomorphisms in A and if Z and Z' are the cofiber products of f with a and a' respectively, and if $a \leqslant a'$, then we get a commutative diagram

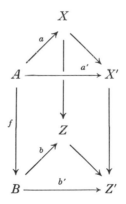

where b and b' are monomorphisms, and $Z \to Z'$ is uniquely determined by $X \to X'$ and b'. f defines a functor $T(f) : T(A) \to T(B)$ which, with the notations of the diagram, assigns to an object a in $T(A)$ the object b in $T(B)$, such that $a \leqslant a'$ implies $T(f)(a) = b \leqslant b' = T(f)(a')$. Since $T(A)$ and $T(B)$ are directed small categories, $T(f)$ is a functor.

If $f : A \to B$ is a monomorphism in $\mathscr{A}$ and if $b, b' \in T(B)$, then in the commutative diagram

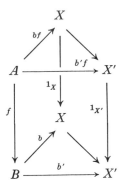

bf and $b'f$ are also monomorphisms and are objects of $T(A)$. If $b \leqslant b'$, then $bf \leqslant b'f$. Thus we get a functor $T^+(f) : T(B) \to T(A)$. If $a \in T(A)$ and $b = T(f)(a)$, then the commutative diagram

$$\begin{array}{ccc} A & \overset{a}{\longrightarrow} & X \\ {\scriptstyle f}\downarrow & & \downarrow \\ B & \overset{b}{\longrightarrow} & Y \end{array}$$

implies that f as well as bf are monomorphisms, and that we have $a \leqslant bf$. Thus for a monomorphism f we have

$$a \leqslant T^+(f)\, T(f)(a)$$

LEMMA 1.   *T is a functor from A into the category of small categories with isomorphism classes of functors as morphisms.*

Proof. The definition of T implies trivially $T(1_A) \cong 1_{T(A)}$. Let morphisms $f : A \to B$ and $g : B \to C$ in $\mathscr{A}$ be given. Let $a \in T(A)$. By Section 2.6, Lemma 3, we have $T(g)\, T(f)(a) \cong T(gf)(a)$. Since all diagrams in $T(C)$ must be commutative, this isomorphism is a natural isomorphism, $T(g)\, T(f) \cong T(gf)$.

Given an additive functor $\mathscr{F} : \mathscr{A} \to \mathscr{C}$. We construct a functor $\mathscr{F}_A{}^* : T(A) \to \mathscr{C}$ for each object $A \in \mathscr{A}$. If $a \in T(A)$ is given, then it defines an exact sequence

$$0 \to A \overset{a}{\to} X \to \operatorname{Cok} a \to 0$$

Since $\mathscr{F}$ is not necessarily exact, $\mathscr{F}$ does not necessarily preserve the kernel A of $X \to \operatorname{Cok} a$, when applied to the above exact sequence. Let us define $\mathscr{F}_A{}^*(a)$ as the kernel of $\mathscr{F}(X) \to \mathscr{F}(\text{Cok } a)$, then we get a commutative diagram with an exact row

$$
\begin{array}{c}
\mathscr{F}(A) \\
\downarrow \quad \searrow {\scriptstyle \mathscr{F}(a)} \\
0 \longrightarrow \mathscr{F}_A{}^*(a) \longrightarrow \mathscr{F}(X) \longrightarrow \mathscr{F}(\text{Cok } a)
\end{array}
$$

where $\mathscr{F}(A) \to \mathscr{F}_A{}^*(a)$ exists uniquely because

$$(\mathscr{F}(A) \to \mathscr{F}(X) \to \mathscr{F}(\text{Cok } a)) = 0$$

If $a \leqslant a'$ in $T(A)$, then there exists a morphism $x : X \to Y$ in $\mathscr{A}$ with $X = R(a)$, $Y = R(a')$, and $xa = a'$. Therefore, we get a commutative diagram with exact rows

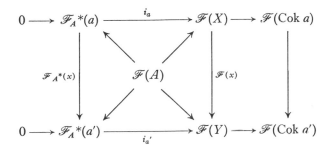

where $\mathscr{F}(\text{Cok } a) \to \mathscr{F}(\text{Cok } a')$ is determined by the natural morphism $\text{Cok } a \to \text{Cok } a'$ and where $\mathscr{F}_A{}^*(x)$ exists because the right square of the diagram is commutative. Because of the uniqueness of the factorizations through kernels and cokernels, $\mathscr{F}_A{}^*(x)$ is uniquely determined by x.

Now we have to show that the morphism $\mathscr{F}_A{}^*(x)$ does not depend on the choice of the representative for $a \leqslant a'$. Thus let also $y : X \to Y$ with $ya = a'$ be given. Then $(x - y)a = 0$. Hence $x - y$ may be factored through $\text{Cok } a$. Then also $\mathscr{F}(x - y)$ may be factored through $\mathscr{F}(\text{Cok } a)$, and we have $\mathscr{F}(x - y)i_a = 0$, hence $\mathscr{F}(x)i_a = \mathscr{F}(y)i_a$. The above diagram implies $i_{a'}\mathscr{F}_A{}^*(x) = i_{a'}\mathscr{F}_A{}^*(y)$ and $\mathscr{F}_A{}^*(x) = \mathscr{F}_A{}^*(y)$. Thus $\mathscr{F}_A{}^*$ is defined on $T(A)$. The functor properties follow trivially from the functor properties of $\mathscr{F}$ and the uniqueness of the factorizations.

Let $f : A \to B$ be a morphism in $\mathscr{A}$. Then there are functors $\mathscr{F}_B{}^*T(f) : T(A) \to \mathscr{C}$ and $\mathscr{F}_A{}^* : T(A) \to \mathscr{C}$ defined. We construct a natural transformation $\mathscr{F}_f{}^* : \mathscr{F}_A{}^* \to \mathscr{F}_B{}^*T(f)$. Let $a : A \to X$ be a monomorphism in $\mathscr{A}$, hence an object in $T(A)$, then $T(f)(a) = b : B \to Y$

is a monomorphism into the cofiber product Y of X and B over A. We get a commutative diagram with exact rows

$$0 \longrightarrow A \longrightarrow X \longrightarrow \mathrm{Cok}\, a \longrightarrow 0$$
$$\downarrow \qquad \downarrow \qquad \downarrow$$
$$0 \longrightarrow B \longrightarrow Y \longrightarrow \mathrm{Cok}\, b \longrightarrow 0$$

This diagram induces another commutative diagram with exact rows

$$0 \longrightarrow \mathscr{F}_A{}^*(a) \longrightarrow \mathscr{F}(X) \longrightarrow \mathscr{F}(\mathrm{Cok}\, a)$$
$$\downarrow \qquad\qquad \downarrow \qquad\qquad \downarrow$$
$$0 \longrightarrow \mathscr{F}_B{}^*(b) \longrightarrow \mathscr{F}(Y) \longrightarrow \mathscr{F}(\mathrm{Cok}\, b)$$

We denote the morphism $\mathscr{F}_A{}^*(a) \to \mathscr{F}_B{}^*(b) = \mathscr{F}_B{}^*T(f)(a)$ by $\mathscr{F}_f{}^*(a)$. It is obviously uniquely determined by f and a. If $g : B \to C$ is another morphism in $\mathscr{A}$, then by the uniqueness the diagram

$$\mathscr{F}_A{}^*(a) \xrightarrow{\;\;\mathscr{F}_f{}^*(a)\;\;} \mathscr{F}_B{}^*T(f)(a)$$

$$\mathscr{F}_{gf}^*(a) \searrow \qquad \swarrow \mathscr{F}_g{}^*T(f)(a)$$

$$\mathscr{F}^*T(gf)(a)$$

is commutative. If $a \leqslant a'$ in $T(A)$ is given, then $T(f)(a) = b \leqslant b' = T(f)(a')$. With the same argument as for the uniqueness of $\mathscr{F}_f{}^*(a)$ one shows that the morphism $\mathscr{F}_A{}^*(a) \to \mathscr{F}_B{}^*(b')$ is uniquely determined. Therefore, the diagram

$$\mathscr{F}_A{}^*(a) \xrightarrow{\;\mathscr{F}_A{}^*(x)\;} \mathscr{F}_A{}^*(a')$$
$$\mathscr{F}_f{}^*(a) \downarrow \qquad\qquad \downarrow \mathscr{F}_f{}^*(a')$$
$$\mathscr{F}_B{}^*(b) \xrightarrow{\;\mathscr{F}_B{}^*(y)\;} \mathscr{F}_B{}^*(b')$$

is commutative, where x is a representative for $a \leqslant a'$ and $y = T(f)(x)$ is a representative for $b \leqslant b'$. Consequently, $\mathscr{F}_f{}^*$ is a natural transformation.

Now we assume that $\mathscr{C}$ is a Grothendieck category. Then there exist direct limits of the functors $\mathscr{F}_A{}^*$. By Section 2.5 there exists a morphism

$$\varinjlim T(f) : \varinjlim \mathscr{F}_B{}^*T(f) \to \varinjlim \mathscr{F}_B{}^*$$

Furthermore, $\mathscr{F}_f{}^*$ induces a morphism

$$\varinjlim \mathscr{F}_f{}^* : \varinjlim \mathscr{F}_A{}^* \to \varinjlim \mathscr{F}_B{}^* T(f)$$

The composition of these two morphisms will be denoted by $(R\mathscr{F})(f)$ and $\varinjlim \mathscr{F}_A{}^*$ with $(R\mathscr{F})(A)$. Then $(R\mathscr{F})(f) : (R\mathscr{F})(A) \to (R\mathscr{F})(B)$ is defined such that the diagram

$$
\begin{array}{ccc}
\mathscr{F}_A{}^*(a) & \xrightarrow{\;\mathscr{F}_f{}^*(a)\;} & \mathscr{F}_B{}^*(b) \\
\downarrow & & \downarrow \\
(R\mathscr{F})(A) & \xrightarrow{\;(R\mathscr{F})(f)\;} & (R\mathscr{F})(B)
\end{array}
$$

is commutative. $(R\mathscr{F})(f)$ is uniquely determined by the fact that all diagrams of this form are commutative for all $a \in T(A)$. The vertical arrows are the injections into the direct limit.

$\mathscr{F}_{1_A}(a) = 1_{\mathscr{F}_A{}^*(a)}$ implies $(R\mathscr{F})(1_A) = 1_{(R\mathscr{F})(A)}$. $\mathscr{F}_g{}^*(b)\,\mathscr{F}_f{}^*(a) = \mathscr{F}_{gf}^*(a)$ implies $(R\mathscr{F})(g)(R\mathscr{F})(f) = (R\mathscr{F})(gf)$. Hence, $(R\mathscr{F})$ is a functor from $\mathscr{A}$ to $\mathscr{C}$. The construction of $\mathscr{F}_A{}^*(a)$ defines a morphism $\mathscr{F}(A) \to \mathscr{F}_A{}^*(a)$ such that for all $a \leqslant a'$ the diagram

$$
\begin{array}{ccc}
 & \mathscr{F}(A) & \\
 \swarrow & & \searrow \\
\mathscr{F}_A{}^*(a) & \xrightarrow{\hspace{3cm}} & \mathscr{F}_A{}^*(a')
\end{array}
$$

is commutative. Thus we get a morphism $\mathscr{F}(A) \to \mathscr{F}_A{}^*(a) \to (R\mathscr{F})(A)$, which is independent of the choice of a. Since for $f : A \to B$, the diagram

$$
\begin{array}{ccc}
\mathscr{F}(A) & \xrightarrow{\;\mathscr{F}(f)\;} & \mathscr{F}(B) \\
\downarrow & & \downarrow \\
\mathscr{F}_A{}^*(a) & \xrightarrow{\;\mathscr{F}_f{}^*(a)\;} & \mathscr{F}_B{}^*(b)
\end{array}
$$

is commutative, also

$$
\begin{array}{ccc}
\mathscr{F}(A) & \xrightarrow{\;\mathscr{F}(f)\;} & \mathscr{F}(B) \\
\downarrow & & \downarrow \\
(R\mathscr{F})(A) & \xrightarrow{\;(R\mathscr{F})(f)\;} & (R\mathscr{F})(B)
\end{array}
$$

is commutative. The morphism $\mathscr{F}(A) \to (R\mathscr{F})(A)$ is a natural transformation, which will be denoted by $\rho : \mathscr{F} \to (R\mathscr{F})$.

LEMMA 2. *Let $\mathcal{G} : \mathcal{A} \to \mathcal{C}$ be a left exact functor and $\varphi : \mathcal{F} \to \mathcal{G}$ be a natural transformation. Then there exists exactly one natural transformation $\psi : (R\mathcal{F}) \to \mathcal{G}$ such that $\psi\rho = \varphi$.*

Proof. Let $a \in T(A)$. Then, be the left exactness of $\mathcal{G}$, we get a commutative diagram with exact rows

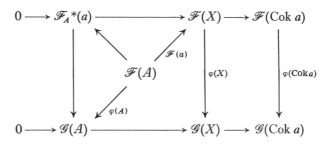

where $\mathcal{F}_A{}^*(a) \to \mathcal{G}(A)$ is uniquely determined by φ. If $a \leqslant a'$, then by this uniqueness the diagram

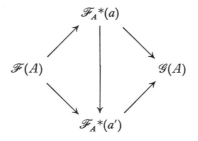

is commutative. Hence we can factor $\varphi(A)$ through $(R\mathcal{F})(A) = \varinjlim \mathcal{F}_A{}^*$:

$$\varphi(A) = (\mathcal{F}(A) \xrightarrow{\ \rho(A)\ } (R\mathcal{F})(A) \xrightarrow{\ \psi(A)\ } \mathcal{G}(A))$$

where $\psi(A)$ is uniquely determined by this property, for $(R\mathcal{F})(A)$ is a direct limit.

We still have to show that ψ is a natural transformation. Let $f : A \to B$ be a morphism in A. Let $b = T(f)(a)$. Then by two-fold application of the first diagram in this proof, together with the construction of b, we get that

$$
\begin{array}{ccc}
\mathcal{F}_A{}^*(a) & \longrightarrow & \mathcal{F}_B{}^*(b) \\
\downarrow & & \downarrow \\
\mathcal{G}(A) & \longrightarrow & \mathcal{G}(B)
\end{array}
$$

is commutative. The direct limit preserves this commutativity, that is, ψ is a natural transformation.

LEMMA 3. *If $f : A \to B$ is a monomorphism in $\mathscr{A}$, then $(R\mathscr{F})(f)$ is a monomorphism in $\mathscr{C}$.*

Proof. Similar to the definition of $\mathscr{F}_j{}^*$ we define a natural transformation $\mathscr{F}_j{}^+ : \mathscr{F}_A{}^* T^+(f) \to \mathscr{F}_B{}^*$ by the commutative diagram

$$
\begin{array}{ccccc}
0 \longrightarrow & \mathscr{F}_A{}^*(bf) & \longrightarrow & \mathscr{F}(Y) & \longrightarrow & \mathscr{F}(\mathrm{Cok}\ bf) \\
& \downarrow & & \downarrow{\scriptstyle \mathscr{F}(1_Y)} & & \downarrow \\
0 \longrightarrow & \mathscr{F}_B{}^*(b) & \longrightarrow & \mathscr{F}(Y) & \longrightarrow & \mathscr{F}(\mathrm{Cok}\ b)
\end{array}
$$

As for $\mathscr{F}_j{}^*$, here again one proves that $\mathscr{F}_j{}^+$ is a natural transformation. But the above diagram implies also that $\mathscr{F}_j{}^+(b) : \mathscr{F}_A{}^*(bf) \to \mathscr{F}_B{}^*(b)$ is a monomorphism because $\mathscr{F}_A{}^*(bf) \to \mathscr{F}(Y)$ is a monomorphism. Since, by hypothesis on $\mathscr{C}$, the Grothendieck condition holds, also

$$
\varinjlim \mathscr{F}_j{}^+ : \varinjlim \mathscr{F}_A{}^* T^+(f) \to \varinjlim \mathscr{F}_B{}^*
$$

is a monomorphism (Section 4.7, Theorem 1).

Let $a \in T(A)$ and $b = T(f)(a)$. The commutative diagram

$$
\begin{array}{ccc}
A & \xrightarrow{\ a\ } & X \\
{\scriptstyle 1_A}\downarrow & & \downarrow \\
A & \xrightarrow{\ bf\ } & Y \\
{\scriptstyle f}\downarrow & & \downarrow{\scriptstyle 1_Y} \\
B & \dashrightarrow{\ b\ } & Y
\end{array}
$$

implies that $\mathscr{F}_j{}^*(a)$ may be factored through

$$
\mathscr{F}_j{}^+(T(f)(a)) : \mathscr{F}_A{}^* T^+(f)\, T(f)(a) \to \mathscr{F}_B{}^* T(f)(a)
$$

where the morphism $\mathscr{F}_A{}^*(a) \to \mathscr{F}_A{}^* T^+(f)\, T(f)(a)$ is induced by $a \leqslant T^+(f)\, T(f)(a)$. This factorization is preserved by the direct limit. Observe that the morphisms $\mathscr{F}_A{}^*(a) \to \mathscr{F}_A{}^* T^+(f)\, T(f)(a)$ give the identity after the application of the direct limit. This implies the assertion of the lemma.

LEMMA 4. *Let $\mathscr{F} : \mathscr{A} \to \mathscr{C}$ be an additive functor which preserves monomorphisms. Then $(R\mathscr{F})$ is left exact.*

Proof. Let $a \leqslant a'$ in $T(A)$ be given. First, we show that the morphism $\mathscr{F}_A{}^*(x) : \mathscr{F}_A{}^*(a) \to \mathscr{F}_A{}^*(a')$ is a monomorphism. We form the cofiber product

$$
\begin{array}{ccc}
A & \xrightarrow{\ a\ } & X \\
{\scriptstyle a'}\downarrow & & \downarrow{\scriptstyle x} \\
Y & \longrightarrow & Z
\end{array}
$$

The composed morphism $a'' : A \to Z$ is a monomorphism because in the cofiber product the morphism $X \to Z$ is a monomorphism. Thus we get a diagram

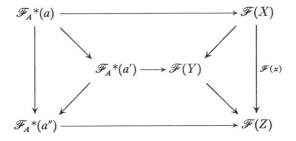

where the two inner quadrangles and the outer quadrangle are commutative, but not necessarily the right triangle. However, because of $a \leqslant a' \leqslant a''$ the left triangle is commutative. Since by hypothesis $\mathscr{F}(x)$ is a monomorphism, we have $\mathscr{F}_A{}^*(a) \to \mathscr{F}(Z)$ and also $\mathscr{F}_A{}^*(a) \to \mathscr{F}_A{}^*(a')$ are monomorphisms.

Let an exact sequence $0 \to A \xrightarrow{f} B \xrightarrow{g} C \to 0$ together with an object $b \in T(B)$ be given. Then we get a commutative diagram with exact rows

$$
\begin{array}{ccccccccc}
0 & \longrightarrow & A & \xrightarrow{\ f\ } & B & \xrightarrow{\ g\ } & C & \longrightarrow & 0 \\
& & {\scriptstyle 1_A}\downarrow & & {\scriptstyle b}\downarrow & & {\scriptstyle c}\downarrow & & \\
0 & \longrightarrow & A & \xrightarrow{\ bf\ } & Y & \longrightarrow & Z & \longrightarrow & 0
\end{array}
$$

where the right square is a cofiber product. The properties of the cofiber product imply that c is a monomorphism and $Y \to Z$ is an epimorphism. By construction, we have $A \subseteq \mathrm{Ker}(Y \to Z)$. To show the converse, we consider the corresponding diagram with Y/A instead of Z. Then we get a morphism $Z \to Y/A$ such that $(Y \to Y/A) = (Y \to Z \to Y/A)$. This means that $\mathrm{Ker}(Y \to Z) \subseteq A$. Since 1_A, b, and c are monomorphisms, we may complete this diagram by the 3×3 lemma. Let $U = \mathrm{Cok}(b)$

and $V = \mathrm{Cok}(c)$, then $U \cong V$ because $\mathrm{Cok}(1_A) = 0$. If we apply $\mathscr{F}$ to the diagram and form the corresponding kernels, then we get a commutative diagram with exact rows and columns

$$
\begin{array}{ccccc}
& & 0 & & 0 \\
& & \downarrow & & \downarrow \\
0 \longrightarrow \mathrm{Ker}(d) \longrightarrow & & \mathscr{F}_B{}^*(b) & \xrightarrow{\ d\ } & \mathscr{F}_C{}^*(c) \\
\downarrow & & \downarrow & & \downarrow \\
0 \longrightarrow \mathscr{F}_A{}^*(bf) \longrightarrow & & \mathscr{F}(Y) & \longrightarrow & \mathscr{F}(Z) \\
& & \downarrow & & \downarrow \\
& & \mathscr{F}(U) & \xrightarrow{\ 1\ } & \mathscr{F}(U)
\end{array}
$$

$(\mathscr{F}_A{}^*(bf) \to \mathscr{F}(Y) \to \mathscr{F}(U)) = 0$ implies that there is exactly one morphism $\mathscr{F}_A{}^*(bf) \to \mathscr{F}_B{}^*(b)$ which makes the diagram commutative. But then $(\mathscr{F}_A{}^*(bf) \to \mathscr{F}_B{}^*(b) \to \mathscr{F}_C{}^*(c)) = 0$, hence $\mathscr{F}_A{}^*(bf) \to \mathscr{F}_B{}^*(b)$ may be uniquely factored through $\mathrm{Ker}(d)$. Consequently, $\mathrm{Ker}(d) \cong \mathscr{F}_A{}^*(bf)$.

For $b \leqslant b'$, we get a commutative diagram with exact rows

$$
\begin{array}{ccccc}
0 \longrightarrow \mathscr{F}_A{}^*T^+(f)(b) & \longrightarrow & \mathscr{F}_B{}^*(b) & \longrightarrow & \mathscr{F}_C{}^*T(g)(b) \\
\downarrow & & \downarrow & & \downarrow \\
0 \longrightarrow \mathscr{F}_A{}^*T^+(f)(b') & \longrightarrow & \mathscr{F}_B{}^*(b') & \longrightarrow & \mathscr{F}_C{}^*T(g)(b')
\end{array}
$$

which after the application of the direct limit becomes the exact sequence

$$
0 \to \varinjlim \mathscr{F}_A{}^*T^+(f) \xrightarrow{\ \varinjlim \mathscr{F}_f{}^+\ } (R\mathscr{F})(B) \xrightarrow{\ \varinjlim \mathscr{F}_g{}^*\ } \varinjlim \mathscr{F}_C{}^*T(g)
$$

From the proof of Lemma 3, we know already that $\varinjlim \mathscr{F}_A{}^*T^+(f) = (R\mathscr{F})(A)$ and $\varinjlim \mathscr{F}_f{}^+ = (R\mathscr{F})(f)$. By definition $(R\mathscr{F})(g) = \varinjlim T(g) \varinjlim \mathscr{F}_g{}^*$. To prove the assertion of the lemma, it is sufficient to show that $\varinjlim T(g)$ is a monomorphism.

Since for $c \leqslant c'$ the morphism $\mathscr{F}_C{}^*(c) \to \mathscr{F}_C{}^*(c')$ is a monomorphism, the morphisms $\mathscr{F}_C{}^*(c) \to (R\mathscr{F})(C)$ are monomorphisms by Section 4.7, Lemma 3. By Section 4.7, Theorem 1(b), $\varinjlim T(g)$ is a monomorphism.

LEMMA 5. $(R\mathscr{F})$ is an additive functor.

Proof. Let A and B be objects in A and let $S = A \oplus B$ be the direct sum. Let an object $c \in T(S)$ be given. If we consider A by $A \to S \xrightarrow{c} X$

as a subobject of X and correspondingly $B \subseteq X$, then the morphism $X \rightarrow X/A \oplus X/B$ induced by $X \rightarrow X/A$ and $X \rightarrow X/B$ is a monomorphism because the kernel is $A \cap B = 0$. The morphism $(S \xrightarrow{c} X \rightarrow X/A \oplus X/B) = d$ is again a monomorphism and we have $c \leqslant d$ in $T(S)$. $(A \rightarrow S \rightarrow X/A) = 0$ and $(B \rightarrow S \rightarrow X/B) = 0$ imply that d is the direct sum of the monomorphisms $(A \rightarrow S \rightarrow X/B) = a$ and $(B \rightarrow S \rightarrow S/A) = b$. Hence the cokernel of d is the direct sum of the cokernels of a and b. Since $\mathscr{F}$ is an additive functor, $\mathscr{F}$ preserves the decompositions into direct sums. Since kernels preserve direct sums, the kernel of $\mathscr{F}(X/A \oplus X/B) \rightarrow \mathscr{F}(\text{Cok } d)$ is the direct sum of the kernels of $\mathscr{F}(X/A) \rightarrow \mathscr{F}(\text{Cok } b)$ and $\mathscr{F}(X/B) \rightarrow \mathscr{F}(\text{Cok } a)$. This construction preserves the corresponding injections and projections. Hence, $\mathscr{F}_S{}^*(d) = \mathscr{F}_A{}^*(a) \oplus \mathscr{F}_B{}^*(b)$. The application of the direct limit gives $(R\mathscr{F})(S) = (R\mathscr{F})(A) \oplus (R\mathscr{F})(B)$. In fact it is sufficient to form the direct limit over those objects $d \in T(S)$ that may be written as a direct sum of objects $a \in T(A)$ with objects $b \in T(B)$ because, to each object c, there exists such an object d with $c \leqslant d$.

LEMMA 6. $R : \mathfrak{A}(\mathscr{A}, \mathscr{C}) \rightarrow \mathfrak{A}(\mathscr{A}, \mathscr{C})$ *is a left exact functor.*

Proof.   Let $0 \rightarrow \mathscr{F} \xrightarrow{\alpha} \mathscr{G} \xrightarrow{\beta} \mathscr{H} \rightarrow 0$ be an exact sequence in $\mathfrak{A}(\mathscr{A}, \mathscr{C})$. For each $A \in \mathscr{A}$ and each $a \in T(A)$, we get a commutative diagram with exact rows and columns

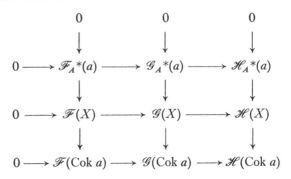

The morphisms $\mathscr{F}_A{}^*(a) \rightarrow \mathscr{G}_A{}^*(a)$ constructed in this way are obviously natural transformations with respect to $A \in \mathscr{A}$ and $a \in T(A)$. Thus we may apply the direct limit over $T(A)$ in the first row to get an exact sequence

$$0 \rightarrow (R\mathscr{F})(A) \xrightarrow{(R\alpha)(A)} (R\mathscr{G})(A) \xrightarrow{(R\beta)(A)} (R\mathscr{H})(A)$$

where the morphisms are uniquely determined by α and β and are natural in A by construction. Because of the uniqueness it is clear that R is a functor. R is a left exact functor by the definition of the exactness in $\mathfrak{A}(\mathscr{A}, \mathscr{C})$.

With these lemmas we now can solve easily the universal problem described in the beginning of this section.

THEOREM 1. *Let $\mathscr{A}$ be a small abelian category and $\mathscr{C}$ be a Grothendieck category. Then $\mathfrak{L}(\mathscr{A}, \mathscr{C})$ is a reflexive subcategory of $\mathfrak{A}(\mathscr{A}, \mathscr{C})$. The reflector $R^0 : \mathfrak{A}(\mathscr{A}, \mathscr{C}) \to \mathfrak{L}(\mathscr{A}, \mathscr{C})$ is called the zeroth right-derived functor.*

Proof. We know that it is sufficient to solve the corresponding universal problem. Let $\mathscr{F} \in \mathfrak{A}(\mathscr{A}, \mathscr{C})$, $\mathscr{G} \in \mathfrak{L}(\mathscr{A}, \mathscr{C})$, and a natural transformation $\varphi : \mathscr{F} \to \mathscr{G}$ be given. By two-fold application of Lemma 2, we get a commutative diagram

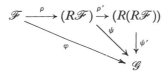

where ρ' is the natural transformation which corresponds to $(R\mathscr{F})$ and is constructed similarly to ρ. ψ and ψ' are uniquely determined by φ. By Lemma 3 $(R\mathscr{F})$ preserves monomorphisms. By Lemma 4, $(R(R\mathscr{F}))$ is left exact. Thus the universal problem is solved. Furthermore, $R^0\mathscr{F} = (R(R\mathscr{F}))$.

COROLLARY 1. *Under the hypotheses of Theorem 1, $\mathfrak{L}(\mathscr{A}, \mathscr{C})$ is an abelian category.*

Proof. The direct sums in $\mathfrak{L}(\mathscr{A}, \mathscr{C})$ and $\mathfrak{A}(\mathscr{A}, \mathscr{C})$ coincide because the direct sum of left exact functors is left exact. Furthermore, the null functor is left exact. By the theorem of Section 4.1, $\mathfrak{L}(\mathscr{A}, \mathscr{C})$ is an additive category.

Let $\varphi : \mathscr{F} \to \mathscr{G}$ be a natural transformation of left exact functors. The kernel of this morphism in Funct$(\mathscr{A}, \mathscr{C})$—hence, argumentwise formed—preserves kernels, that is, is left exact. We denote this functor by Ker(φ). This functor has, also in $\mathfrak{L}(\mathscr{A}, \mathscr{C})$, the property of a kernel. Let $\mathscr{H}$ be the cokernel of φ in Funct$(\mathscr{A}, \mathscr{C})$. Let $\psi : \mathscr{G} \to \mathscr{K}$ be a morphism in $\mathfrak{L}(\mathscr{A}, \mathscr{C})$ with $\psi\varphi = 0$. Then we get a commutative diagram

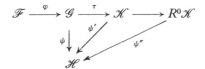

where ψ'' is uniquely determined by ψ. Hence $R^0\mathcal{K} = \text{Cok}(\varphi)$ is the cokernel of φ in $\mathfrak{L}(\mathscr{A}, \mathscr{C})$.

In $\mathfrak{A}(\mathscr{A}, \mathscr{C})$ we have an exact sequence

$$0 \to \text{Ker}(\tau) \to \mathscr{G} \overset{\tau}{\to} \mathscr{K} \to 0$$

Since R is left exact by Lemma 6, R^0 is also left exact. So we get the exact sequence

$$0 \to R^0\text{Ker}(\tau) \to \mathscr{G} \to R^0\mathscr{K}$$

in $\mathfrak{A}(\mathscr{A}, \mathscr{C})$ (and also in $\mathfrak{L}(\mathscr{A}, \mathscr{C})$) because $\mathscr{G} = R^0\mathscr{G}$, since $\mathscr{G}$ is left exact. Let $\mathscr{L}$ be the cokernel of $\text{Ker}(\varphi) \to \mathscr{F}$ in $\mathfrak{A}(\mathscr{A}, \mathscr{C})$. Then we get an exact sequence

$$0 \to \text{Ker}(\varphi) \to \mathscr{F} \to R^0\mathscr{L}$$

Since $\mathscr{L}$ is the coimage of φ in $\mathfrak{A}(\mathscr{A}, \mathscr{C})$ and $\text{Ker}(\tau)$ is the image of φ, we have that $\mathscr{L} \cong \text{Ker}(\tau)$. Hence we also have $R^0\mathscr{L} = R^0\text{Ker}(\tau)$. The last two exact sequences show that $R^0\mathscr{L}$ is the coimage of φ in $\mathfrak{L}(\mathscr{A}, \mathscr{C})$ and $R^0\text{Ker}(\tau)$ is the image of φ in $\mathfrak{L}(\mathscr{A}, \mathscr{C})$. Hence, $\mathfrak{L}(\mathscr{A}, \mathscr{C})$ is an abelian category.

THEOREM 2. *Let $\mathscr{A}$ be a small abelian category and $\textbf{Ab}$ be the category of abelian groups. Then $\mathfrak{L}(\mathscr{A}, \textbf{Ab})$ is a Grothendieck category with a generator.*

Proof. Funct$(\mathscr{A}, \textbf{Ab})$ has coproducts; coproducts of additive functors are additive, hence, $\mathfrak{A}(\mathscr{A}, \textbf{Ab})$ is cocomplete. Since $\mathfrak{L}(\mathscr{A}, \textbf{AB})$ is a full reflexive subcategory of $\mathfrak{A}(\mathscr{A}, \textbf{Ab})$, $\mathfrak{L}(\mathscr{A}, \textbf{Ab})$ is also cocomplete (Section 2.11, Theorem 3).

We show that the Grothendieck condition holds in Funct$(\mathscr{A}, \textbf{Ab})$. Let $\{\mathscr{F}_i\}$ be a directed family of subfunctors of $\mathscr{G}$ and $\mathscr{H}$ be a subfunctor of $\mathscr{G}$. Since subfunctors are kernels in Funct$(\mathscr{A}, \textbf{Ab})$, the corresponding monomorphisms are pointwise monomorphisms. Since limits and colimits are formed pointwise in Funct$(\mathscr{A}, \textbf{Ab})$, intersections and unions of functors are formed pointwise also:

$$\left(\left(\bigcup \mathscr{F}_i\right) \cap \mathscr{H}\right)(A) = \left(\left(\bigcup \mathscr{F}_i(A)\right) \cap \mathscr{H}(A)\right) = \bigcup (\mathscr{F}_i(A) \cap \mathscr{H}(A))$$

$$= \bigcup (\mathscr{F}_i \cap \mathscr{H})(A)$$

Thus direct limits in Funct$(\mathscr{A}, \textbf{Ab})$ are exact. Since they preserve additive functors, they are also exact $\mathfrak{A}(\mathscr{A}, \textbf{Ab})$. Since kernels in $\mathfrak{L}(\mathscr{A}, \textbf{Ab})$ coincide with kernels in $\mathfrak{A}(\mathscr{A}, \textbf{Ab})$, the monomorphisms also coincide. Direct limits preserve monomorphisms in $\mathfrak{A}(\mathscr{A}, \textbf{Ab})$, hence they also preserve monomorphisms in $\mathfrak{L}(\mathscr{A}, \mathbf{Ab})$, for direct limits of left exact functors are again left exact by the Grothendieck condition. Consequently, direct limits in $\mathfrak{L}(\mathscr{A}, \mathbf{Ab})$ are exact, that is, the Grothendieck condition holds.

To show that $\mathfrak{L}(\mathscr{A}, \mathbf{Ab})$ is locally small, it is sufficient to know that there is a generator in $\mathfrak{L}(\mathscr{A}, \mathbf{Ab})$. We claim $\coprod_{A \in \mathscr{A}} h^A = G$ is a generator. First, h^A is left exact for all $A \in \mathscr{A}$. Then the coproduct of left exact functors is left exact. (Section 2.7, Corollary 2), hence $G \in \mathfrak{L}(\mathscr{A}, \mathbf{Ab})$. Let φ and ψ be two different natural transformations from $\mathscr{F}$ to $\mathscr{G}$ in $\mathfrak{L}(\mathscr{A}, \mathbf{Ab})$. Then there is at least one $A \in \mathscr{A}$ with $\varphi(A) \neq \psi(A)$. Hence the product morphisms from $\prod_{A \in \mathscr{A}} \mathscr{F}(A)$ to $\prod_{A \in \mathscr{A}} \mathscr{G}(A)$ are different. By the Yoneda lemma these are induced by the morphisms $\mathrm{Mor}_f(G, \varphi)$ and $\mathrm{Mor}_f(G, \psi)$ because we have $\mathrm{Mor}_f(G, \mathscr{F}) \simeq \prod_{A \in \mathscr{A}} \mathscr{F}(A)$ and $\mathrm{Mor}_f(G, \mathscr{G}) \simeq \prod_{A \in \mathscr{A}} \mathscr{G}(A)$. Since $\mathscr{F}(A) \neq \varnothing$ for all $A \in \mathscr{A}$, also $\mathrm{Mor}_f(G, \mathscr{F}) \neq \varnothing$ for all $\mathscr{F} \in \mathfrak{L}(\mathscr{A}, \mathbf{Ab})$. Consequently, G is a generator for $\mathfrak{L}(\mathscr{A}, \mathbf{Ab})$.

COROLLARY 2. $\mathfrak{L}(\mathscr{A}, \mathbf{Ab})$ *is an abelian category with an injective cogenerator.*

Proof. The corollary is implied by Section 4.9, Corollary 3.

THEOREM 3. *The contravariant representation functor* $h : \mathscr{A} \to \mathfrak{L}(\mathscr{A}, \mathbf{Ab})$ *is full, faithful, and exact.*

Proof. We denote the injective cogenerator of $\mathfrak{L}(\mathscr{A}, \mathbf{Ab})$ by $\mathscr{K}$. The functor $\mathrm{Mor}_f(-, \mathscr{K}) : \mathfrak{L}(\mathscr{A}, \mathbf{Ab}) \to \mathbf{Ab}$ is faithful and exact by definition of $\mathscr{K}$. By Section 4.3, Lemma 2 and Section 2.12, Lemma 1, a sequence in $\mathfrak{L}(\mathscr{A}, \mathbf{Ab})$ is exact if and only if the image under $\mathrm{Mor}_f(-, \mathscr{K})$ is exact. Let $0 \to A \to B \to C \to 0$ be an exact sequence in $\mathscr{A}$. Then the sequence $0 \to h^C \to h^B \to h^A$ is exact, since for all $D \in \mathscr{A}$ the sequence $0 \to h^C(D) \to h^B(D) \to h^A(D)$ is exact and since kernels in $\mathfrak{L}(\mathscr{A}, \mathbf{Ab})$ are formed pointwise. Thus the sequences $\mathrm{Mor}_f(h^A, \mathscr{K}) \to \mathrm{Mor}_f(h^B, \mathscr{K}) \to \mathrm{Mor}_f(h^C, \mathscr{K}) \to 0$ and $\mathscr{K}(A) \to \mathscr{K}(B) \to \mathscr{K}(C) \to 0$ are exact. But $\mathscr{K}$ is a left exact functor, thus even $0 \to \mathscr{K}(A) \to \mathscr{K}(B) \to \mathscr{K}(C) \to 0$ and also $0 \to \mathrm{Mor}_f(h^A, \mathscr{K}) \to \mathrm{Mor}_f(h^B, \mathscr{K}) \to \mathrm{Mor}_f(h^C, \mathscr{K}) \to 0$ are exact. Thus by the above remark

$$0 \to h^C \to h^B \to h^A \to 0$$

is exact. We know already from Section 2.12, Proposition 2 that the representation functor is full and faithful.

4.14   Embedding Theorems

We have investigated the importance of full faithful functors in Section 2.12. For abelian categories, there is an additional very important notion, namely that of an exact functor. Again the behavior of functors with respect to diagrams is of interest. Since the corresponding diagram schemes, however, are not abelian categories in general, we shall have to reformulate the exactness.

Let us discuss the example of a part of the assertion of the 3×3 lemma. Given a commutative diagram with exact columns and an exact first and second row in an abelian category $\mathscr{C}$,

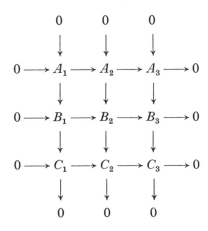

then the third row is also exact. How can we formulate this assertion in the language of diagram schemes? First, let a diagram scheme $\mathscr{D}$ with the corresponding objects $A_i{}'$, $B_i{}'$, $C_i{}'$ $(i = 1, 2, 3)$ and $0'$ be given. When we define the morphisms of $\mathscr{D}$, we may already take into account the existing commutativity relations. Let $\mathscr{F}$ be the functor which maps $\mathscr{D}$ to our given diagram. The assertions about the exactness have to be checked in $\mathscr{C}$. But we can say in $\mathscr{D}$ for which pairs of morphisms we have to check the exactness, namely for

$$(0' \to A_1{}'', A_1{}' \to A_2{}') \ ,..., \ (B_3{}' \to C_3{}', C_3{}' \to 0')$$

however, not for

$$(0' \to C_1{}', C_1{}' \to C_2{}'), \quad (C_1{}' \to C_2{}', C_2{}' \to C_3{}') \quad \text{and} \quad (C_2{}' \to C_3{}', C_3{}' \to 0')$$

If these pairs of morphisms become exact after the application of $\mathscr{F}$, then by the 3×3 lemma also the pairs $(0' \to C_1{}', C_1{}' \to C_2{}'),...,$

$(C_2' \to C_3', C_3' \to 0')$ will become exact after the application of $\mathscr{F}$. But here we did not yet take into account that $\mathscr{F}(0')$ shall be the zero object of $\mathscr{C}$. Certainly we can ask for this property separate from the exactness conditions. But there is an exactness condition which implies this condition automatically. If $(0' \xrightarrow{1} 0', 0' \xrightarrow{1} 0')$ becomes exact after the application of $\mathscr{F}$, then $\mathscr{F}(0')$ can only be a zero object of $\mathscr{C}$. Later we shall express other conditions by exactness conditions. First, we want to formalize the considerations we made up to now.

Let $\mathscr{D}$ be a diagram scheme. A set E of pairs of morphisms in $\mathscr{D}$ is called a set of *exactness conditions* if we have $R(a) = D(b)$ for each pair $(a, b) \in E$, that is, if the two morphisms in a pair may be composed in $\mathscr{D}$. Let $\mathscr{F} : \mathscr{D} \to \mathscr{C}$ be a diagram over $\mathscr{D}$ in $\mathscr{C}$. We say that $\mathscr{F}$ satisfies the exactness conditions E if for each pair $(a, b) \in E$ the sequence

$$\mathscr{F}(D(a)) \xrightarrow{\mathscr{F}(a)} \mathscr{F}(R(a)) \xrightarrow{\mathscr{F}(b)} \mathscr{F}(R(b))$$

is exact. Let us denote by E_1 the exactness conditions for the zero object and the exactness of the columns and the first and second row and by E_2 the exactness conditions for the exactness of the last row of the given diagram, then the 3×3 lemma may be formulated in the following way. Each diagram $\mathscr{F}$ which satisfies the exactness conditions E_1 also satisfies the exactness conditions E_2.

If $\mathscr{F}$ satisfies a set of given exactness conditions, then it is possible that certain parts of the diagram become commutative where the commutativity in $\mathscr{D}$ was not given or not recognizable. The commutativity of diagrams may also be expressed by a set K of pairs of morphisms in $\mathscr{D}$ for which $(a, b) \in K$ always implies $D(a) = D(b)$ and $R(a) = R(b)$. Such a set K is also called a set of *commutativity conditions*. We say that $\mathscr{F}$ satisfies the commutativity conditions K if for each pair $(a, b) \in K$ we have $\mathscr{F}(a) = \mathscr{F}(b)$. An *exact categorical statement* in an abelian category $\mathscr{C}$ with respect to the diagram scheme $\mathscr{D}$ with the exactness conditions E and E' and the commutativity conditions K and K' is an assertion of the following form: Each diagram $\mathscr{F}$ over $\mathscr{D}$ in $\mathscr{C}$ which satisfies the exactness conditions E and the commutativity conditions K satisfies also the exactness conditions E' and the commutativity conditions K'.

Since the identities and compositions of morphisms may already be formulated in $\mathscr{D}$ and are preserved by the functor $\mathscr{F}$ some of the notions in an abelian category may be defined by exactness and commutativity conditions. Since we are only interested in functors $\mathscr{F}$ which satisfy the given exactness and commutativity conditions, we can formulate the defining exactness and commutativity conditions in $\mathscr{C}$ for the particular notions independently of the diagram scheme $\mathscr{D}$.

The following assertions hold in any abelian category $\mathscr{C}$:

$A = 0$ if and only if $A \xrightarrow{1} A \xrightarrow{1} A$ is exact.
$(A \to B) = 0$ if and only if $A \to B \xrightarrow{1} B$ is exact.
$A \to B$ is a monomorphism if and only if $0 \to A \to B$ is exact.
$(A \to B) = \mathrm{Ker}(B \to C)$ if and only if $0 \to A \to B \to C$ is exact.
$S = A \oplus B$ with projections and injections $S \to A$, $S \to B$, $A \to S$, and $B \to S$ respectively if and only if $A \to S \to B$ is exact, $B \to S \to A$ is exact, $(A \to S \to A) = (A \xrightarrow{1} A)$, and $(B \to S \to B) = (B \xrightarrow{1} B)$.

$C \to S$ is the morphism into the direct sum induced by $C \to A$ and $C \to B$ if and only if $(C \to S \to A) = (C \to A)$ and $(C \to S \to B) = (C \to B)$.

The diagram

is a fiber product if and only if $0 \to P \to A \oplus B \to C$ is exact.

Beyond these examples there are many more notions which may be represented in a similar way. In particular, finite limits and colimits together with their universal properties may be defined in this way.

LEMMA 1. *Let $\mathscr{G} : \mathscr{B} \to \mathscr{C}$ be a faithful exact functor between abelian categories. Assume that the exact categorical statement defined by $(\mathscr{D}, E, K, E', K')$ is true in $\mathscr{C}$. Then it is also true in $\mathscr{B}$.*

Proof. We have to show that a diagram $\mathscr{F} : \mathscr{D} \to \mathscr{B}$ which satisfies the exactness conditions E and the commutativity conditions K also satisfies the exactness conditions E' and the commutativity conditions K'. By hypothesis, $\mathscr{G}\mathscr{F} : \mathscr{D} \to \mathscr{C}$ satisfies the conditions E' and K'. In fact, if $\mathscr{F}$ satisfies E and K, then $\mathscr{G}\mathscr{F}$ satisfies conditions E and K because $\mathscr{G}$ is exact. Since $\mathscr{G}$ is faithful, the conditions K' have to be satisfied already in $\mathscr{B}$. We only have to show that a sequence $A \to B \to C$ in $\mathscr{B}$ is exact if $\mathscr{G}(A) \to \mathscr{G}(B) \to \mathscr{G}(C)$ is exact in $\mathscr{C}$. In fact, then E' also holds in $\mathscr{B}$.

Let $A \xrightarrow{f} B \xrightarrow{g} C$ in $\mathscr{B}$ be not exact. Then $(A \to B \to C) \neq 0$ or $(\mathrm{Ker}(g) \to B \to \mathrm{Cok}(f)) \neq 0$. Since $\mathscr{G}$ is faithful and exact, $\mathscr{G}$ preserves kernels, cokernels, and nonzero morphisms. Hence $(\mathscr{G}(A) \to \mathscr{G}(B) \to \mathscr{G}(C)) \neq 0$ or $(\mathrm{Ker}(\mathscr{G}(g)) \to \mathscr{G}(B) \to \mathrm{Cok}(\mathscr{G}(f))) \neq 0$. Hence, also $\mathscr{G}(A) \to \mathscr{G}(B) \to \mathscr{G}(C)$ cannot be exact (Section 4.3, Lemma 1).

With this lemma we can test the truth of an exact categorical statement via faithful exact functors. Since a diagram consists always only of a set of objects and morphisms, it is interesting to know if each diagram in an abelian category is already in a small abelian category. Later on we shall see that for small abelian categories there are faithful exact test functors into the category of abelian groups.

PROPOSITION 1. *Each set of objects in an abelian category lies in a small full exact abelian subcategory.*

Proof. Let $\mathscr{A}_0$ be the full subcategory of the abelian category $\mathscr{C}$ with the given set of objects in $\mathscr{C}$ as objects. Now we construct a sequence of full subcategories $\mathscr{A}_i$ of $\mathscr{C}$ by the following construction. If $\mathscr{A}_i$ is given, then let $\mathscr{A}_{i+1}$ consist of the kernels and cokernels of all morphisms of $\mathscr{A}_i$ as well as of all direct sums of objects of $\mathscr{A}_i$ where the kernels, cokernels, and direct sums have to be formed in $\mathscr{C}$ and where we take for each morphism only one kernel and cokernel and to each finite set of objects only one direct sum. Let $\mathscr{A}_{i+1}$ be the full subcategory of $\mathscr{C}$ defined by these objects. Since $\mathscr{A}_i$ is small also $\mathscr{A}_{i+1}$ is small. Furthermore, we have $\mathscr{A}_i \subseteq \mathscr{A}_{i+1}$ if, for example, we use A as the kernel of $0 : A \to A$. Thus $\mathscr{A}_0$ is in $\mathscr{B} = \bigcup_{i=0}^{\infty} \mathscr{A}_i$ and $\mathscr{B}$ is a small full exact abelian subcategory of $\mathscr{C}$. By definition $\mathscr{B}$ is a small full subcategory. $\mathscr{B}$ contains the zero object of $\mathscr{C}$ as kernel of an identity and the morphism sets of $\mathscr{B}$ form abelian groups in the same way as they do in $\mathscr{C}$. Furthermore, for each finite set of objects in $\mathscr{B}$ there exists a direct sum in $\mathscr{B}$ since the finite set has to lie already in one of the $\mathscr{A}_i$. Therefore, $\mathscr{B}$ is an additive category. Furthermore, kernels and cokernels of morphisms in $\mathscr{B}$ coincide with kernels and cokernels in $\mathscr{C}$ by definition, and they exist. The natural morphism from the coimage into the image of a morphism in $\mathscr{B}$ coincides with the one formed in $\mathscr{C}$, so it has an inverse morphism which is also in $\mathscr{B}$. Thus $\mathscr{B}$ is abelian and the embedding is exact.

THEOREM 1. *Let $\mathscr{A}$ be a small abelian category. Then there exists a covariant faithful exact functor $\mathscr{F} : \mathscr{A} \to \mathbf{Ab}$ from $\mathscr{A}$ into the category of abelian groups.*

Proof. We apply Section 4.13, Theorem 3 and Corollary 2. The contravariant representation functor $h : \mathscr{A} \to \mathfrak{L}(\mathscr{A}, \mathbf{Ab})$ is faithful and exact. Let $\mathscr{K}$ be an injective cogenerator in $\mathfrak{L}(\mathscr{A}, \mathbf{Ab})$. Then the contravariant representable functor $\mathrm{Mor}_f(-, \mathscr{K}) : \mathfrak{L}(\mathscr{A}, \mathbf{Ab}) \to \mathbf{Ab})$ is faithful and exact by the definition of the injective cogenerator. The composition of these two functors is covariant, faithful, and exact and we have

$\mathrm{Mor}_f(-, \mathscr{K})h \cong \mathscr{K}$. Hence, $\mathscr{K} : \mathscr{A} \to \mathbf{Ab}$ is a covariant faithful exact functor.

Now by Lemma 1, it is sufficient to test the truth of exact categorical statements only in the category of abelian groups $\mathbf{Ab}$. This is also true for an arbitrary abelian category $\mathscr{C}$, since each diagram is already in a small abelian category $\mathscr{A}$ by Proposition 1 and since the exactness in $\mathscr{A}$ and in $\mathscr{C}$ is the same. Since we can check the exactness and equality of morphisms in $\mathbf{Ab}$ elementwise, many proofs will be considerably simplified. We formulate this fact in the metatheorem that follows.

METATHEOREM 1.   *An exact categorical statement which is true in the category $\mathbf{Ab}$ of abelian groups is true in each abelian category.*

As an application of this metatheorem, we show that in each abelian category the lattice of subobjects of an object is modular. A lattice is called *modular* if for elements A, B, and C of the lattice $A \subseteq C$ implies $A \cup (B \cap C) = (A \cup B) \cap C$. We always have $A \cup (B \cap C) \subseteq (A \cup B) \cap C$ by the hypothesis $A \subseteq C$. To prove the equality in the lattice of the subobjects, we have to show that the morphism $A \cup (B \cap C) \subseteq (A \cup B) \cap C$ is an isomorphism. For the formulation of an intersection and a union, we may use finite limits and colimits. Hence, the modularity of the lattice of the subobjects of an object in an abelian category is an exact categorical assertion. We need check it in $\mathbf{Ab}$ only. But if $c \in (A \cup B) \cap C$, then $c = a + b$ with $a \in A$ and $b \in B$. Since $A \subseteq C$ we get $c - a = b \in C$, hence $b \in B \cap C$. This proves that $c = a + b \in A \cup (B \cap C)$, that is, $A \cup (B \cap C) = (A \cup B) \cap C$.

COROLLARY 1.   *The lattice of the subobjects of an object in an abelian category is modular.*

With our example of the 3×3 lemma we were only able to cover a part of the lemma as an exact categorical statement. Although in this case it is easy to prove the existence of the morphisms in the lower row, which make the diagram commutative, it is of principal interest to carry even this task over into another category by a suitable functor. This problem deals with two diagram schemes with the same objects where the morphisms of the first diagram scheme are also morphisms of the second diagram scheme, but in the second diagram scheme there are more morphisms.

Let $\mathscr{D}$ be a diagram scheme with the exactness conditions E and the commutativity conditions K. Let $\mathscr{D}'$ be another diagram scheme with the exactness conditions E' and the commutativity conditions K'. Let

$\mathscr{I} : \mathscr{D} \to \mathscr{D}'$ be a functor which is bijective on the objects. ($\mathscr{I}$, $\mathscr{D}$, $\mathscr{D}'$, E, K, E', K') defines a *full exact categorical statement* with respect to an abelian category $\mathscr{C}$ of the following form: To each diagram $\mathscr{F} : \mathscr{D} \to \mathscr{C}$ which satisfies the exactness conditions E and the commutativity conditions K, there exists a diagram $\mathscr{F}' : \mathscr{D}' \to \mathscr{C}$ with $\mathscr{F}'\mathscr{I} = \mathscr{F}$ which satisfies the exactness conditions E' and the commutativity conditions K'. Hence the 3×3 lemma is a full exact categorical statement which is true in each abelian category.

LEMMA 2. *Let $\mathscr{G} : \mathscr{B} \to \mathscr{C}$ be a full faithful exact functor between abelian categories. Let the full exact categorical statement defined by ($\mathscr{I}$, $\mathscr{D}$, $\mathscr{D}'$, E, K, E', K') be true in $\mathscr{C}$. Then it is also true in $\mathscr{B}$.*

Proof. Assume that $\mathscr{F} : \mathscr{D} \to \mathscr{B}$ satisfies the conditions E and K. Then also $\mathscr{G}\mathscr{F} : \mathscr{D} \to \mathscr{C}$ satisfies the conditions E and K, because $\mathscr{G}$ is exact. Hence there is a diagram $\mathscr{F}'' : \mathscr{D}' \to \mathscr{C}$ which satisfies the conditions E' and K'. By Section 1.15, Lemma 2, $\mathscr{F}''$ may be uniquely factored through $\mathscr{B}$ with a diagram $\mathscr{F}' : \mathscr{D}' \to \mathscr{B}$ and $\mathscr{F}'' = \mathscr{G}\mathscr{F}'$. Since $\mathscr{G}$ is faithful and exact and since $\mathscr{G}\mathscr{F}'$ satisfies the conditions E' and K', so does $\mathscr{F}'$. This has already been proved in Lemma 1.

By Proposition 1 we may decide each full exact categorical statement already in a small abelian category, namely in the small full exact abelian subcategory which contains all objects of the diagram $\mathscr{F} : \mathscr{D} \to \mathscr{C}$. This category certainly depends on the choice of the diagram $\mathscr{F}$. However, if we show that a full exact categorical statement in each small full exact abelian subcategory of $\mathscr{C}$ is true, then it is also true in $\mathscr{C}$. For the following considerations, we still need another theorem.

THEOREM 2. *Let $\mathscr{C}$ be a cocomplete abelian category with a projective generator P. Let $\mathscr{A}$ be a small full exact abelian subcategory of $\mathscr{C}$. Then there exists a full faithful exact covariant functor $\mathscr{F} : \mathscr{A} \to \mathbf{Mod}_R$ from $\mathscr{A}$ into a category of R-modules.*

Proof. The proof goes analogously to the proof of Section 4.11, Theorem 1. Since P is not finite, we shall not try find epimorphisms from coproducts of P with itself to the particular objects, but only epimorphisms from some projective generator. Since each coproduct of copies of P is again a projective generator we choose the number of factors large enough such that each object A of $\mathscr{A}$ may be reached by an epimorphism $\coprod P \to A$. This is possible because $\mathscr{A}$ is small. Let us call $\coprod P = P'$ and $R = \mathrm{Hom}_C(P', P')$. Since P' is a projective generator, the functor $\mathrm{Hom}_{\mathscr{C}}(P', -) : \mathscr{C} \to \mathbf{Mod}_R$ is faithful and exact. We still have to show that the restriction $\mathscr{F}$ of $\mathrm{Hom}_{\mathscr{C}}(P', -)$ to the subcategory $\mathscr{A}$ is full. Then $\mathscr{F}$ is full, faithful, and exact. Let $\mathscr{G} = \mathrm{Hom}_{\mathscr{C}}(P', -)$.

Let $f : \mathscr{F}A \to \mathscr{F}B$ be given for objects A, $B \in \mathscr{A}$. We have to find a morphism $f' : A \to B$ with $Ff' = f$. Let $a : P' \to A$ and $b : P' \to B$ be epimorphisms. Since the ring R is projective we get a commutative diagram

$$\mathrm{Ker}(\mathscr{G}a) \longrightarrow R \xrightarrow{\ \mathscr{G}a\ } \mathscr{F}A$$

$$\mathscr{G}g \downarrow \qquad\qquad \downarrow f$$

$$R \xrightarrow{\ \mathscr{G}b\ } \mathscr{F}B$$

The morphism $R \to R$ may be represented in the form $\mathscr{G}g$ because $\mathrm{Hom}_{\mathscr{C}}(P', P') \cong \mathrm{Hom}_R(R, R)$ by the functor $\mathrm{Hom}_{\mathscr{C}}(P', -)$. Since $\mathscr{G}$ is exact, $\mathrm{Ker}(\mathscr{G}a) \cong \mathscr{G}(\mathrm{Ker}(a))$. Since $\mathscr{G}$ is faithful, $(\mathrm{Ker}(\mathscr{G}a) \to R \to R \to \mathscr{F}B) = 0$ implies $(\mathrm{Ker}(a) \to P' \to P' \to B) = 0$. Thus in the diagram

$$\mathrm{Ker}(a) \longrightarrow P' \xrightarrow{\ a\ } A$$

$$g \downarrow \qquad\qquad \downarrow f'$$

$$P' \xrightarrow{\ b\ } B$$

there exists exactly one morphism f' which makes the square commutative. Hence, the upper diagram becomes commutative also if we replace f by $\mathscr{F}f'$. But since $\mathscr{G}a$ is an epimorphism we get $f = \mathscr{F}f'$.

THEOREM 3 (Mitchell). *Let $\mathscr{A}$ be a small abelian category. Then there exists a covariant full faithful exact functor $\mathscr{F} : \mathscr{A} \to \mathbf{Mod}_R$ from $\mathscr{A}$ into a category of R-modules.*

Proof. The functor $h : \mathscr{A} \to \mathfrak{L}(\mathscr{A}, \mathbf{Ab})$ is contravariant, full, faithful, and exact. Let h^0 be the corresponding functor from $\mathscr{A}$ into the category $\mathfrak{L}^0(\mathscr{A}, \mathbf{Ab})$ dual to $\mathfrak{L}(\mathscr{A}, \mathbf{Ab})$ which is cocomplete by Section 4.13 and has a projective generator. Then h^0 is covariant, full, faithful, and exact. Let $\mathscr{B}$ be the small full exact abelian subcategory of $\mathfrak{L}^0(\mathscr{A}, \mathbf{Ab})$ which is generated by $h^0(\mathscr{A})$ by Proposition 1. Then by Theorem 2, there exists a full faithful exact functor $\mathscr{B} \to \mathbf{Mod}_R$ for a ring R. Hence also $\mathscr{A} \to \mathscr{B} \to \mathbf{Mod}_R$ is covariant, full, faithful, and exact.

As in the case of the Metatheorem 1, Lemma 2 and Theorem 3 imply the following result.

METATHEOREM 2. *A full exact categorical statement which is true in all module categories is true in each abelian category.*

Now with this theorem we can also decide about the existence of morphisms in relatively simple categories, namely module categories where one can compute elementwise. So the 3×3 lemma need only be proved with these means in an arbitrary module category. This then implies that it holds in all abelian categories.

The best-known application of this theorem is the existence of the *connecting homomorphism.*

COROLLARY 2. *Let the diagram*

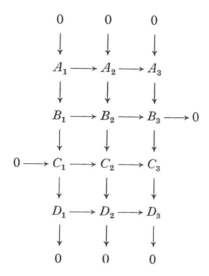

be commutative with exact rows and columns in an abelian category $\mathscr{C}$. Then there is a morphism $\delta : A_3 \to D_1$ called the connecting homomorphism such that the sequence

$$A_2 \to A_3 \to D_1 \to D_2$$

is exact.

Proof. The assertion of the corollary is a full exact categorical statement. So we need only check it in a module category. We define the following application

$$A_3 \ni a_3 \mapsto b_3 \mapsto b_2 \mapsto c_2 \mapsto c_1 \mapsto d_1 \in D_1$$

Here the elements are in the modules with the corresponding subscripts. Let b_2 be chosen such that b_2 is mapped onto b_3 by $B_2 \to B_3$. Since c_2 is mapped onto 0 by $C_2 \to C_3$, c_2 is already an element in C_1 which we denote by c_1. The only ambiguity of this application is the choice of

b_2 . This choice is unique up to a summand $b_1' \in B_1$. But we have $b_2 + b_1' \mapsto c_2 + c_1' \mapsto c_1 + c_1' \mapsto d_1$ because $(B_1 \to C_1 \to D_1) = 0$. Obviously this map is a homomorphism which we denote by $\delta : A_3 \to D_1$.

If $\delta(a_3) = 0$, then there exists a $b_1' \in B_1$ with $b_1' \mapsto c_1$ by $B_1 \to C_1$. Therefore, $b_2 - b_1' \mapsto 0$ by $B_2 \to C_2$. Hence, there exists exactly one a_2 with $a_2 \mapsto b_2 - b_1'$. But then $a_2 \mapsto a_3$ by $A_2 \to A_3$, hence $A_2 \to A_3 \to D_1$ is exact.

Let $d_1 \in D_1$ be given such that d_1 is mapped to 0 by $D_1 \to D_2$, then there exists a c_1 with $c_1 \mapsto d_1$ and c_1 is mapped to 0 by $C_1 \to C_2 \to D_2$. Hence there exists a b_2 with $b_2 \mapsto c_2$ and $c_1 \mapsto c_2$. Therefore, b_2 is mapped to 0 by $B_2 \to B_3 \to C_3$, that is, there exists an a_3 with $a_3 \mapsto b_3$ and $b_2 \mapsto b_3$. By definition of δ we have $\delta(a_3) = d_1$. Consequently, the sequence

$$A_2 \to A_3 \xrightarrow{\delta} D_1 \to D_2$$

is exact.

Problems

4.1. Show that Example 2 of Section 4.1 is not an abelian category.

4.2. The sequence $0 \to A \to B \to 0$ is exact if and only if $A \to B$ is an isomorphism.

4.3. Let $\mathscr{C}$ be an abelian category. If the following diagram in $\mathscr{C}$

$$
\begin{array}{ccccccccc}
0 & \longrightarrow & A & \xrightarrow{f} & B & \xrightarrow{g} & C & \longrightarrow & 0 \\
& & \downarrow{u} & & \downarrow{v} & & \downarrow{w} & & \\
0 & \longrightarrow & A' & \xrightarrow{f'} & B' & \xrightarrow{g'} & C' & \longrightarrow & 0
\end{array}
$$

is commutative and if both rows are short exact sequences, then: (1) if u and w are monomorphisms, then v is a monomorphism; (2) if u and w are epimorphisms, then v is an epimorphism.

4.4 Dualize Lemma 2 of Section 4.3.

4.5. Let $0 \to A \xrightarrow{f} B \xrightarrow{g} C \to 0$ be an exact sequence. The following are equivalent:
(1) f is a section.
(2) g is a retraction.
(3) $B = A \oplus C$ and $f : A \to A \oplus C$ is the injection with respect to A.

4.6. Show that the category of ordered abelian groups is not an abelian category. An abelian group G is *ordered* if G is an ordered set (Section 1.1, Example 2) such that $a \leqslant b$ implies $a + x \leqslant b + x$ for all $a, b, x \in G$. Let G and G' be ordered abelian groups. A homomorphism $f : G \to G'$ is called *order-preserving* if $a \leqslant b$ implies $f(a) \leqslant f(b)$. The ordered abelian groups together with the order-preserving homomorphisms form an additive category, the category of ordered abelian groups.

4.7. Show that the assertion of Section 4.5, Lemma 1 holds without the assumption that C/A is simple.

4.8. Find an object of finite length with infinitely many different subobjects in an abelian category.

4.9. Show that $_R\mathbf{Mod}$ is a Grothendieck category for each unitary associative ring R.

4.10. In a module category $_R\mathbf{Mod}$ the union (in the categorical sense) of submodules of a module is the sum (in the module theoretical sense) of these submodules.

4.11. Prove the Steinitz exchange theorem for vector spaces by Section 4.10, Theorem 5.

4.12. Show that in Section 4.9, Corollary 4 the module R/M for a local ring R is not a cogenerator, so that in general $\coprod R/M$ is not a cogenerator.

4.13. An additive functor between abelian categories is faithful if and only if it reflects exact sequences (Section 4.14, Lemma 1).

4.14. Does Section 4.10, Corollary 1 hold for arbitrary equationally defined algebras instead of R-modules?

4.15. (a) Let $M \in {}_R\mathbf{Mod}$. Let $\{G_i\}_{i \in I}$ be the set of large submodules of M and $\{E_j\}_{j \in J}$ be the set of simple submodules of M. Then $\bigcap G_i = \coprod_{j \in K} E_j$ for suitable subset $K \subseteq J$ and is called socle of M.

(b) $M \in {}_R\mathbf{Mod}$ is called *cocompact* if M is compact in $_R\mathbf{Mod}^0$. M is cocompact if and only if the socle of M is large in M and finitely generated.

4.16. Let $\mathscr{S} : \mathscr{C} \to \mathscr{D}$ be an additive functor between abelian categories with an exact right adjoint functor $\mathscr{T}$. Then $\mathscr{S}$ preserves injective objects.

4.17. Let $\mathscr{C}$ be an abelian cocomplete category with a finitely generated generator and let $G, G' \in \mathscr{C}$.

(a) If for all simple objects U there is a commutative diagram

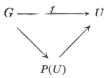

with an epimorphism f and a projective object $P(U)$, then G is a generator.

(b) If for all simple objects U there is a commutative diagram

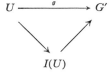

with a monomorphism g and a projective object $I(U)$, then G' is a cogenerator.

Appendix

Fundamentals of Set Theory

We shall give an outline of those facts of set theory which are not too well known from naïve set theory. As a basis we shall use the set of axioms of Gödel and Bernays. The difference between sets and classes and the consequences of the strong axiom of choice play an important part in the theory of categories. Since the axiomatic description of set theory is very formalistic, we shall try to express most of the formulas in ordinary language. Observe that, for an axiomatic representation of a theory, we prove theorems on and within this theory, but that the models which satisfy the axioms of this theory do not belong to the theory itself. So axiomatic set theory involves computations with the given formulas; the "class of all sets," however, or better, a model for the class of all sets will not be given. The axioms and the theorems derived from the axioms, however, should always have a meaning for naïve set theory.

We agree on the following *symbols*: class variables X, Y, Z,...; special classes $\varnothing$, $\mathfrak{U}$, A_1, A_2,...; set variables x, y, z,..., and formulas φ, ψ,... . We may use subscripts with the symbols so that we have countably many symbols at hand in this way. Equality $=$ and element of $\in$ are used between set variables, class variables, and special classes, where on both sides different kinds of these symbols may be used. Logical symbols are: "not" $\neg$, "or" $\vee$, "and" $\wedge$, "implies" $\Rightarrow$, "if and only if" $\Leftrightarrow$, "there exists" $\vee$, "there exists exactly one" $\vee!$, and "for all" $\wedge$. The symbol $\neg$ precedes formulas. The symbols $\vee$, $\wedge$, $\Rightarrow$, $\Leftrightarrow$ are used between formulas. The symbols $\vee$, $\vee!$, and $\wedge$ are used in front of variables, they are put in parentheses, and are followed by a formula or some other sequence of symbols.

There are relations between the logical symbols through which all logical symbols may be reduced to the three logical symbols $\neg$, $\wedge$, and $\vee$ (and the equality sign). The other symbols may be considered as abbreviations in the following way:

$\varphi \vee \psi$ is equivalent to $\neg(\neg\varphi \wedge \neg\psi)$.

$\varphi \Rightarrow \psi$ is equivalent to $\neg(\varphi \wedge \neg\psi)$.
$\varphi \Leftrightarrow \psi$ is equivalent to $(\varphi \Rightarrow \psi) \wedge (\psi \Rightarrow \varphi)$.
$(\wedge X)\varphi$ is equivalent to $\neg((\vee X) \neg \varphi)$.
$(\vee ! X)\varphi$ is equivalent to $(\vee X)\varphi \wedge ((\vee Y)\varphi \Rightarrow (X = Y))$.

A *formula* is inductively defined for variables or special classes Λ, Γ by

(1) $\Lambda \in \Gamma$ is a formula.

(2)   If φ and ψ are formulas, then also $\neg\varphi$, $\varphi \wedge \psi$, and $(\vee x)\varphi$ are formulas where x may be replaced by any other set variable and where we admit abbreviations (e.g., with other logical symbols).

(3)   Only those sequences of symbols which arise from (1) and (2) are called formulas.

If one of the variables occurs together with one of the so-called *quantifiers* $\vee$, $\wedge$, or $\vee !$ (e.g., $(\vee X)...$, $(\wedge X)...$, $(\vee ! y)...$), then the variable is called a *bound variable*, otherwise it is called a *free variable*.

The axioms of set theory are subdivided into several groups. The axioms of group A are:

$$x \text{ is a class} \tag{A1}$$

Each set is a class.

$$X \in Y \Rightarrow X \text{ is a set} \tag{A2}$$

Each class which is an element of another class is a set.

$$(\wedge u)(u \in X \Leftrightarrow u \in Y) \Rightarrow X = Y \tag{A3}$$

Axiom of extensionality: If two classes have the same elements, then they are equal. (If two classes are equal, then they also have the same elements by the logical properties of the equality sign.)

$$(\wedge u, v)(\vee w)(x \in w \Leftrightarrow x = u \vee x = v) \tag{A4}$$

For any two sets u, v there exists another set w which contains exactly u and v as elements.

Only sets may occur as elements of classes or sets. In particular elements are not objects different from sets, contrary to the view of naïve set theory. Talking about elements is nothing more than the colloquial transcription of the symbol $\in$.

We introduce a number of abbreviations which will be admitted also in formulas except for the first two abbreviations. Here ":$\equiv$" has the meaning of "is an abbreviation of".

$S(X)$	$:\equiv$	X is a set.
$C(X)$	$:\equiv$	X is a class but not a set.
$X \neq Y$	$:\equiv$	$\neg\, X = Y$.
$X \notin Y$	$:\equiv$	$\neg\, X \in Y$.
$\{xy\}$	$:\equiv$	the set defined by (A4) which contains exactly x and y and which is uniquely determined by (A3).
$\{x\}$	$:\equiv$	$\{xx\}$, hence $\{x\} = \{xx\}$.
$\langle xy \rangle$	$:\equiv$	$\{\{x\}\{xy\}\}$, the ordered pair of x and y.
$\langle x \rangle$	$:\equiv$	x.
$\langle x_1 \cdots x_n \rangle$	$:\equiv$	$\langle x_1 \langle x_2 \cdots x_n \rangle \rangle$ for all positive integers n. Thus finite ordered sets are defined.
Empty(X)	$:\equiv$	$\neg\, ((\vee u)(u \in X))$, X is empty.
Ex(X, Y)	$:\equiv$	$\neg\, ((\vee u)(u \in X \wedge u \in Y))$, X and Y do not have a common element.
Un(X)	$:\equiv$	$(\wedge u, v, w)((\langle vu \rangle \in X \wedge \langle wu \rangle \in X) \Rightarrow w = v)$, the subclass of X that contains only ordered pairs contains to each u, at most one pair $\langle vu \rangle$, that is, X has uniquely defined values.
$X \subseteq Y$	$:\equiv$	$(\wedge u)(u \in X \Rightarrow u \in Y)$.
$X \subset Y$	$:\equiv$	$(X \subseteq Y) \wedge (X \neq Y)$.

The axioms of the other groups B, C, and D are:

$$(\vee A)(\wedge x, y)(\langle xy \rangle \in A \Leftrightarrow x \in y) \tag{B1}$$

There is a class A which contains the ordered pair $\langle xy \rangle$ if and only if $x \in y$ holds.

$$(\wedge A, B)(\vee C)(\wedge u)((u \in A \wedge u \in B) \Leftrightarrow u \in C) \tag{B2}$$

For any two classes A and B there exists a class C, the *intersection* $A \cap B$ of A and B, which consists of exactly those sets which are elements as well of A as of B.

$$(\wedge A)(\vee B)(\wedge u)(u \notin A \Leftrightarrow u \in B) \tag{B3}$$

To each class A there exists a class B, the *complement* $-A$ of A, which contains exactly those sets which are not contained in A.

$$(\wedge A)(\vee B)(\wedge u)(u \in B \Leftrightarrow (\vee y)(\langle yu \rangle \in A)) \tag{B4}$$

To each class A there exists a class B, the *domain* $\mathfrak{D}(A)$ of A, which contains exactly the second components of the ordered pairs in A.

$$(\wedge\, A)(\vee\, B)(\wedge\, xy)(\langle\, yx\rangle \in B \Leftrightarrow x \in A) \tag{B5}$$

To each class A there exists a class B, which contains an ordered pair if and only if the second component of the ordered pair is an element of A. Nothing is said about the elements of B which are not ordered pairs. (B5) serves to construct the *product*.

$$(\wedge\, A)(\vee\, B)(\wedge\, xy)(\langle xy\rangle \in A \Leftrightarrow \langle\, yx\rangle \in B) \tag{B6}$$

To each class A there exists a class B which contains as ordered pairs exactly the ordered pairs of A with reversed order.

$$(\wedge\, A)(\vee\, B)(\wedge\, x, y, z)(\langle xyz\rangle \in A \Leftrightarrow \langle\, yzx\rangle \in B) \tag{B7}$$

$$(\wedge\, A)(\vee\, B)(\wedge\, x, y, z)(\langle xyz\rangle \in A \Leftrightarrow \langle xzy\rangle \in B) \tag{B8}$$

To each class A there exists a class B which contains as triples exactly the triples of A where the order is changed in correspondence with (B7) or (B8).

$$(\vee\, a)(\neg\, \text{Empty}(a) \wedge (\wedge\, x)(x \in a \Rightarrow (\vee\, y)(y \in a \wedge x \subset y))) \tag{C1}$$

There exists a set a which has at least *countably (infinitely) many elements*.

$$(\wedge\, x)(\vee\, y)(\wedge\, u, v)(u \in v \wedge v \in x \Rightarrow u \in y) \tag{C2}$$

To each set x there exists a set y which contains the *union* of those sets which are elements of x.

$$(\wedge\, x)(\vee\, y)(\wedge\, u)(u \subseteq x \Rightarrow u \in y) \tag{C3}$$

To each set x there exists a set y which contains each *subset* of x as an element.

$$(\wedge\, x, A)(\text{Un}(A) \Rightarrow (\vee\, y)(\wedge\, u)(u \in y \Leftrightarrow (\vee\, v)(v \in x \wedge \langle uv\rangle \in A))) \tag{C4}$$

To each class A with unique values (an *application*) and to each set x there exists a set y which consists of exactly those elements which are the values of the elements of x under the application A.

$$\neg\, \text{Empty}(A) \Rightarrow (\vee\, u)(u \in A \wedge \text{Ex}(u, A)) \tag{D}$$

Axiom of foundation: Each nonempty class contains an element which is disjoint to the given class.

LEMMA 1. *There exists exactly one class $\varnothing$ with $(\wedge u)(u \notin \varnothing)$ and exactly one class $\mathfrak{U}$ with $(\wedge u)(u \in \mathfrak{U})$.*

Proof. By axiom (B1) there exists a class A. By (B3) the complement $B = -A$ of A exists. By (B2) the intersection C of A and B with $(\wedge u)(u \in C \Leftrightarrow u \in A \wedge u \in B)$, that is, $(\wedge u)(u \in C \Leftrightarrow u \in A \wedge \neg (u \in A))$, exists. Hence we get $(\wedge u)(u \notin C)$ because $u \in A \wedge \neg (u \in A)$ is always wrong. We set $C = \varnothing$. By (A3) the class $\varnothing$ is uniquely determined. Let $\mathfrak{U}$ be the complement of $\varnothing$ (B3). Also $\mathfrak{U}$ is uniquely determined.

We call $\mathfrak{U}$ the *universal class* and $\varnothing$ the *empty set*. We shall show later on that $\varnothing$ is a set.

METATHEOREM OF CLASS FORMATION. *Let $\varphi(x_1 \cdots x_n)$ be a formula with no other free variables than $x_1, ..., x_n$. Then there exists exactly one class A such that the following holds:*

$$(\wedge u)(u \in A \Leftrightarrow (\vee x_1, ..., x_n)(u = \langle x_1 \cdots x_n \rangle \wedge \varphi(x_1 \cdots x_n)))$$

Proof. (1) We may assume that in φ there is no special class at the left side of $\in$ because of

$$(A_k \in \Gamma) \Leftrightarrow ((\vee x)(x = A_k \wedge x \in \Gamma))$$

(2) We may assume that, except special classes and variables, there occur only $\in$, $\neg$, $\wedge$, and $\vee$ (with parentheses) in the formulas (and no equality sign) because of

$$(\Lambda = \Gamma) \Leftrightarrow ((\wedge x)(x \in \Lambda \Leftrightarrow x \in \Gamma))$$

(3) Let $\varphi = (x_r \in x_s)$. If $r = s$, then $\varphi = (x_r \in x_r)$. But $x_r \in x_r$ and $x_r \in \{x_r\}$ implies $-_1 Ex(x_r, \{x_r\})$ a contradiction to axiom (D). We set $A_1 = \varnothing$. If $r < s$, then we get by (B1)

$$(\vee A_1)(\wedge x_r, x_s)(\langle x_r x_s \rangle \in A_1 \Leftrightarrow x_r \in x_s)$$

If $r > s$, then we get by (B1) and (B6)

$$(\vee A_1)(\wedge x_r, x_s)(\langle x_s x_r \rangle \in A_1 \Leftrightarrow x_r \in x_s)$$

By (B5), (B6), (B7), and (B8) we get in all three cases with $1 \leqslant r \leqslant n$ and $1 \leqslant s \leqslant n$:

$$(\vee A_2)(\wedge x_1, ..., x_n)(\langle x_1 \cdots x_n \rangle \in A_2 \Leftrightarrow x_r \in x_s)$$

(4)   Let $\varphi = (x_r \in A_k)$. Then we get $(\vee A_k)(x_r \in A_k \Leftrightarrow x_r \in A_k)$. By (B5)–(B8) we get for $1 \leqslant r \leqslant n$

$$(\vee A_2)(\wedge x_1, ..., x_n)(\langle x_1 \cdots x_n \rangle \in A_2 \Leftrightarrow x_r \in A_k)$$

(5)   Now we make an induction with respect to the number of logical symbols $\neg$, $\wedge$, and $\vee$. The necessary induction steps are

$\neg \varphi$:   By (B3)

$$(\wedge x_1, ..., x_n)(\langle x_1 \cdots x_n \rangle \in A_2 \Leftrightarrow \varphi(x_1 \cdots x_n))$$
$$\Rightarrow (\wedge x_1, ..., x_n)(\langle x_1 ... x_n \rangle \in -A_2 \Leftrightarrow \neg \varphi(x_1 \cdots x_n))$$

$\varphi \wedge \psi$:   By (B2)

$$(\wedge x_1, ..., x_n)(\langle x_1 \cdots x_n \rangle \in A_2 \Leftrightarrow \varphi(x_1 \cdots x_n))$$
$$\wedge (\wedge x_1, ..., x_n)(\langle x_1 \cdots x_n \rangle \in A_3 \Leftrightarrow \psi(x_1 \cdots x_n))$$
$$\Rightarrow (\wedge x_1, ..., x_n)(\langle x_1 \cdots x_n \rangle \in A_2 \cap A_3 \Leftrightarrow (\varphi \wedge \psi)(x_1 \cdots x_n))$$

$(\vee x)$:   By (B4)

$$(\wedge x, x_1, ..., x_n)(\langle xx_1 \cdots x_n \rangle \in A_2 \Leftrightarrow \varphi(xx_1 \cdots x_n))$$
$$\Rightarrow (\wedge x_1, ..., x_n)(\langle x_1 \cdots x_n \rangle \in \mathfrak{D}(A_2) \Leftrightarrow (\vee x)(\varphi(xx_1 \cdots x_n)))$$

(6)   We define $A \times B$ by

$$(\wedge x)(x \in A \times B \Leftrightarrow (\vee y, z)(x = \langle yz \rangle \wedge y \in A \wedge z \in B))$$

Furthermore, let $A^n = A \times A^{n-1}$. In particular, we get

$$(\wedge u)(u \in \mathfrak{U}^n \Leftrightarrow (\vee x_1, ..., x_n)(u = \langle x_1 \cdots x_n \rangle))$$

We replace the class $B(= -A_2, A_2 \cap A_3, \mathfrak{D}(A_2))$ defined by (5) by the class $A = B \cap \mathfrak{U}^n$. Then by (A3) the class A is uniquely determined by

$$(\wedge u)(u \in A \Leftrightarrow (\vee x_1, ..., x_n)(u = \langle x_1 \cdots x_n \rangle \wedge \varphi(x_1 \cdots x_n)))$$

The class A constructed in the Metatheorem of class formation is also written as $A = \{\langle x_1 \cdots x_n\rangle \mid \varphi(x_1 \cdots x_n)\}$. Thus we get further abbreviations:

$$
\begin{array}{lll}
A - B & :\equiv & \{x \mid x \in A \wedge x \notin B\}, \\
A \cup B & :\equiv & \{x \mid x \in A \vee x \in B\}, \\
\bigcup X & :\equiv & \{x \mid (\vee y)(x \in y \wedge y \in X)\}, \\
\bigcap X & :\equiv & \{x \mid (\wedge y)(y \in X \Rightarrow x \in y)\}, \\
\mathfrak{P}(X) & :\equiv & \{x \mid x \subseteq X\}, \\
X^{-1} & :\equiv & \{x \mid (\vee y, z)(x = \langle yz\rangle \wedge \langle zy\rangle \in X)\}, \\
\mathfrak{R}(X) & :\equiv & \mathfrak{D}(X^{-1}) \text{ (range of } X) \\
F((X)) & :\equiv & \mathfrak{R}(F \cap (\mathfrak{U} \times X)) \text{ (image of } X \text{ under } F, \text{ that is, the} \\
& & \text{class of those elements which occur as images of ele-} \\
& & \text{ments of } X \text{ under the application of } F).
\end{array}
$$

A series of new formulas is defined by

$$
\begin{array}{lll}
\mathrm{Rel}(X) & :\equiv & X \subseteq \mathfrak{U}^2, \\
\mathrm{Equ.Rel}(X) & :\equiv & \mathrm{Rel}(X) \wedge (\wedge x)(x \in \mathfrak{D}(X) \Rightarrow \langle xx\rangle \in X) \\
& & \wedge (\wedge x, y)(\langle xy\rangle \in X \Rightarrow \langle yx\rangle \in X) \\
& & \wedge (\wedge x, y, z)(\langle xy\rangle \in X \wedge \langle yz\rangle \in X \\
& & \Rightarrow \langle xz\rangle \in X), \\
\mathrm{Map}(X) & :\equiv & \mathrm{Rel}(X) \wedge \mathrm{Un}(X), \\
F \text{ map on } X & :\equiv & \mathrm{Map}(F) \wedge \mathfrak{D}(F) = X, \\
F \text{ map from } X \text{ to } Y & :\equiv & F \text{ map on } X \wedge \mathfrak{R}(F) \subseteq Y, \\
\mathrm{bijective}\,(F) & :\equiv & \mathrm{Un}(F) \wedge \mathrm{Un}(F^{-1}).
\end{array}
$$

Let F be a class and x be a set. Then $F(x)$ is uniquely defined by

$$
(((\vee! y)(\langle yx\rangle \in F)) \Rightarrow (\langle F(x)\, x\rangle \in F)) \wedge ((\neg (\vee! y)(\langle yx\rangle \in F)) \Rightarrow F(x) = \varnothing)
$$

Let F map from X to Y be given. F is called *injective*, if $\mathrm{Un}(F^{-1})$. F is called *surjective* if $\mathfrak{R}(F) = Y$. Instead of F map from X to Y, we often write $F : X \to Y$ or $X \ni x \mapsto F(x) \in Y$ or $X \xrightarrow{F} Y$. Observe that the arrow $\mapsto$ is used between sets which are assigned to each other, whereas the arrow $\to$ is used between sets or classes the elements of which are assigned to each other. A family F of elements of Y with index set X is (F map from X to Y).

We have the following *rules of set theory*:

$$
\begin{array}{ll}
\text{(a)} & \bigcap \varnothing = \mathfrak{U}; \quad \bigcap \mathfrak{U} = \varnothing; \quad \bigcup \varnothing = \varnothing; \quad \bigcup \mathfrak{U} = \mathfrak{U}; \\
\text{(b)} & \varnothing \subseteq X \subseteq \mathfrak{U}; \\
\text{(c)} & X = Y \Leftrightarrow X \subseteq Y \wedge Y \subseteq X; \\
\text{(d)} & \mathfrak{D}(\mathfrak{U}) = \mathfrak{U}; \quad \mathfrak{R}(\mathfrak{U}) = \mathfrak{U}; \\
\text{(e)} & \mathfrak{P}(\mathfrak{U}) = \mathfrak{U}; \\
\text{(f)} & \mathsf{S}(\varnothing); \quad \mathsf{C}(\mathfrak{U});
\end{array}
$$

(g) $S(X) \Rightarrow S(X \cap Y) \wedge S(\mathfrak{P}(X)) \wedge S(\bigcup X)$;

(h) $X \neq \varnothing \Rightarrow S(\bigcap X)$;

(i) $S(X) \wedge (Y \subseteq X) \Rightarrow S(Y)$;

(j) $S(X) \wedge S(Y) \Rightarrow S(X \times Y) \wedge S(X \cup Y)$;

(k) F map on $x \Rightarrow S(F) \wedge S(\mathfrak{R}(F)) \wedge S(F((x)))$;

(l) $C(X) \Rightarrow C(\mathfrak{P}(X)) \wedge C(\bigcup X) \wedge C(X \cup Y) \wedge C(X - y)$;

(m) $C(X) \wedge Y \neq \varnothing \Rightarrow C(X \times Y)$;

(n)   bijective$(F) \wedge X \subseteq \mathfrak{D}(F) \wedge C(X) \Rightarrow C(F((X)))$;

(o) F map on $A \wedge G$ map on $A \Rightarrow ((\wedge u)(u \in A \Rightarrow F(u) = G(u))$
       $\Rightarrow F = G)$.

Proof. It is trivial to verify (a), (b), (c), (d), and (e).

(i) Let $A = \{\langle zz \rangle \mid z \in Y\}$, then A has uniquely defined values (Un(A)). By axiom (C4), we get $y = Y$, that is, $S(Y)$.

(g) $S(X \cap Y)$ trivially by (i). (i) implies also $S(\mathfrak{P}(X))$ and $S(\bigcup X)$ by axioms (C2) and (C3).

(j) $\{X, Y\}$ is a set by axiom (A4). (g) implies $S(X \cup Y)$. $X \times Y \subseteq \mathfrak{P}\mathfrak{P}(X \cup Y)$ implies $S(X \times Y)$ by (i) and (g).

(k) $S(\mathfrak{R}(F))$ and $S(F((x)))$ hold by axiom (C4). $F \subseteq x \times \mathfrak{R}(F)$ implies $S(F)$. (l), (m), and (n) are proved analogously.

(o) holds by definition of $F(x)$.

(f) $\varnothing \subseteq X$ and the existence of a set (axiom(C1)) imply $S(\varnothing)$. Assume $S(\mathfrak{U})$. Then $\mathfrak{U} \in \mathfrak{U}$ and $\mathfrak{U} \in \{\mathfrak{U}\}$ contradicting axiom D. Hence $C(\mathfrak{U})$.

(h) $y \in X$ and $\bigcap X \subseteq y$ imply $S(\bigcap X)$.

The strong axiom of choice of Gödel is equivalent to the axiom of choice we use here and is particularly suitable for the application in categories. (The equivalence of these two axioms holds only if the axiom of foundation holds.) The axiom of choice is

$$\text{Equ. Rel } R \Rightarrow (\vee X)(\wedge u)(u \in \mathfrak{D}(R) \Rightarrow (\vee! v)(v \in X \wedge \langle uv \rangle \in R))$$

To each equivalence relation R on $\mathfrak{D}(R)$ there exists a complete system of representatives $X \cap \mathfrak{D}(R)$.

THEOREM. *The axiom of choice is equivalent to the following axiom of choice of Gödel*

$$(\vee A)(\text{Un}(A) \wedge (\wedge x)(\neg \text{ Empty}(x) \Rightarrow (\vee y)(y \in x \wedge \langle yx \rangle \in A)$$

(*There is a class with uniquely defined values (an application) which assigns to each nonempty set x one of its elements.*)

Proof. Assume that the axiom of choice holds. Let E be the class of the $\in$-relation: $E = \{\langle xy \rangle \mid x \in y\}$. Let

$$R = \{\langle wxyz \rangle \mid \langle wx \rangle \in E \wedge \langle yz \rangle \in E \wedge x = z\}$$

Then R is an equivalence relation on E. Let A be a complete system of representatives for R. If $y \neq \varnothing$, then there is exactly one x with $\langle xy \rangle \in A \subseteq E$. Thus A is the choice function for the strong axiom of choice of Gödel.

We shall only indicate the converse of the proof. Gödel's strong axiom of choice implies that $\mathfrak{U}$ may be well-ordered. If R is an equivalence relation, then

$$X = \{x \mid x \in \mathfrak{D}(R) \wedge \langle \wedge y \rangle (y \in \mathfrak{D}(R) \wedge \langle xy \rangle \in R \Rightarrow x \leqslant y\}$$

is a complete system of representatives.

The axiom of choice implies in particular Zorn's Lemma. We define a *chain* K in an ordered set X (in the sense of Section 1.1, Example 2) to be a subset of X such that for any two elements $x, y \in K$ always $x \leqslant y$ or $y \leqslant x$ holds. An *upper bound* for a chain K in X is an element $b(K) \in X$ such that $x \leqslant b(K)$ for all $x \in K$. A *maximal element* $m \in X$ is an element with the property that $m \leqslant x$ implies $m = x$ for all $x \in X$. Observe that a chain may be empty and that every element of X is an upper bound for the empty chain.

ZORN'S LEMMA. *If X is an ordered set and if each chain K in X has an upper bound, then there is a maximal element in X.*

We have to refer the reader to text books on set theory for the proof of this and the following lemma on ordinals.

LEMMA 2. *Let K be a well-ordered set of ordinals α, let γ be the first ordinal with $|K| < |\gamma|$ and $|\alpha| < |\gamma|$ for all $\alpha \in K$. Then there is an ordinal β with $\beta < \gamma$ and $\alpha < \beta$ for all $\alpha \in K$.*

BIBLIOGRAPHY

Brinkmann, H. B., and Puppe, D., "Kategorien und Funktoren," Lecture Notes 18. Springer, Berlin, 1966.

Eckman, B. (ed.), "Seminar on Triples and Categorical Homology Theory," Lecture Notes 80. Springer, Berlin, 1969.

Ehresmann, C., "Catégories et structures." Dunod, Paris, 1965.

Eilenberg, S., *et al.* (eds.), "Proceedings of the Conference on Categorical Algebra-LaJolla-1965." Springer, Berlin, 1966.

Freyd, P., "Abelian Categories." Harper, New York, 1964.

Gabriel, P., Des catégories abéliennes. *Bull. Soc. Math. France,* **90,** 323–448 (1962).

Hasse, M., and Michler, L., "Theorie der Kategorien." Deut. Verlag. Wiss., Berlin, 1966.

Lambek, J., "Completion of Categories," Lecture Notes 24. Springer, Berlin, 1966.

MacLane, S., Categorical algebra, *Bull. Amer. Math. Soc.,* **71,** 40–106 (1965).

Mitchell, B., "Theory of Categories." Academic Press, New York, 1965.

Index

Pure and Applied Mathematics

A Series of Monographs and Textbooks

Editors

Paul A. Smith and Samuel Eilenberg

Columbia University, New York

Pure and Applied Mathematics

A Series of Monographs and Textbooks

In preparation

EDUARD PRUGOVEČKI. Quantum Mechanics in Hilbert Space.